Collins

Collins Revision

KS3

Science

Revision Guide

Levels 3–6

Patricia Miller

Revision contents

Revision material covers each section of the curriculum

Download free clips to help you revise
www.collinseducation.com/revision

Workbook contents

free downloads

free downloads

Watch and listen to worked questions and answers with tips

Revise on your PC/Mac + iPod/mobile phone
www.collinseducation.com/revision

Cell structure

level 3

Cell structure

There are many different types of cells which all have different jobs.
Most cells have certain things the same.

- The **cell membrane** controls what goes in and out of the cell.
- **Cytoplasm** is a kind of chemical soup which makes up most of the cell in both plants and animals.
- The **nucleus** controls the chemical activity of the cell.

level 3

Structure of plant cells

Plant cells have extra things which are not found in animal cells.

- Plant cells have a **cell wall** as well as a cell membrane.
- The cell wall is made of cellulose and helps plants to keep their shape, or rigid.
- The **vacuole** is a bag-like structure in the middle of the cytoplasm. It holds water and pushes the cytoplasm up against the cell wall to keep the cell rigid.
- **Chloroplasts** contain the green pigment **chlorophyll**. Chlorophyll is used by plants in photosynthesis – the process by which plants make their own food (see page 16).
- Remember! Plants do not have a skeleton – they keep their rigid shape because of the cell wall and the vacuole.

Plant cell

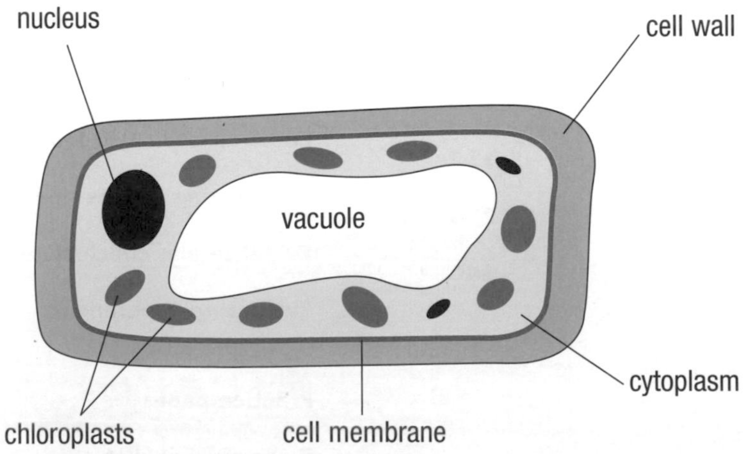

level 3

Structure of animal cells

- Simple animal cells have the basic structure shown in the diagram below.
- They are different from plant cells because:
  - they have only a cell membrane, not a cell wall
  - they do not have chloroplasts or a vacuole.
- As you will see on page 7, many animal cells have very different structures to enable them to carry out their special jobs.

Animal cell

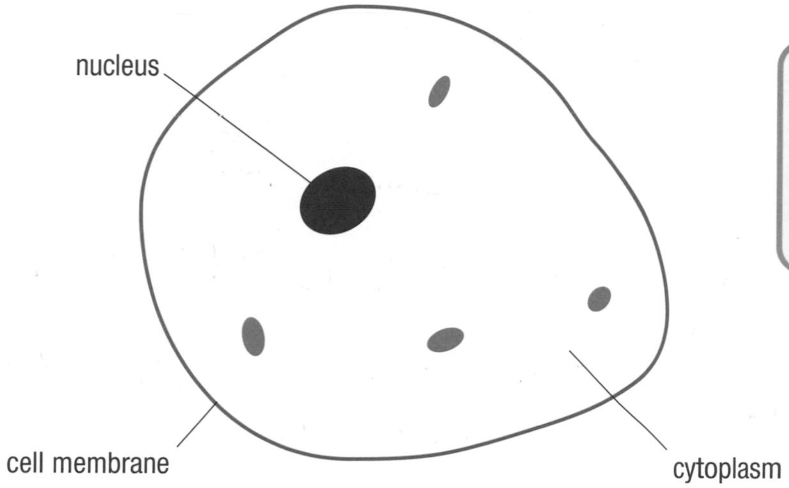

Top Tip!

You must remember the things that are the same about plant and animal cells and the things that are different.

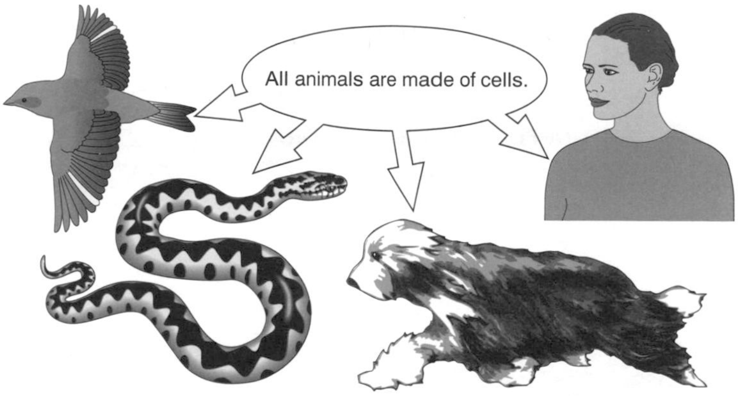

Did You Know?

An amoeba is an animal that is so small it is made from a single cell.

A human body is made of millions of cells.

Spot Check

1 Which **three** of these structures are common to animal and plant cells?

cell membrane **cell wall** **nucleus**
cytoplasm **chloroplasts** **vacuole**

2 Which part of a plant cell helps the plant to keep its shape even though it does not have a skeleton?

3 Which part of both plant and animal cells controls what goes in and out of the cell?

Specialist cells

level 4

Specialist plant cells

Although all plant cells have the same basic structure, many are adapted to carry out a special job within the plant.

levels 4-5

Palisade cells

- **Palisade cells** have a lot of extra chloroplasts to help with **photosynthesis** (see page 16). They are mostly found in the top surface of leaves.

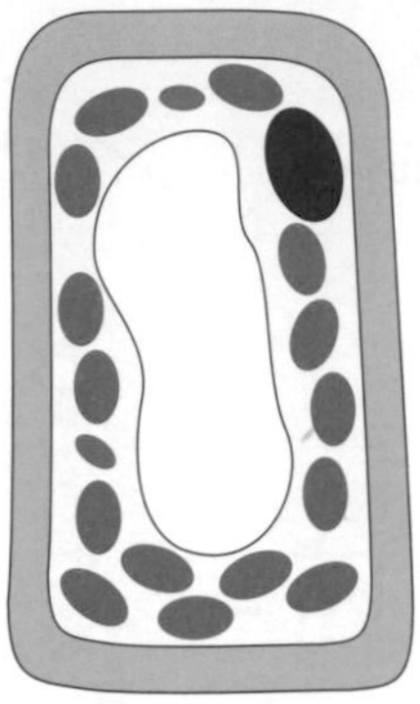

levels 4-5

Root hair cells

- **Root hair cells** have no chloroplasts at all as they do not need chlorophyll to carry out their role. They are long and thin to enable the plant to draw water from deep down in the soil.

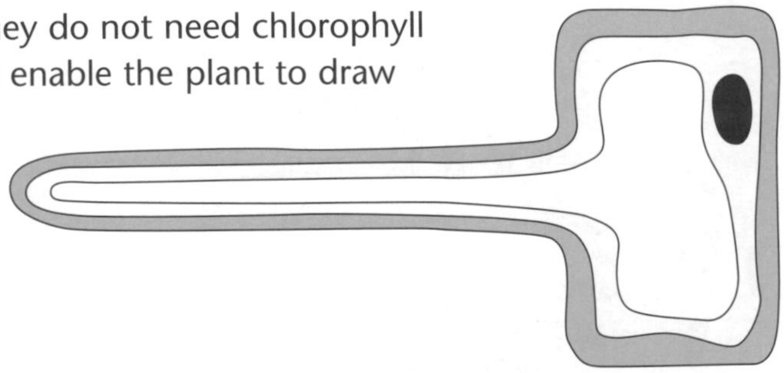

level 4

Size of cells

- On average, single cells are 0.05 mm in diameter and can only be seen under a microscope. However, some cells measure 0.2 mm and certain nerve cells in animals can be as long as 1 m.

Top Tip!

Think carefully about the way in which specialised cells are adapted – and how this enables them to carry out their special job.

level 5

Specialist animal cells

Some animal cells have very complicated adaptations to help them do their job within the animal.

Type of cell	Special task	Adaptation
Nerve cells 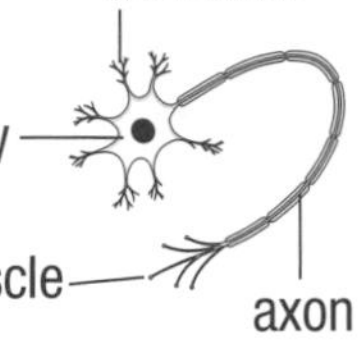	Carry messages from the brain to other parts of the body.	Very long and thin – up to 1 metre long.
Ciliated epithelial cells 	Keep the airways clean by trapping dust and microbes.	Tiny hairs all along the upper surfaces.
Red blood cells 	Carry oxygen around in the blood.	No nucleus and **bi-concave** shape to give the biggest surface area for absorbing oxygen.
Sperm cells 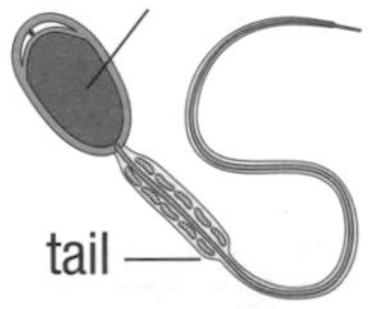	Carry the male genetic information and fertilise the egg to create a new animal.	A tail for swimming and a tough head for penetrating the egg – and half the usual number of **chromosomes** in the nucleus. Smaller than an egg cell.
Egg cells (ova) 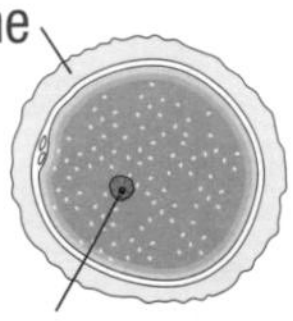	Carry the female genetic information and join with a sperm cell to make a new animal.	Carry a supply of food for energy for the embryo until it is implanted. Half the number of chromosomes in the nucleus just like the sperm cell. When the sperm and the ovum join together in fertilisation, the new cell has the full number of chromosomes.

Did You Know?
When a baby girl is born she has all the eggs she will need already in her body.

Spot Check

1 Why do root hair cells not have any chloroplasts even though they are plant cells?
2 Which type of animal cell is adapted to have the biggest possible surface area, and how does this enable it to do its special job?
3 Which kind of cell needs to be very long and thin, and how does this adaptation help it to perform its function?

Tissues and organs

Organisation

level 4

- Apart from the very simplest organisms, plants and animals are made of lots of cells.
- The cells group together to form **tissues**, and tissues group together to form **organs**.

Growth

level 4

- A plant or animal grows because its cells divide and make new cells not because the cells get bigger and bigger.

The nucleus of the cells splits in two. | A new cell membrane forms in the middle. | The new daughter cells get bigger. | Once the daughter cells are full-size, they too can divide.

Tissues

level 4

- Cells have different structures so that they can perform different functions in the animal or plant.
- Groups of the same cell join together to make tissues.

Examples of tissues

level 4

- Muscle cells are grouped to form muscle tissue.

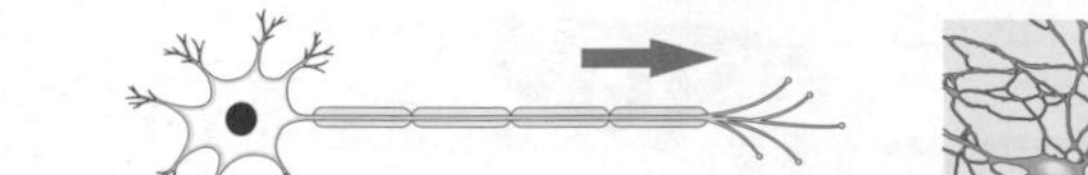

- Nerve cells join together to make the nerve tissues which carry messages from the brain to all parts of the body.

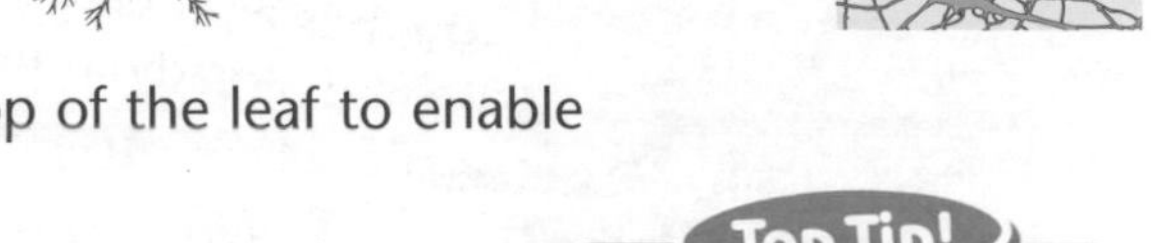

- In plants, palisade cells (see page 6) cluster near the top of the leaf to enable the plant to make food.
- Root hair cells join together to make root hair tissue.

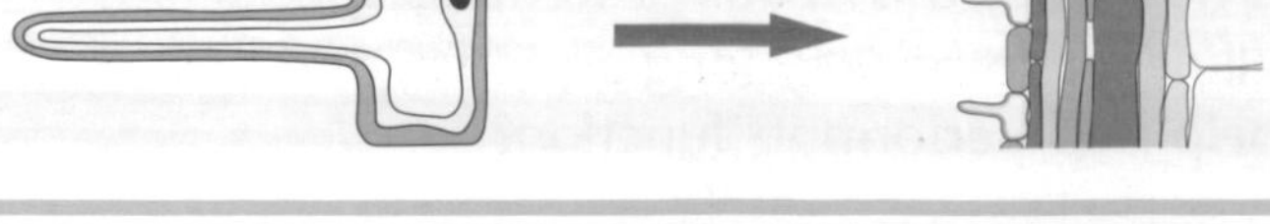

Top Tip!

One organ may contain more than one type of tissue.
The heart, for example, contains muscle tissue and nerve tissue.

Organs

level 4

- Groups of different tissues join together to form organs.
- The heart, lungs, liver, brain and stomach are all examples of organs. They each have a particular job to do and consist of groups of tissues made of specialist cells to enable them to do that job.
- In plants, the leaves and roots are organs.

Systems

levels 4-5

- Everything that living things do relies on an organ or a group of organs. A group of organs working together makes up a **system**. In mammals it works like this:

Characteristics of living things	Systems that enable this to happen	Organs in this system
Movement	Skeletal system in animals	Bones and muscles
Respiration	Respiratory system	Lungs
Sensitivity	Nervous system	Brain, nerves and the sensing organs including eyes, ears and the skin.
Growth	All systems – growth happens by cell division.	All the specialist tissues that make up the organs of the body.
Reproduction	Reproductive system	Reproductive organs such as the ovaries and womb in females and the penis and testes in males.
Excretion	Excretory system	The kidneys are the most obvious organs but the lungs and the skin are also used by the body to get rid of waste.
Nutrition	Digestive system allows food to be broken down so that the body can make use of it.	The organs involved in digestion include the mouth, stomach and intestines.

Did You Know?

Dolphins can hear sounds made by other dolphins and whales over distances up to 300 miles.

Spot Check

1 What do cells do so that the plant or animal can grow bigger?
2 Which organs make up the nervous system?
3 Which system in animals allows them to move?

The digestive system

level 3

Food

- Plants make their own food using the energy from sunlight (see page 16) but animals have to take in food and break it down to release energy.

level 4

Digestion

- **Digestion** starts in the mouth where food is broken down into smaller pieces. **Saliva** contains an enzyme that starts to break down the starch into smaller sugar molecules.
- From the mouth food travels down the **oesophagus** until it reaches the **stomach**.

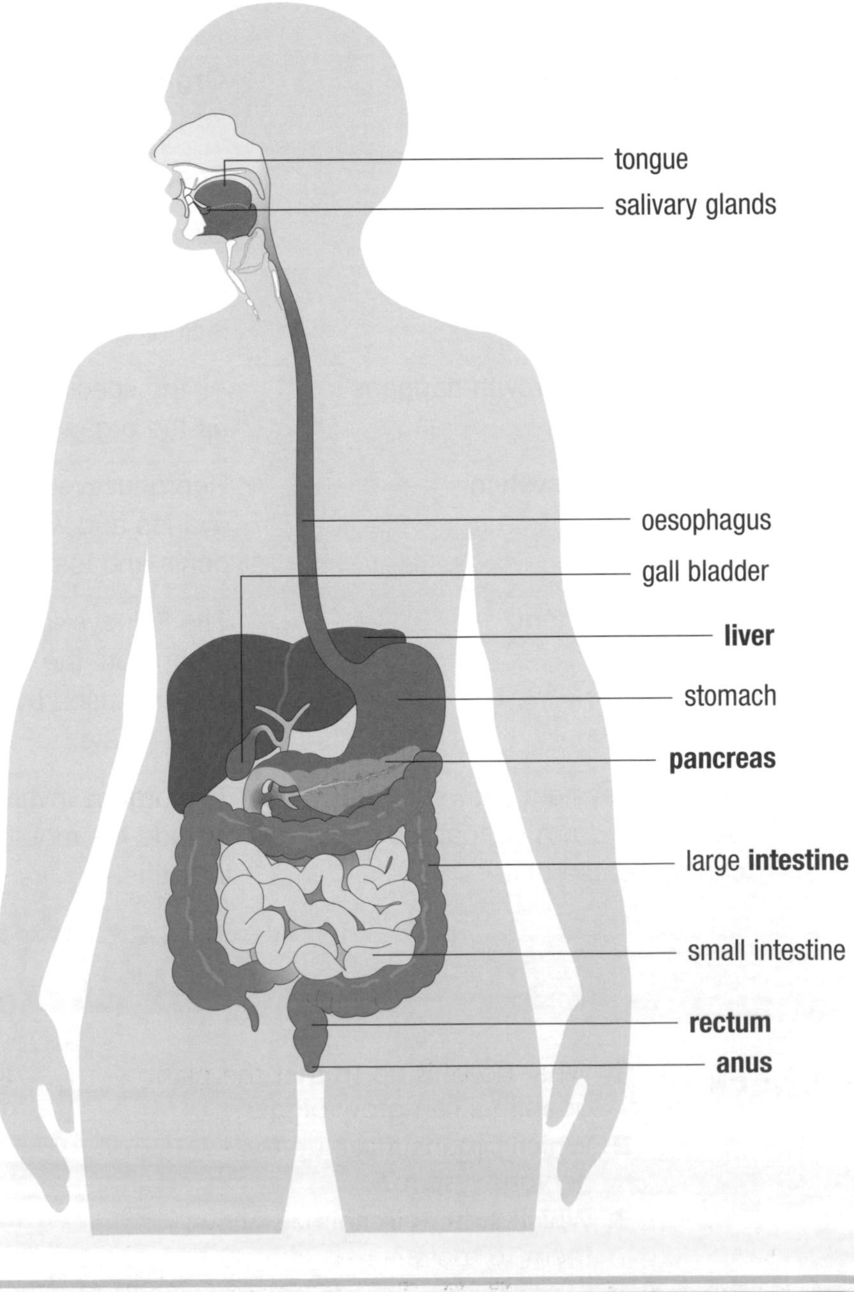

levels 4-5

Organs of the digestive system

Organ	Function in digestion
Digestion starts when food enters the mouth. The food then moves down the oesophagus to …	
Stomach	Muscular walls churn up the food. At the same time **gastric** juices mix with the chopped up food to produce a sort of mushy, soup-like substance which then passes into the small intestine. Protein digestion starts in the stomach.
Liver	The food does not pass through the liver on its way through the body – but the liver produces a liquid called **bile** which helps in the breakdown of fats. Bile is stored in the gall bladder.
Small intestine	This is where the mush from the stomach is further broken down so that the molecules become small enough to pass through the intestine wall into the bloodstream. Enzymes from the pancreas help with this chemical breakdown.
Large intestine	In this final stage, water is absorbed back into the body and the remaining solid waste is passed into the rectum where it is stored until it is passed out of the body through the anus.

level 6

Digestion and energy

Digestion releases energy for growth

Digestion releases energy for movement

Digestion releases energy for warmth

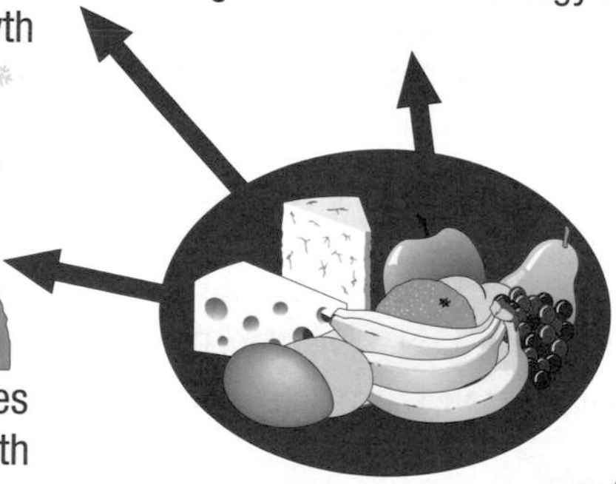

Did You Know?

If the tubes in a French Horn were straightened out it would be over 6 m long – and human intestines are a little bit longer.

Top Tip!

Anything to do with the stomach is described as 'gastric'.
The chemicals that break down the molecules in food into smaller molecules are called enzymes.

Spot Check

1. Digestion releases energy from food for **three** important uses. What are they?
2. What is the name of the fluid in the mouth that contains an enzyme that begins to break down starch?
3. In which organ of the digestive system is water absorbed back into the body?

CELLS

The reproductive system

level 3

Reproduction

- One of the key characteristics of living things is that they can make new organisms like themselves – this is called reproduction.

Top Tip!

This system has a lot of organs! You need to learn them all and know what each one does.

levels 3-4

Organs of reproduction in humans

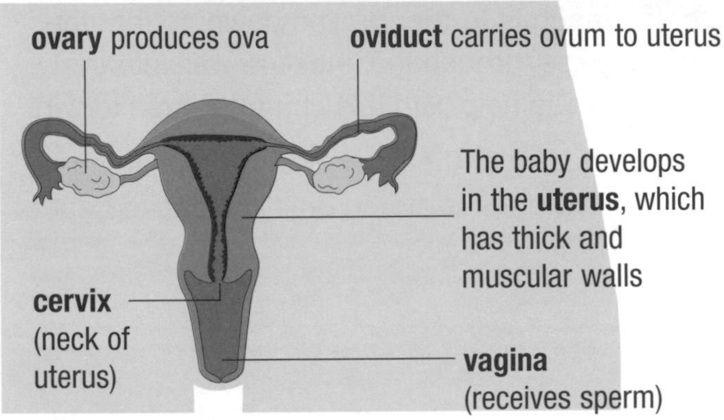

Female reproductive organs

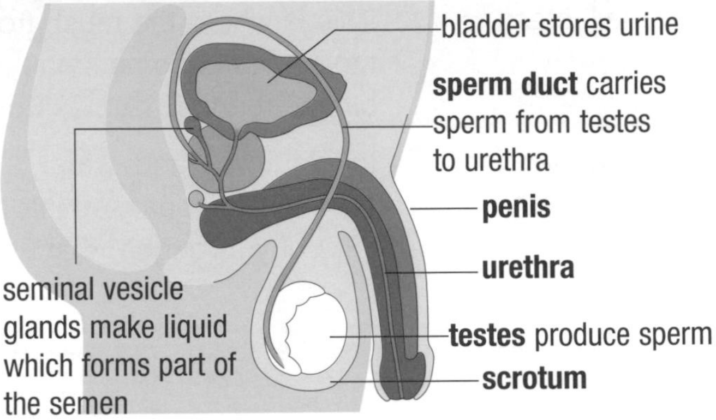

Male reproductive organs

level 4

Fertilisation

- A new human being is made when an egg cell (or ovum) in a female is fused with a sperm cell from a male. This fusion is called **fertilisation**.
- The chromosomes in the nucleus contain DNA – the genetic material. The DNA for the new human comes from the parents – half from the sperm and half from the egg.

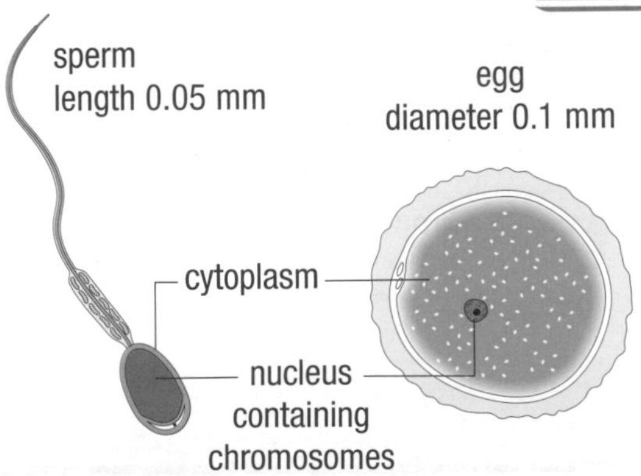

Spot Check

1 What is the name of the fusion of an egg and a sperm cell to make a new human being?
2 What is the name of the organ through which the foetus gets the nutrients and oxygen it needs?
3 What happens at around day 14 of the menstrual cycle?

Did You Know?

A human foetus takes about 9 months to develop in its mother's uterus – for elephants this gestation period is 22 months, but for hamsters it is only 16 days!

levels 5-6

The menstrual cycle

- An adult female releases an ovum from one of her ovaries about every 28 days. Before the ovum is released, the uterus prepares to accept a fertilised ovum – just in case fertilisation takes place. These events are part of the menstrual cycle.

Time in cycle	What happens	
Day 0–5	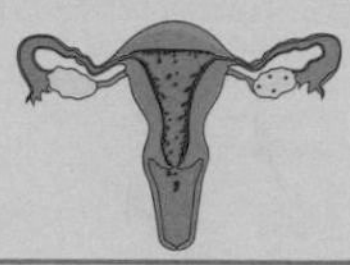	If there is no fertilised ovum, the uterus lining breaks down and is passed out of the vagina. This is called a **period** or **menstruation**.
Day 6–13	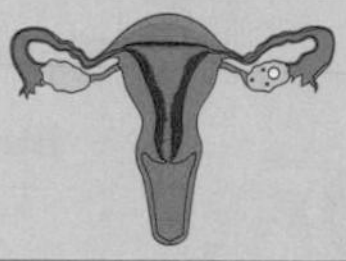	Uterus lining starts to thicken in case it has to receive a fertilised ovum.
Day 14	**Ovulation** – a mature ovum is released from the ovary.	
Day 15	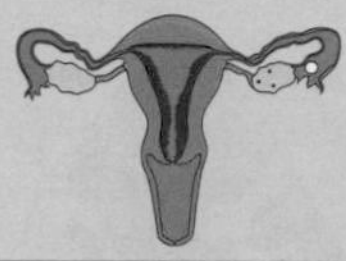	The ovum starts to move along the oviduct.
Day 16–21	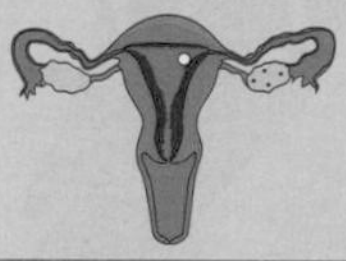	The uterus lining remains thick with a good blood supply in case a fertilised ovum needs to be implanted.
Day 22–28	The lining of the uterus stops developing and if there is no fertilised ovum it starts to break down and the cycle begins again.	

level 6

Pregnancy and birth

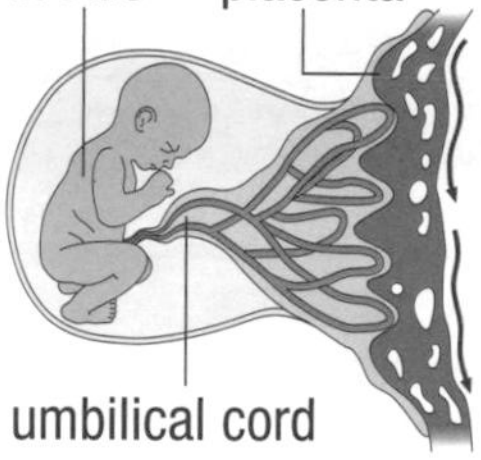

- If an egg is fertilised in the oviduct it starts to divide straight away. By the time it reaches the uterus it is a ball of cells ready to implant in the prepared lining of the uterus.
- After about 6 weeks, the tiny **embryo** floats in a sac of amniotic fluid that protects it until it is ready to be born. The developing **foetus** gets the nutrients and oxygen it needs from the **placenta** via the **umbilical cord**.
- Approximately 9 months (40 weeks) after fertilisation the baby is ready to be born. It is pushed out through the vagina by strong muscular contractions of the wall of the uterus.

level 6

Pregnancy and lifestyle

- A woman's lifestyle choices during pregnancy can affect the health of her baby. If she drinks, smokes or takes drugs then these substances will pass through her placenta to the developing baby. These substances can affect the baby's birth weight and make it more likely that the baby will be ill in early life. In extreme cases the baby will be born already addicted to whatever its mother has been taking.

CELLS The circulation system

levels 3-4

Deliveries and removals

Every cell in the body needs a supply of food and oxygen – and every cell produces waste products which need to be removed. This is done by the circulation system.

levels 4-5

Organs of the circulation system

- The major organ in the circulation system is the heart.
- The heart is a powerful muscular pump which sends blood to all of the body.
- 'Pulmonary' means to do with the lungs. The pulmonary artery carries blood to the lungs and the pulmonary vein carries blood away from the lungs.

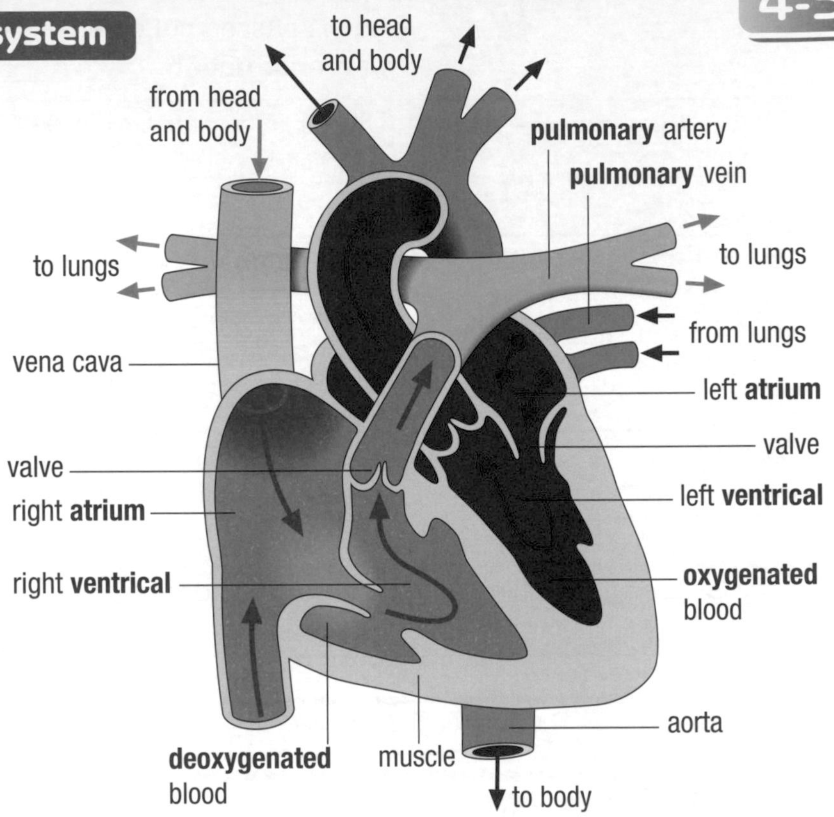

Top Tip!

Diagrams of the heart are always drawn as if you are looking at a heart inside a person's chest. This means the left side of the heart is always drawn on the right-hand side of the page.

levels 5-6

Gas exchange

- The blood goes from the right-hand side of the heart to the lungs where the red blood cells collect oxygen. It is then called oxygenated blood. The oxygenated blood goes through the left-hand side of the heart and is sent all around the body.
- Each cell in the body exchanges oxygen for carbon dioxide. The deoxygenated blood then comes back to the right-hand side of the heart. From there it is sent back to the lungs where it exchanges its carbon dioxide for oxygen – and the cycle begins again.

Spot Check

1 Name the four sections or chambers of the heart.
2 Which type of blood vessel has thick muscular walls?
3 Which gas is the waste product of respiration that passes from the blood into the lungs to be exhaled from the body?

Did You Know?

The surface area of the lungs of an adult human is almost 100 m^2 – and the same person's skin will be only about 2 m^2.

level 4

Blood vessels

- There are three types of blood vessels: **arteries** **veins** **capillaries**
- The structure of each is adapted to allow it to carry out its function.

level 5

Blood vessel functions

- Thick muscular walls allow the arteries to carry blood at high pressure as it is pumped away from the heart.
- Veins have thinner walls as the blood they carry is moving more slowly and at a lower pressure going back towards the heart. Veins have valves on the insides of their walls to make sure the blood does not flow in the wrong direction.
- Capillaries have walls only one cell thick so that oxygen, carbon dioxide and other food and waste products can pass in and out of them easily.

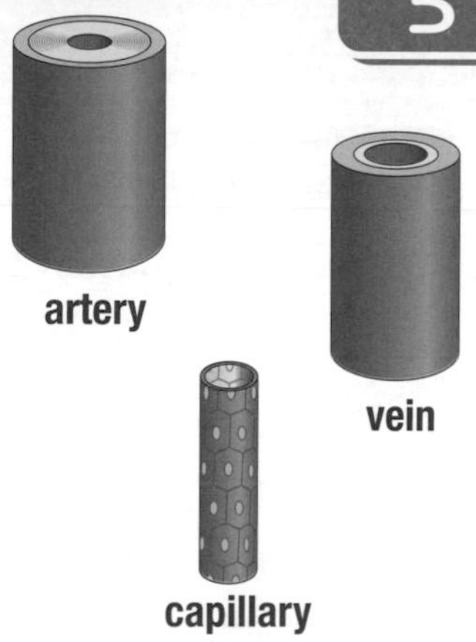

levels 5-6

Respiration and breathing

- **Respiration** and **breathing** are NOT the same thing, although they are connected, so it is an easy mistake to make.
- Breathing means taking air, containing plenty of oxygen, into our lungs and expelling air, containing little oxygen and a lot of carbon dioxide, from our lungs.
- Respiration is the chemical reaction which takes place in every cell in our bodies to release energy from food. We need oxygen to make this reaction happen. Carbon dioxide is given out by the cells as a result of this reaction.
- The circulation system is able to respond to different situations. For example, when a person exercises, the heart beats faster so that blood carrying oxygen and glucose reaches the muscle cells more quickly. This means that the muscle cells can release more energy using respiration.

level 6

Organisms

- The lungs are part of the respiratory or breathing system – they work with the circulation system to deliver oxygen to the cells for respiration. This is an example of how all the systems work together to form a whole organism.

CELL → TISSUE → ORGAN → SYSTEM → ORGANISM

Photosynthesis

level 3

Sunlight

Photosynthesis is the process by which green plants make their own food. They make use of our principal energy source – the Sun.

- Green plants are able to make their own food. This is why all food chains begin with green plants – called the **producers**.

levels 3-4

Chlorophyll

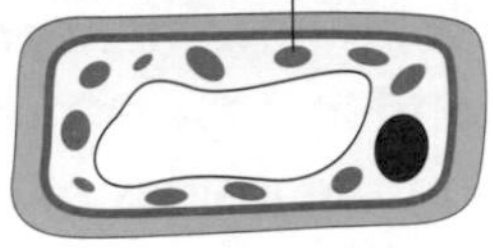

- Plants make food in the cells that contain **chloroplasts**. Chloroplasts are green because they contain the green pigment **chlorophyll**.
- Cells near the top of the leaf always have a large number of chloroplasts so that they can absorb a lot of sunlight for photosynthesis.
- Root hair cells have no chloroplasts – being far away from the sunlight they do not take part in photosynthesis.
- Plants that have **variegated** leaves – that is leaves that are part green and part white – only carry out photosynthesis in the green part of these leaves.

variegated leaf

level 4

Water and carbon dioxide

- As well as chlorophyll and sunlight, a plant needs two important ingredients for photosynthesis: water and carbon dioxide. As it is a chemical reaction we call the ingredients 'reactants'.

level 4

Photosynthesis and competition

- Plants compete with each other to get what is necessary for photosynthesis. There is often a patch of bare earth under a large tree or dense bush because plants growing underneath get too little light, are not be able to make enough food and so they die.

level 4

Plants and food

- Plants make their own food through photosynthesis. They do NOT take in food through their roots. Garden centres sell containers labelled 'Plant Food'. These contain the minerals and trace elements that plants need to stay healthy, BUT plant 'food' is the glucose they make by photosynthesis.

level 5

Photosynthesis as a chemical reaction

- Photosynthesis mostly happens in leaves, although any plant cell that has chloroplasts can carry out photosynthesis.
- We can describe photosynthesis using a word equation like this:

Water + carbon dioxide —(**light energy** / **chlorophyll**)→ **glucose + oxygen**

Top Tip!

All green plants carry out photosynthesis and the chemical reaction is always the same. Don't be put off by unfamiliar plant names!

- This means that the cells of a green plant take in water and carbon dioxide. If there is light and chlorophyll present they can make glucose. Oxygen is released as a waste product.

Photosynthesis

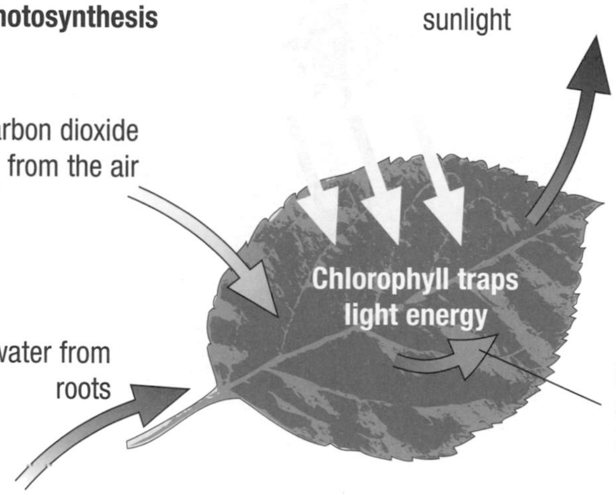

Did You Know?

The world's tallest tree is a Coast Redwood which stands 112 m tall – that is 19 m taller than the Statue of Liberty – and all that growth has come from photosynthesis.

level 6

Photosynthesis and respiration

- Plants need to take in carbon dioxide for photosynthesis, and they give out oxygen. Plant cells also carry out respiration to free the energy from glucose. For this they need to take in oxygen and give out carbon dioxide.
- During the day, there will be more photosynthesis than respiration. The plant will therefore take in more carbon dioxide than it gives out and will give out more oxygen than it takes in. At night, there is only respiration taking place, so plants only take in oxygen and give out carbon dioxide.
- Photosynthesis is one of the most important chemical reactions on earth. It is how we trap the energy from sunlight AND how we replace the oxygen we use up in respiration.

Spot Check

1 Why do food chains always start with a green plant?
2 What gas does a plant take in to carry out photosynthesis?
3 Was does the word 'variegated' mean, and how is it connected to photosynthesis?

Energy resources

level 3

Non-renewable energy resources

- These are also known as **fossil fuels**: **coal**, **oil** and **natural gas**.
- They are the remains of plant and animal life that lived millions of years ago which have been squashed below the Earth's surface to form fuels. They are very concentrated sources of energy but will one day run out. Because they have taken millions of years to produce, we can't make any more so they are **non-renewable**.

Top Tip!

Don't confuse sources of energy with energy itself. Fuels are not energy, they are sources of energy.

level 3

Renewable energy resources

- Renewable energy resources are:
  - **solar** power
  - **wind** power
  - **tidal** and **wave** power
  - water stored behind dams for **hydroelectric** power
  - **geothermal** power (energy from hot rocks)
  - **biomass** (wood, straw, etc.)
- These are not such concentrated forms of energy – but they will not run out in the way that fossil fuels will, so we call them renewable.

Solar power

levels 3-4

Using energy sources

Fossil fuels can be transported and used anywhere once they have been brought up from below the ground. Renewable energy resources are not as flexible.

- You can only use solar panels in the daytime.
- Wind turbines only work on top of a hill or in open areas where there is a lot of wind.
- Tidal and wave power can only be used where the conditions are right. There are only two places in Britain where we can use tidal power.
- You can only use the energy from hot rocks to heat water if you live near some hot rocks.

Geothermal power

Wind power

level 5

Energy resources and the environment

- When fossil fuels are burned to release their store of energy, a large amount of carbon dioxide is released into the air. This carbon dioxide goes up into the atmosphere and forms an insulating layer.
- This means that, although the heat energy from the Sun can get into the Earth's atmosphere, the lower energy (reflected waves of radiant heat) cannot get out again. (See also Energy transfer on page 26.)
- This is called the **greenhouse effect** and the increase of this effect is the cause of **global warming**.
- Burning fossil fuels also releases sulphur and sulphur dioxide This can combine with water in the clouds to produce **acid rain** which damages trees and buildings.
- Renewable energy resources are mostly much cleaner and do not have any of these effects on the environment.
- However, burning biomass such as wood and straw does release carbon dioxide.

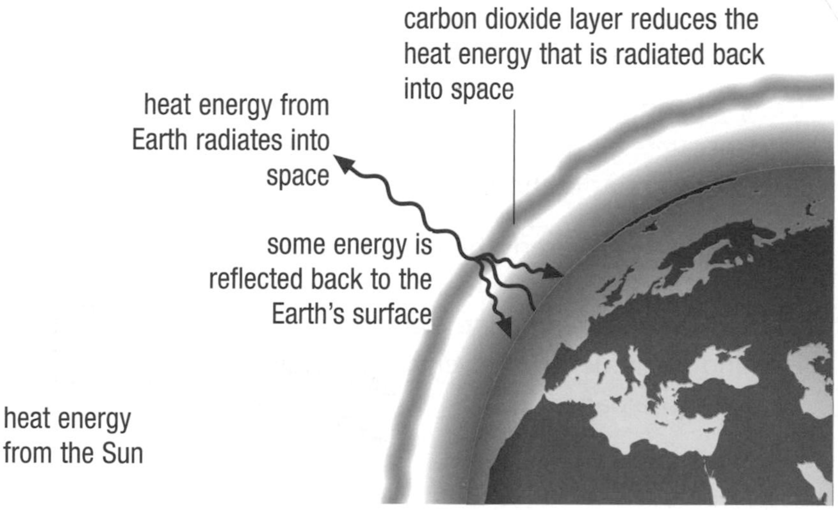

level 4

Nuclear power

- The energy stored in the atoms of radioactive materials such as uranium (a naturally occurring metallic element) can be released to produce energy to generate electricity.
- **Nuclear** power is not really renewable – but it is not a fossil fuel either.

Spot Check

1. Name three fossil fuels.
2. What is the name of the gas given off when we burn fossil fuels and which is causing the greenhouse effect?
3. Why are coal, oil and natural gas called non-renewable energy resources?

Did You Know?

On Earth we get 700 000 000 000 000 000 000 (seven hundred million million million) watts of energy from the Sun every second.

Generating and using electricity

level 4

Generating electricity

One of the most important uses of fossil fuels and renewable energy resources is to **generate** electricity. This can then be used in our homes, schools and workplaces to give us heat, light and other forms of energy.

level 4

Using fossil fuels to generate electricity

- Coal, oil and gas are all used in power stations to generate electricity. The energy stored in coal, oil and gas is chemical energy.
- Whichever fuel is used, the process is always the same. Burning fossil fuels is the most efficient way of generating electricity – but burning fossil fuels causes environmental damage (see page 19).

Fuel is burned in a **furnace** to release energy in the form of heat.

↓

The heat from the furnace heats the water in the boiler, which creates steam.

↓

The steam turns the **turbine**.

↓

The turbine turns a magnet inside a **generator**, which produces the electricity.

Top Tip!

Remember that electricity is a kind of energy that has to be produced using another energy source.

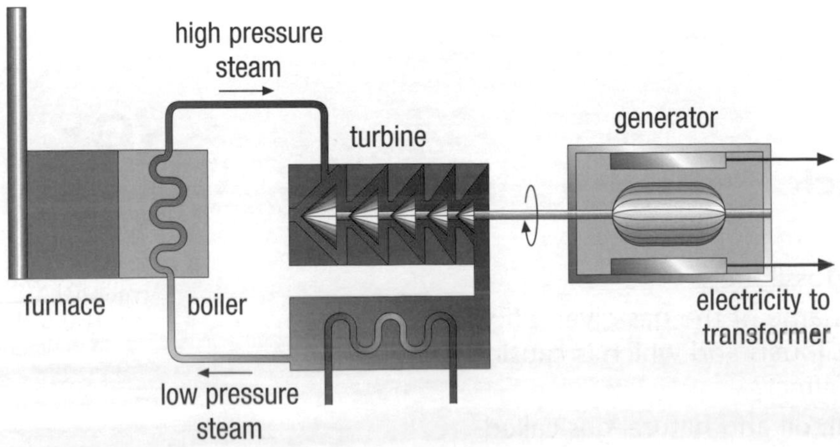

Did You Know?

If 1 million homes all had solar panels it would still only produce 0.1% of the 50 thousand million watts of electrical energy we use in the UK each year.

levels 4-5

Generating electricity from renewable energy resources

- Using wind turbines or tidal or wave power or water stored behind a dam to generate **hydroelectric** power relies on turning the **turbine** directly. There is no burning of fuel to heat water to make the steam to turn the turbine.
- **Solar panels** trap the energy of the Sun and use it to make electricity.
- These are more environmentally friendly ways of generating electricity but they are much less efficient.

level 4

Using electricity

- We use electricity for all sorts of purposes at home, at school and in the workplace.
- To conserve fossil fuel supplies and to reduce environmental damage, we need to try to cut down on the amount of electricity we use.
- These are examples of ways to reduce the energy we use:

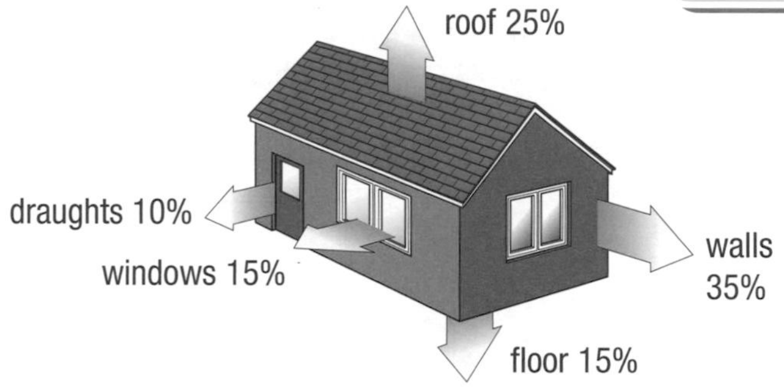

Heat loss from a house

Example of energy use	Way of reducing energy use
Heating our homes	Good insulation reduces the heat that is wasted. This can be done through double glazing, loft insulation and remembering to shut the doors and windows.
Lighting our homes	Use energy efficient light bulbs and turn off lights that are not necessary.
Washing ourselves and our clothes	Baths use much more hot water than showers. Always put a full load in the washing machine.
Boiling the kettle	Only boil the amount you need – don't boil a full kettle to make one cup of tea.

Spot Check

1 What does steam do in a power station?
2 What is the biggest difference in the process of generating electricity from renewable energy resources such as wind, tidal or wave power rather than from using fossil fuels?
3 Name **three** ways of reducing heat loss from our homes.

ENERGY Electrical circuits

level 3

Electrical circuits

We can only make use of electricity if we can provide a **circuit** for it to travel around. The circuit has to be made of the right materials and set up correctly for it to work.

level 3

Simple electric circuits

- Circuits must be made of materials that can carry electricity; these are called **conductors**. All metals conduct electricity and almost all non-metals are **insulators**.
- In order to work, electric circuits must be complete. We always draw them using symbols to stand for the component parts of the circuit. It is much easier to draw circuits using symbols – and everyone understands them.

Picture	Symbol	Component
	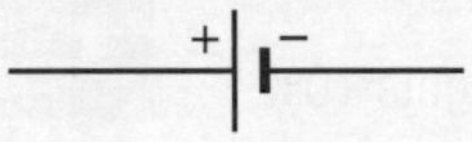	A single **cell**
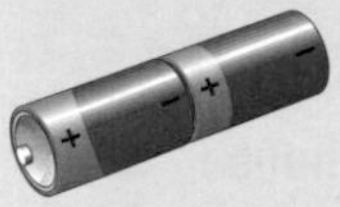	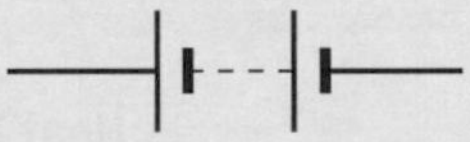	A **battery** of cells
	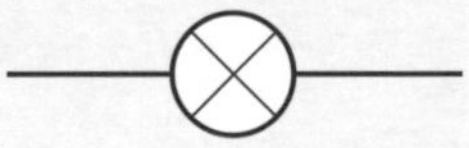	A **lamp** or bulb
	———	A connecting wire
		A **switch**

Top Tip!

Always draw circuits as a rectangle with the connecting wires drawn as straight lines even though real wires are often far from straight. Remember that for an electric current to flow, you MUST have a complete circuit.

level 5

Series and parallel circuits

- In a circuit, all the components can be one after the other – we call this a **series circuit**.
- Or the circuit can have two or more branches with components in each of the branches – this is called a **parallel circuit**.

download, watch and listen to help you revise
www.collinseducation.com/revision

level
5

Series circuits

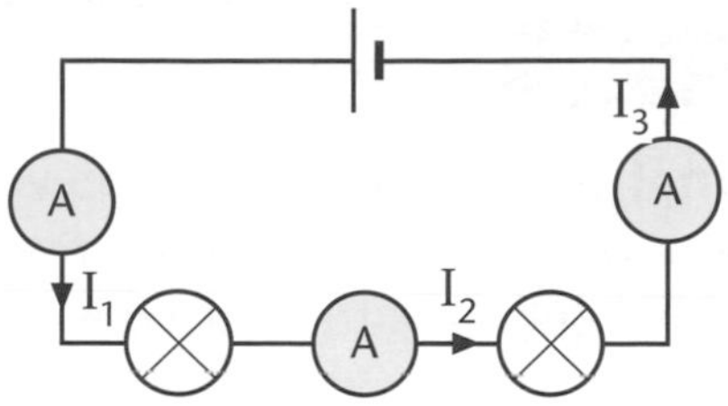

- A series circuit looks like this:
- When you see the letter I on a circuit diagram, it means the current.

On the diagram above $I_1 = I_2 = I_3$ as the current is the same at all points in the circuit.

The symbol (A) stands for an **ammeter** which is the instrument we use to measure current.

- In a series circuit, the current is always the same wherever you measure it. So the reading on all the ammeters in the diagram above would be the same. In a series circuit if one bulb breaks, it breaks the whole circuit and all the bulbs go out.
- This means you can always predict the current at any point in a series circuit provided you know what the current is at one given point.

Did You Know?

Bee keepers never put their hives near to electric power lines as this can affect the ability of the bees to make honey!

level
5

Parallel circuits

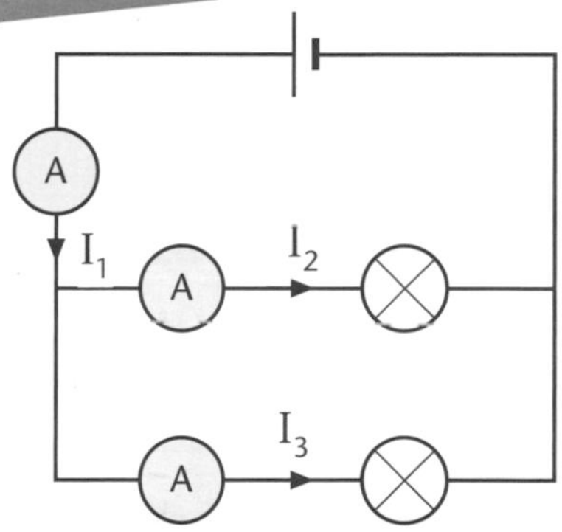

- A parallel circuit looks like this:
- In a parallel circuit, the current divides into two branches so $I_1 = I_2 + I_3$. If one of the bulbs breaks, there will still be a complete circuit to the other bulb, so it will stay alight.
- If all the bulbs in a set of Christmas tree lights are connected in series and one bulb breaks, all the lights go out. If they are connected in parallel and one goes out, then the others stay on! This is true for any parallel circuit whatever the situation described.
- Again you can always predict the current in one part of a parallel circuit provided you are given some information about the total current and what each of the branches looks like.

Spot Check

1 What name is given to an electrical circuit in which all the components are connected one after the other?
2 What is the key feature of current in a series circuit?
3 If one bulb breaks in a parallel circuit with several bulbs in it, what happens to the other bulbs?

ENERGY Energy transformation

Thermal energy

level 5

- Heat or **thermal** energy is there during every energy transfer – some energy is transformed into heat energy and given out to the surroundings. Often this is lost energy as it is too small to measure. Thermal energy is transferred in different ways (see page 27).

Top Tip!

Energy may change its form, but it is never created or destroyed. The same total amount of energy exists at the end of a series of transfers as at the beginning.

Light and sound energy

level 5

- These two types of energy travel as waves.
- Light energy or visible light is a kind of electromagnetic radiation which travels as a wave and transfers energy from place to place (see page 31).
- Sound energy is also a wave that transfers energy from place to place. Sound waves need particles to vibrate in order for them to travel – unlike light (see page 30).

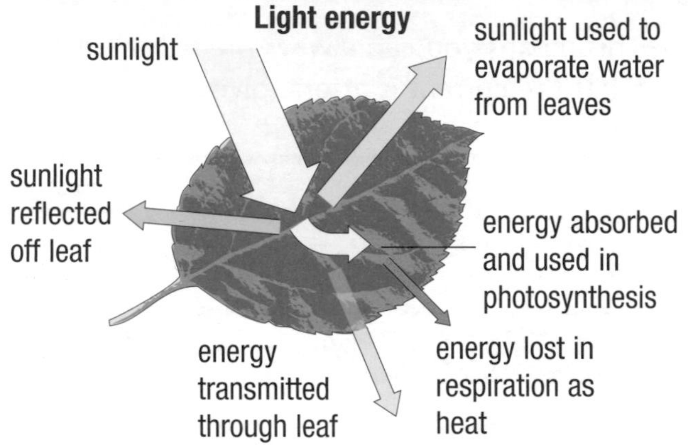

Sound energy

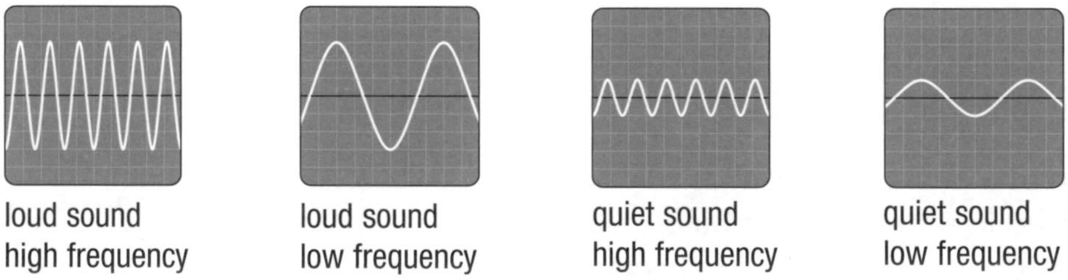

Kinetic energy

level 5

- **Kinetic** energy is the energy that all objects have when they are moving. It is sometimes called movement energy.

Electrical energy

level 5

- Electrical energy is the transfer of energy in an electric circuit. Electrical energy is very useful in our homes (see page 21).

level 5

Types of potential energy

- The forms of energy on page 24 are all visible 'energies at work', but before an object has any of these energies it needs to have some stored or **potential energy**.
- Potential energy is the store of energy that an object has because of where or what it is. There are different kinds of potential energy: **gravitational** **elastic** **chemical**

levels 5-6

Gravitational potential energy

- When an object is raised above the ground it gains a supply of **gravitational potential energy**. The vase on the shelf has gravitational potential energy.
- When it falls, that energy becomes kinetic energy as the vase moves towards the ground.

levels 5-6

Elastic potential energy

- When an elastic band or a bow string is stretched it gains a store of **elastic potential energy**.
- When the bow is released the energy becomes the kinetic energy of the moving arrow.

levels 5-6

Chemical potential energy

- **Chemical potential energy** is the store of energy inside the petrol you put in the car or the food you eat. A candle stores chemical potential energy which is then transformed into heat energy and light energy and transferred to the surroundings when the candle burns.

Spot Check

1 What name is given to all forms of stored energy?
2 What form of energy is always part of every energy transfer?
3 What is the biggest difference between the transfer of light energy and of sound energy?

Did You Know?

Energy transfers are not very efficient! A car engine only transfers about one third of the stored energy in petrol into movement – the rest is lost overcoming friction in the engine and changes to heat, making the car bonnet feel warm at the end of the journey.

ENERGY Energy transfer

level 5

Transferring energy

Energy can never be destroyed – it is just **transferred** from place to place. Sometimes it changes its form – and sometimes, when it is transferred, it is not in the form we want.

Top Tip!

Remember that energy is never used up. For example, when a battery is flat, it means that its store of energy has been transferred elsewhere, and then lost to the surroundings.

levels 5-6

Everyday energy transfers

- When we switch on an electric light, the energy has been transferred from a power station to our homes by the National Grid. The energy is then transferred to the light bulb and eventually to the surroundings.
- It is sometimes easier to think of the energy as changing its form. For example, in a light bulb it changes from electrical energy to the heat and light given out to the surroundings.

levels 5-6

Sankey diagrams

- We can show these energy transfers on a diagram as branching arrows. This is called a Sankey diagram. **Joules** are the units of energy.

For a coal-fired power station:

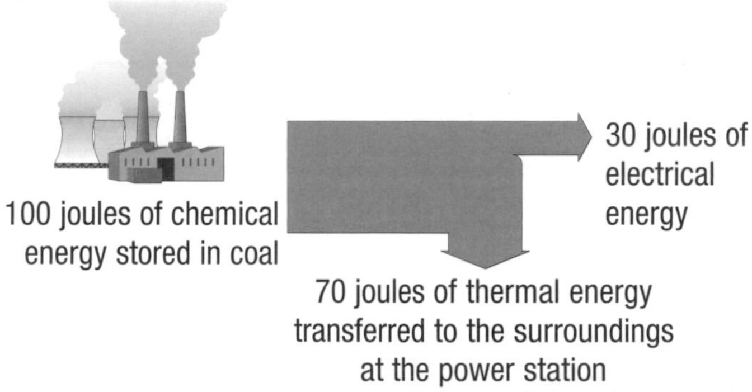

For an electric light bulb:

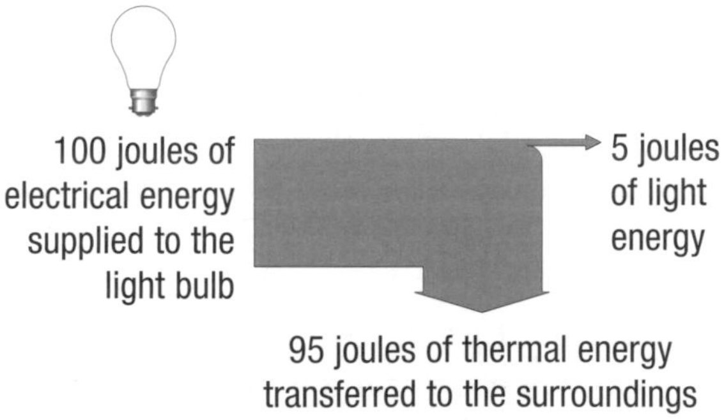

levels 5-6

Thermal energy transfer

- There are a lot of situations where we want to transfer thermal energy. Thermal energy can be transferred in three different ways:

conduction **convection** **radiation**

Did You Know?

'Radiators' in our homes transfer heat by setting up convection currents in the air – rather than by radiation.

levels 5-6

Conduction

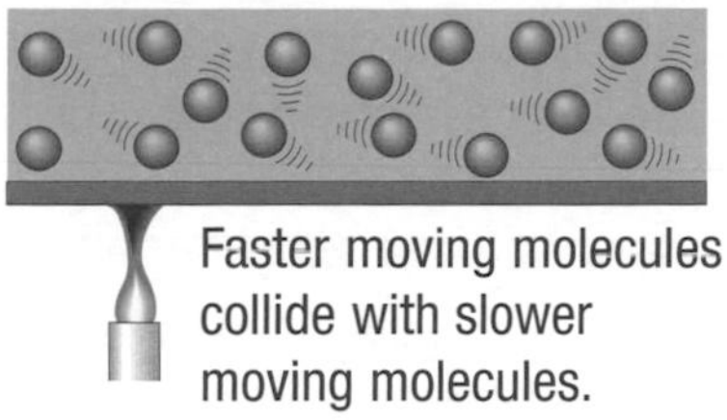

- Conduction is the transfer of thermal energy through solids.
- Metals are good conductors of heat, non-metals are not. Saucepans are made of metal to transfer the heat to the food. A wooden spoon is used to stir the food because wood is not a good conductor of heat so you will not burn your fingers.
- Thermal energy makes the molecules move faster. As the faster molecules collide with slower moving molecules, the energy is passed through the material.

levels 5-6

Convection

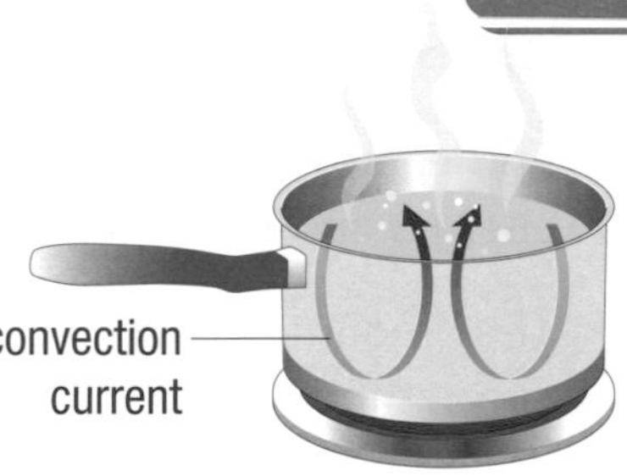

- Convection is the movement of heat through liquids and gases.
- The particles in the hot liquid (or gas) move faster and further away from each other. This makes the hot liquid less dense so it rises and the cold, more dense, liquid falls down to take its place. This process produces convection currents.

levels 5-6

Radiation

- Radiation is the heat given off by any object that is hotter than its surroundings. Black objects radiate heat more than white or silver ones. It is the way heat can move through a vacuum and is how the heat from the Sun reaches the Earth.

levels 5-6

Mixed heat transfers

- Sometimes heat transfer can be by more than one method. In the diagram on the right, heat is conducted through the cup wall and is radiated to the surroundings. Warm air above the cup rises by convection after being heated by the drink.

Spot Check

1 Of every 100 joules of energy supplied to a hairdryer, 30 joules of energy goes to the kinetic energy and sound energy of the fan. What are the other 70 joules transferred as?

2 How is thermal energy transferred through liquids and gases?

3 What happens to the particles in a piece of metal when it is heated at one end?

Energy from food

level 4

Capturing the Sun's energy

All the Earth's energy from food comes from the Sun. The Sun's energy is trapped by plants during the process of photosynthesis (see page 16).

level 5

Energy transfers from food

- The food we eat is a store of chemical **energy**. The energy is released by the chemical reaction of **respiration** which happens in every cell in our bodies.
- We can show respiration in a word equation like this:

  Glucose + oxygen → carbon dioxide + water + energy

- This energy is then used by our bodies as heat (thermal energy) and for movement (kinetic energy) and for all the processes that living things carry out (see page 15).
- The amount of food we need to take in depends on the amount of energy we are going to use. Surplus food is stored by our bodies – and this is when we put on weight!

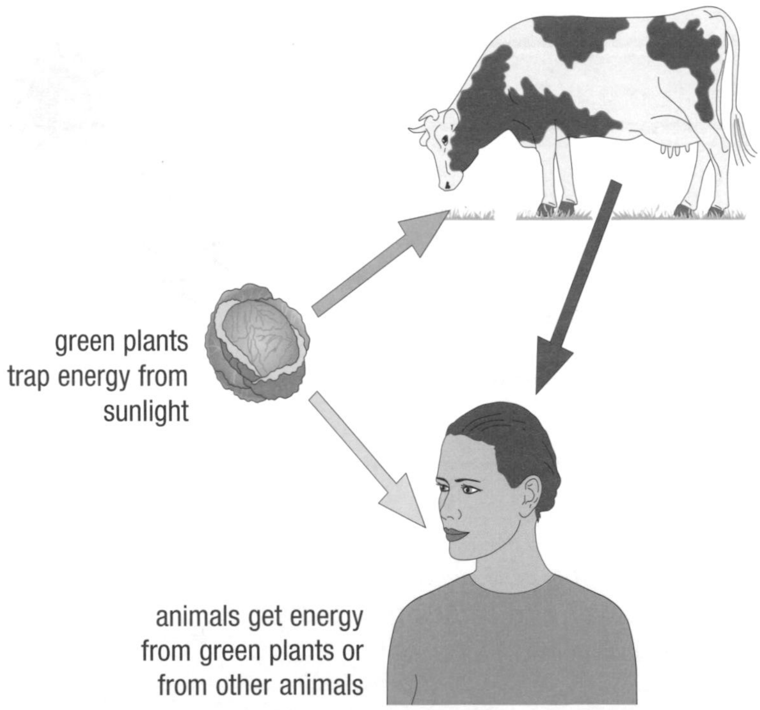

Top Tip!

A green plant always starts every food chain because only green plants can trap the energy from sunlight. Animals need to eat plants, or other animals that have eaten plants, so they can get the energy they need.

Did You Know?

Plants trap energy from sunlight and that is how we get our energy – but they only trap about 1% of the huge amount of energy that comes from the Sun.

Spot Check

1 Write the word equation for respiration.
2 How would you carry out an experiment to compare the energy values in different foods?
3 Which type of food is especially important to young people who are still growing?

Food labels

level 5

- Food labels always say how much energy is in a particular foodstuff. The one shown here is from a breakfast cereal. The energy content is given in **kilojoules** (kJ) and **kilocalories** (kcal).
- Energy values are given per 100 g – so that you can compare different foods – and for a normal serving, in this case 30 g of cereal with 125 ml of semi-skimmed milk.

Nutrition		
Typical values	Per 30g with 125ml semi-skimmed milk	Per 100g
Energy	738kJ **174kcal**	1624kJ **383kcal**
Protein	**5.8g**	**5.5g**
Carbohydrate	**31.7g**	**84.8g**
of which sugars	17.8g	38.3g
Fat	**2.7g**	**2.4g**
of which saturates	1.7g	1.4g
Fibre	**0.6g**	**1.9g**
Sodium	**0.6g**	**1.4g**

Matching our energy needs

level 5

- The recommended daily kilocalorie intake for women is 2000 kcal. For men it is 2500 kcal.
- Growing children, pregnant women, athletes and those who do hard, physical work need to take in more energy than adults who sit in an office all day.
- By carrying out an experiment to burn different foods and using the energy to heat water, we can see that different foods have different amounts of energy. A high energy food (high calorie value) will raise the temperature of water more than a low energy food.

Food groups

level 5

- Different food groups have different uses in our bodies:

Food group	Examples of foods that are good sources	What the body uses this for
Protein	Meat, fish, eggs, cheese, milk and other dairy products	Growth and repair
Carbohydrate	Bread, cake, rice, pasta, potatoes	Energy
Fat	Butter, cheese	Energy, especially long-term energy stores
Fibre	Vegetables, wholemeal bread, cereal	Helps the movement of digested food and encourages good bacteria to grow. Not digested – passes out of the body as part of solid waste.
Vitamins and minerals	Fruit and vegetables	Lack of these causes disease.

- The amount of each type of food we eat depends on the kind of life we lead. A healthy, balanced diet contains food from all these groups.
- To match examples of food intake to the right people, think about their needs. A pregnant woman or a young child will need extra protein for growth. A marathon runner will need extra carbohydrate to provide energy for running.

Sound and light

level 3

Waves for energy transfer

Sound and light are both ways of transferring energy from one place to another. They both use waves to do this but in different ways. Sound uses particles but light doesn't.

level 4

Sound

- Sound travels by making particles vibrate. Where there are no particles, sound cannot travel, but light can.
- Space has no atmosphere – and no particles – so we cannot hear the explosions on the Sun, but we can see the light that they produce.
- It is also why astronauts on the moon need radios to communicate with each other even if they are close together – there are no air particles in space to carry the vibrations.

level 4

Hearing sound

- We hear sounds because our eardrum vibrates and passes the **vibration** through to the inner ear where nerves pass the impulses to the brain. As we get older we lose the ability to hear very high-pitched and very low-pitched sounds. Very loud sounds can damage our hearing as loud sounds mean very big vibrations which can be harmful.

Top Tip!

Remember that the amplitude of a sound wave is related to the loudness of a sound and its frequency is related to pitch.

levels 5-6

Sound waves

- Sound can be described as a wave. What the wave looks like shows us what the sound will be like. The **pitch** of a sound depends on the **frequency** of the waves – that is how close together the waves are or how many waves pass a given point in one second. The **loudness** of a sound depends on the **amplitude** or height of the wave.

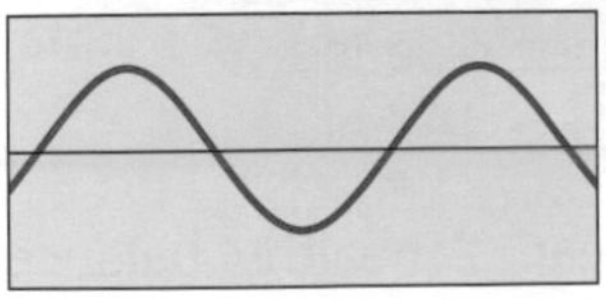

The sound on the left would have a lower pitch than the sound on the right.

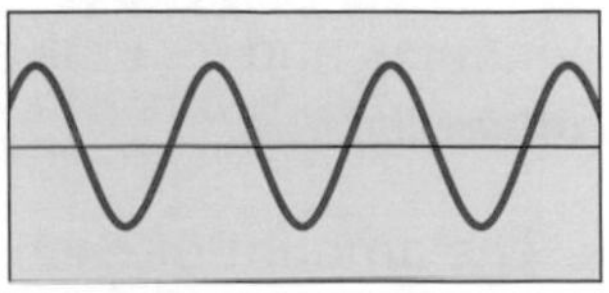

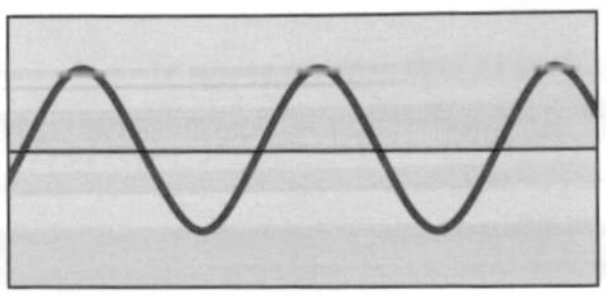

The sound on the left would be quieter than the sound on the right.

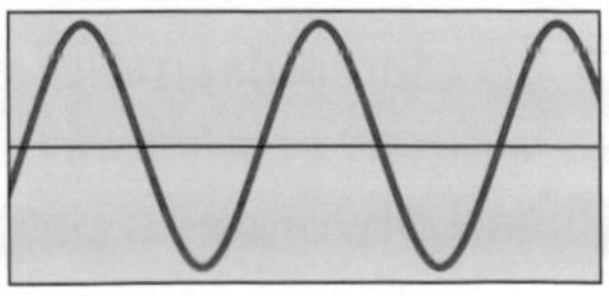

Did You Know?

'Laser' stands for Light Amplification by Stimulated Emission of Radiation. Lasers are single colour, concentrated beams of light. High power lasers can be used for cutting through metal.

level 4

Light

- Light also travels as a wave – but unlike sound it does not depend on vibrations and does not need a material to travel through.
- A few things give off their own light, for example, stars (but not planets), light bulbs, candles and fires. These are called **luminous** objects.
- We see everything else because the light is **reflected** into our eyes.

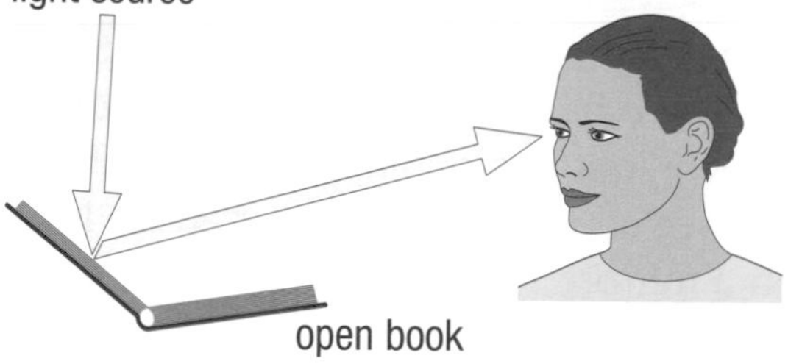

level 4

Seeing straight

- Light travels in straight lines. Light can only go through materials that are **transparent**. We cannot see through brick walls because they are **opaque**. Some things, like frosted bathroom windows, are **translucent** which means they will let some light through.
- Light cannot go through opaque objects and, because it travels in straight lines, it cannot go round them and this explains why opaque objects make shadows.
- We can only see things when reflected light reaches our eyes – and light travels in straight lines. The cyclist and the car driver will only be able to see each other when there is a straight line between them and nothing opaque in between – that is when the car gets to point B.

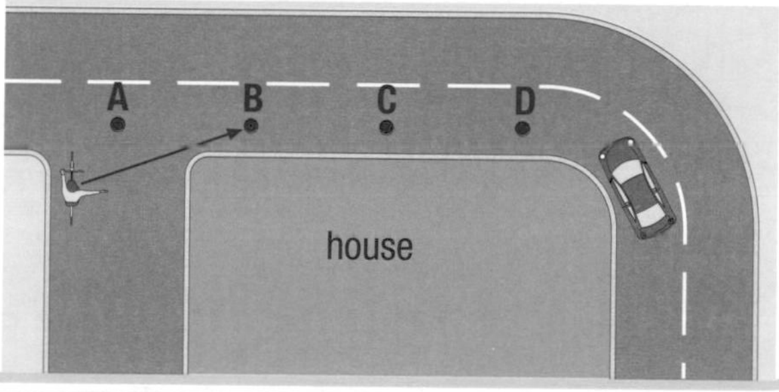

level 4

Comparing light and sound

You need to be able to compare the behaviour of light and sound waves.

- Sound will only travel where there are particles to vibrate. Light only will travel in straight lines through air, a vacuum or transparent materials.
- Light travels very much faster than sound – about a million times as fast. This is why we always see lightning before we hear thunder; the gap between the two gives us an idea of how far away the storm is. The storm will be about 1 km away for every 3 seconds you count.

Spot Check

1. What is the proper name for the height of a wave?
2. If a sound wave has a high frequency, what will this mean for the sound?
3. What do we call an object that gives off its own light?

Reflection, refraction and seeing colour

level 4

Reflection

When light hits an opaque surface, some of it is reflected back into our eyes and we see the object. When light hits a shiny surface all of it is reflected and we see an image, such as when we look at ourselves in a mirror.

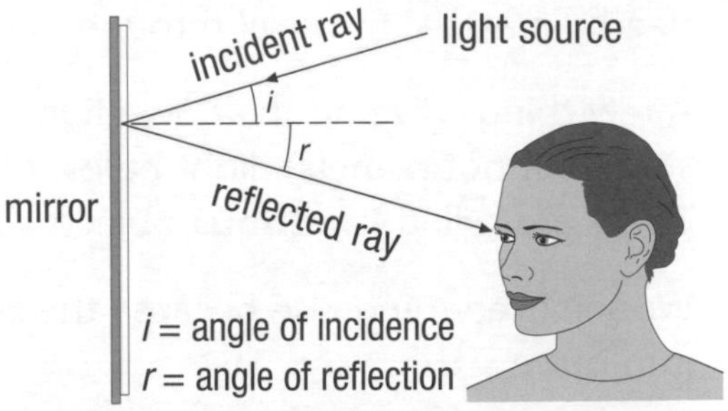

Top Tip!

When you draw a ray of light, make sure it is a straight line (drawn with a ruler) and has an arrow to show its direction. If it is going to someone's eye – make sure it goes right to the eye.

level 4

Rays

- The light rays hitting the mirror are called **incident** rays and those coming out again are called **reflected** rays.
- The angle at which the light hits the mirror is called the angle of incidence.
- The angle at which the light is reflected is called the angle of reflection.

The angle of incidence = the angle of reflection

- This means that the light leaves the mirror at the same angle as it hits the mirror.
- We can use this fact to help us to see over high walls and around corners using a **periscope**. The light coming into the periscope hits the first mirror at 45 degrees and so is reflected out at 45 degrees which means the light has turned through 90 degrees. The same then happens at the second mirror.

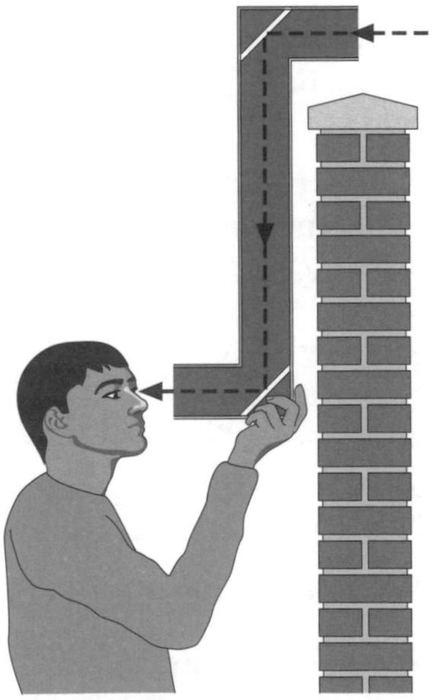

Spot Check

1 What is the name of a device that uses two mirrors to help us to see over high walls and around corners?
2 What is the proper scientific word to describe how a ray of light bends when it goes from air to glass or water to air?
3 If an object looks black, what is happening to the light that falls on it?

Refraction

level 5

- Light travels in straight lines but it does change direction if it hits the boundary between two different materials at an angle. This is called **refraction**.
- Refraction explains:
  - why water always looks shallower than it is
  - why it is hard to tell where an underwater object really is
  - why a straw in water looks bent.

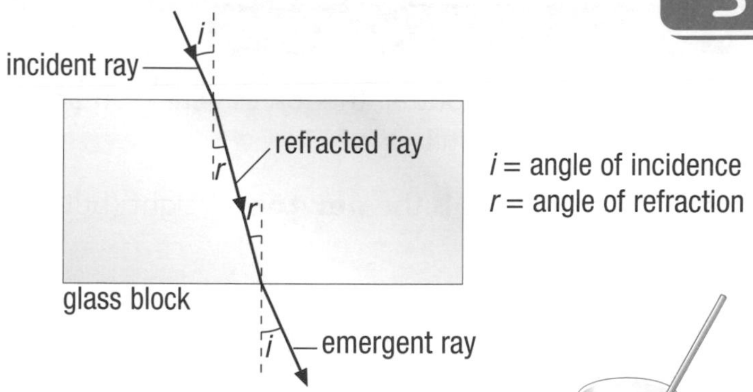

The spectrum

level 6

- White light is a mixture of the seven colours of the **spectrum**. White light can be split into a spectrum using a **prism**.
- The colours of the spectrum – Red, Orange, Yellow, Green, Blue, Indigo and Violet – can be remembered like this: Richard Of York Gave Battle In Vain.

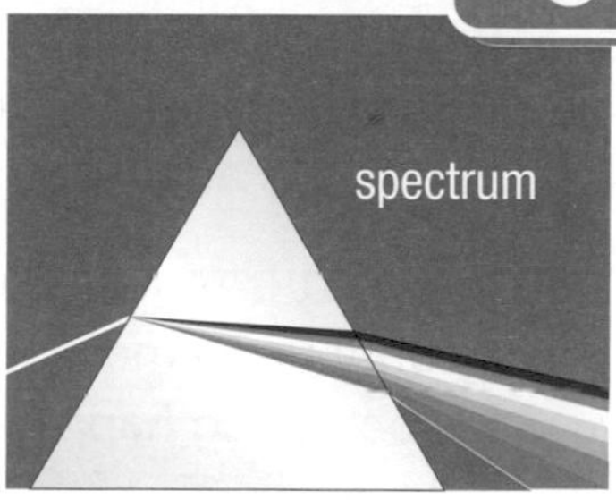

Did You Know?

Sir Isaac Newton was the first person to look at white light through a prism and see it split into the colours of the spectrum. When we see a rainbow, white light from the Sun is being split into colours because raindrops in the air act as prisms.

Seeing colour

level 6

- We see things as being coloured because, when the white light falls on them, only part of the spectrum is reflected into our eyes. Red objects reflect red light; blue objects blue light, etc. White objects reflect all the colours of light. Black objects look black because they absorb all the light and do not reflect any of it.
- Coloured filters only allow that colour of light to pass through and absorb the rest of the spectrum. A red traffic light is a bulb giving off white light behind a red filter that only lets red light through.
- Light travels in straight lines but water, mirrors and coloured filters can affect what we see and how we see it.

Balanced and unbalanced forces

level 4

Forces acting on an object

You need to think about all the forces acting on an object and how they combine to make the object move or stay still.

The unit for all forces is the **newton**. Weight (but not mass) is a force and so is measured in newtons (N).

level 4

Balanced forces

- Look at the picture of a man standing on a bench.
- The weight of the man pushes down on the bench with a force of 750 N. The bench pushes back up with a force of 750 N. The forces are **balanced**.
- Stationary objects have balanced forces acting on them. They do not move because the forces are balanced NOT because there are no forces at all – forces are acting on everything all the time.
- If an object is moving and the forces on it are balanced, then it will continue to move at the same speed in the same direction until something happens to make the forces **unbalanced**.
- This boat is floating because the weight of the boat acting downwards is exactly balanced by the upthrust from the water acting upwards. The forces are balanced.

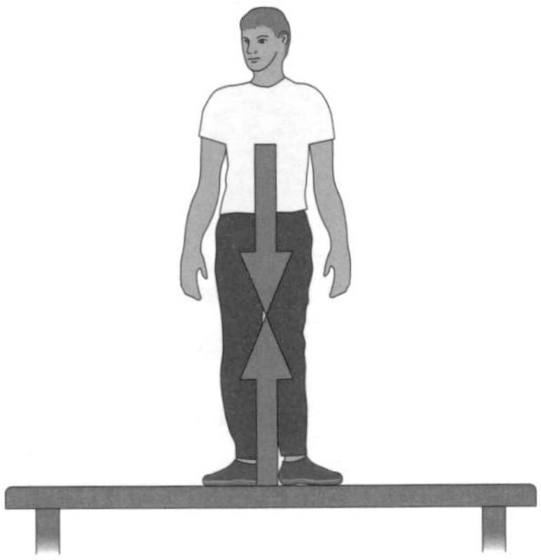

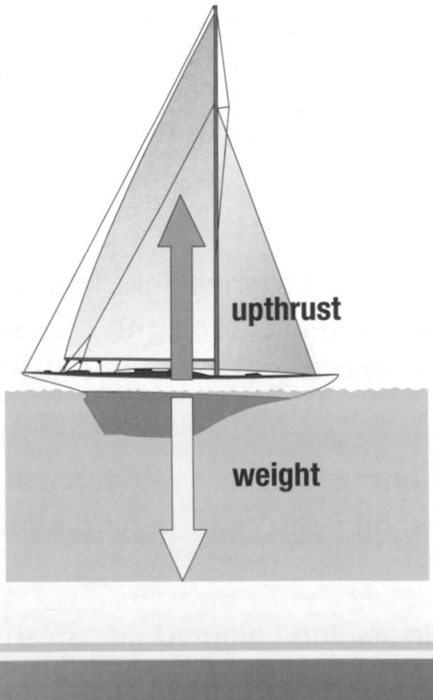

Top Tip!

A mass of 100 g has a force of about 1 N due to gravity.
A mass of 1 kg has a force of about 10 N due to gravity.

Did You Know?

The line painted on the side of cargo ships is called the Plimsoll line – after Samuel Plimsoll. When fully loaded, a ship can safely go down in the water to this level. Upthrust from the sea will balance the load and the ship will float. The temperature of the water and its salinity determine the level of the line.

Unbalanced forces

levels 3-4

- Unbalanced forces make things change:

speed **direction** **shape**

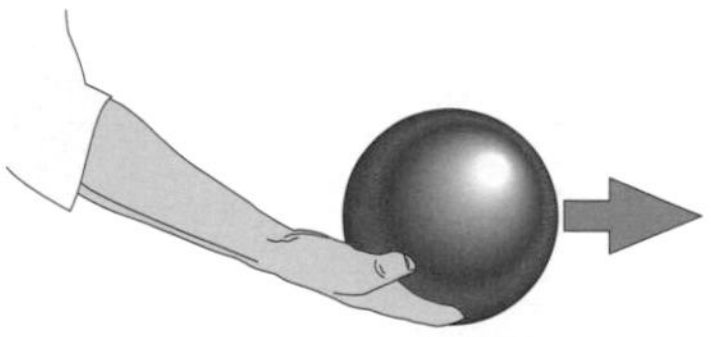

Pushing a bowling ball
The **push** force makes the ball move as it is greater than the other forces, such as friction, which act on the ball.

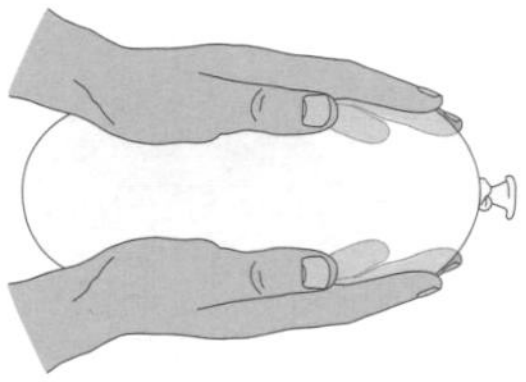

Squashing a balloon
The balloon is squashed and changes shape because the push of the hands is greater than the force of the air acting on the inside of the balloon.

Twisting a bottle top
The **twist** force on the bottle top is greater than the friction, so the top starts to move.

Pulling a water skier
The **pull** force of the boat on the skier is greater than the drag of the water, so the skier moves forward.

Speeding up and slowing down

level 5

- For a car to increase its speed, the force from the engine (using the accelerator) must be greater than the **air resistance** and the **friction**, which act to slow it down.
- To make a car reduce its speed, the forward force from the engine must be reduced by not pressing the accelerator pedal and the friction increased by putting on the brake. There is more about air resistance on page 41 and about friction on page 38.

Pressure

level 5

- The pressure arising from a force acting on any object will be greater if the force acts over a smaller area. That is why knife blades and the points of needles are very narrow – to make the pressure as great as possible.
- Skis and tractor tyres have the largest possible area to spread the force and make the pressure as low as possible to stop them sinking into the ground.

Spot Check

1. What **three** things can an unbalanced force change in a moving object?
2. If the forces on a moving object are balanced, what will happen to the moving object?
3. How can you increase the pressure on an object without increasing the size of the force?

Speed and motion

levels 4-5

Speed

- If a car travels a **distance** of 50 kilometres in one hour, we say it has travelled at a **speed** of 50 kilometres per hour (km/h). If a person walks 10 metres in 10 seconds we say they have walked at a speed of 1 metre per second (m/s).
- If we know the distance travelled and the **time** taken, we can calculate speed using the equation:

  Speed = distance ÷ time

  If a car travels 200 km in 4 h then:

  Speed = distance ÷ time
  = 200 ÷ 4
  = 50 km/h
- The units used for speed not only need to be correct, but also suitable for the purpose. Speeds are generally measured in metres per second (m/s) but for a car or an aeroplane, kilometres per hour (km/h) or miles per hour (mph) is better. For something moving very slowly then it might be millimetres per second (mm/s) or even millimetres per hour (mm/h).

levels 4-5

Distance

- We can also calculate the distance travelled if we know the speed at which an object was moving and the length of time for which it moved at that speed.

  Distance = speed × time

  If you walk at a steady pace of 2 m/s for 30 min, then you can calculate the distance.

  Change minutes to seconds first: 30 × 60 = 1800 s

  Distance = speed × time
  = 2 × 1800
  = 3600 m

levels 4-5

Time

- And finally, we can work out the time it will take for a particular journey if we know the distance we have to travel and the speed we will be moving at.

  Time = distance ÷ speed

  If an aeroplane travels at 450 miles per hour, then you can calculate the time taken for a journey of 9000 miles.

  Time = distance ÷ speed
  = 9000 ÷ 450
  = 20 h

Top Tip!

Always include the units with your answer when working out speed, distance or time.

levels 4-5

The speed triangle

- You can use this triangle to help you remember these equations. Just cover the quantity you want to find and the triangle shows how to work it out.

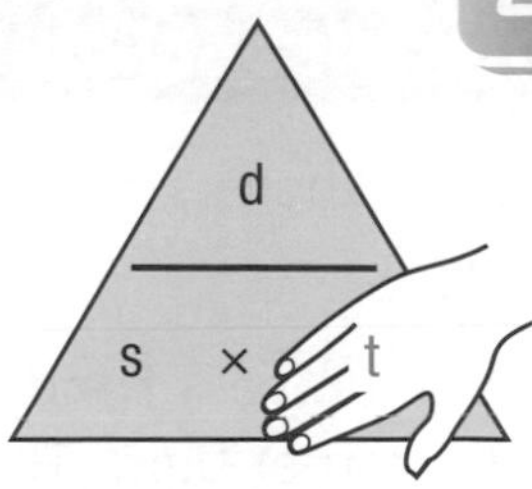

levels 4-5

Average speed

- It would be most unusual for any journey to be travelled at exactly the same speed all the way. A bus stops to pick up passengers, a car slows down at traffic lights and roundabouts and even a person walking has to stop before they cross the road. It would be very complicated to work out the individual speeds for each part of any journey, which is why we use the total distance and the total time to give us the **average speed**:

$$\textbf{Average speed} = \frac{\textbf{total distance travelled}}{\textbf{total time taken}}$$

Did You Know?

The current land speed record is 763 mph.

levels 4-5

Distance-time graphs

- We can show what an actual journey looks like on a distance-time graph.
- Between A and B the bus is moving at a steady speed. The line is going up and is straight.
- Between B and C it is stationary. The line doesn't go up.
- It then moves at a slow, steady speed between C and D. The line is not very steep.
- It then moves at its fastest speed for the journey – it covers more distance in the time – from D to E. Here the line is steepest.
- Between E and F it is stationary again.

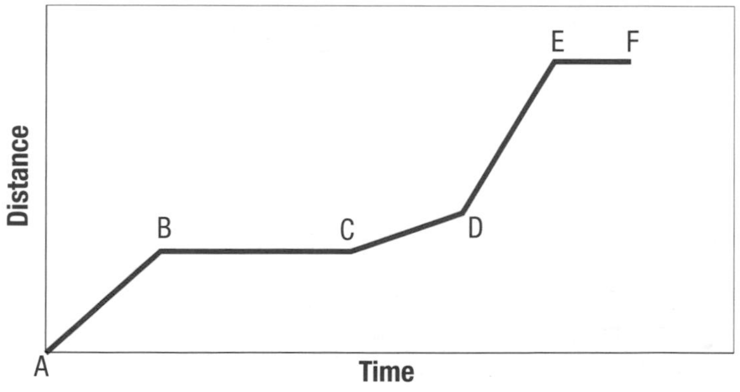

Spot Check

1. If a train journey of 150 miles takes 3 hours, what was the average speed of the train?
2. Does this mean that the train travelled at a steady speed for the whole journey?
3. What would be suitable units to describe the speed of a sprinter running a 110 m race?

Friction

level 5

Friction between moving objects

Wherever there is movement there is **friction** – and friction always acts against the movement causing it.

- If you rub your hands together very quickly they will get hot. If you slide on a carpet you may get a carpet burn. These are both everyday examples of friction.
- Whenever two solid touching surfaces move, there is friction. The rougher the surfaces, and the faster they move, the more friction there will be.

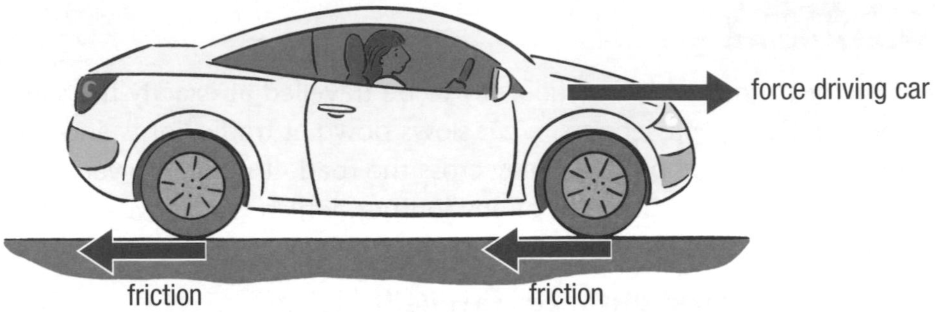

level 5

Balancing friction

- In this diagram, it is the friction between the chain and the table that is stopping the chain from falling off the table. The two forces of weight and friction are balanced.

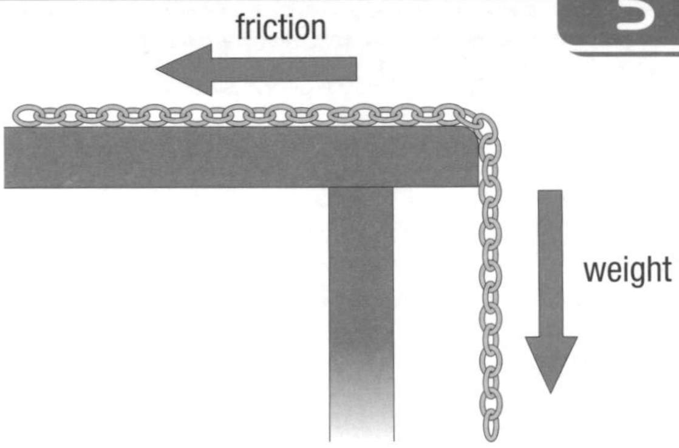

Top Tip!

Don't forget friction when thinking about whether forces are balanced or unbalanced.

level 5

Overcoming friction

- The force you need to apply to move this box will have to be greater than the friction between the box and the floor. If the size of the push is less than or equal to the friction, then the box will stay still.

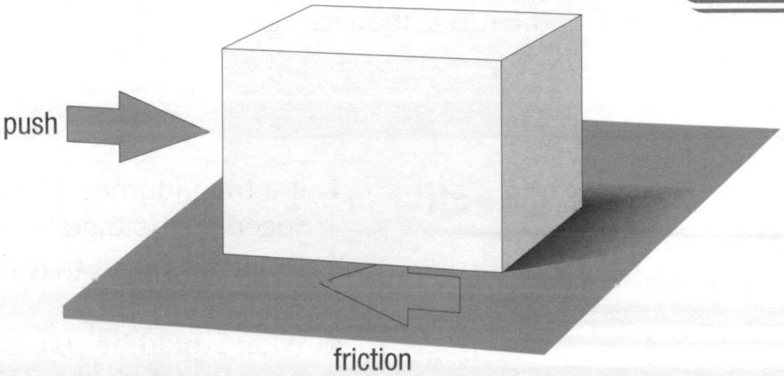

levels 5-6

Effects of reduced friction

Friction can be a great nuisance – it causes wear on all sorts of moving parts in many types of machinery. It is also, however, something we could not manage without.

- When you slip on an icy pavement on a winter morning, it is because there is not enough friction between your shoes and the pavement.
- Cars take longer to stop on wet or icy roads because there is less friction between the tyres and the road.
- Worn tyres are dangerous because they reduce the friction between the car and the road.

Did You Know?

The first bicycles appeared in Paris is 1791. By the 1880s they had become very fashionable, especially the penny farthing with its large front wheel and a small back wheel.

level 6

Using friction

- Think about all the points where friction is involved when riding a bike:

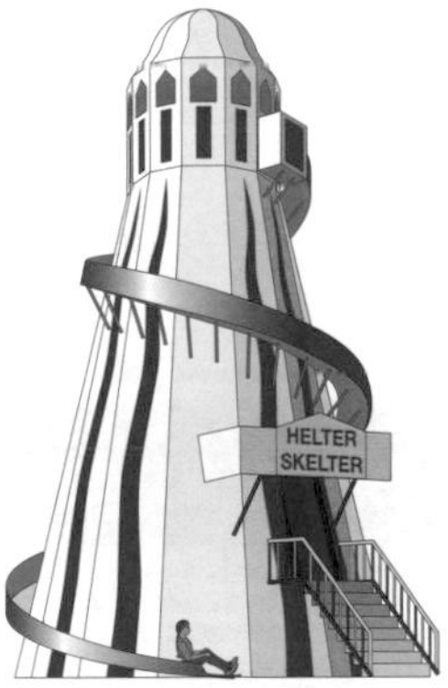

- On a slide, friction will slow you down, which may or may not be a good thing. A slippery mat will help you go faster because it will reduce the friction between your body and the slide.

Spot Check

1 Read these statements about the friction acting on a moving car carefully. Which ones are examples of **useful** friction?

- **a** The friction between the tyres and the road.
- **b** The friction between the moving parts of the engine.
- **c** The friction between the brake blocks and the wheels.
- **d** The friction between the wipers and the windscreen.
- **e** The friction between the driver's hand and the steering wheel.

2 A person is trying to move a heavy block that is resting on the ground by pushing it. What will be the size of the push force compared to the friction force at the point when the block starts to move?

FORCES

Streamlining and air resistance

levels 5-6

Friction in liquids and gases

Friction does not only happen between solid surfaces. Liquids and gases exert a kind of friction on objects moving through them as well.

levels 5-6

Air resistance

- Liquids and gases both exert friction on objects moving through them. The **drag** that a car, aeroplane or a parachutist feels when moving quickly through the air is called **air resistance**.
- Air resistance increases the faster you move, until the air resistance is so great that you cannot go any faster. This is why everything has a top speed. Cars, aeroplanes and even cyclists' helmets are designed to reduce air resistance and make the top speed as high as possible.

levels 5-6

Streamlining

- If cars have a **streamlined** shape it not only makes the top speed greater, but it also reduces the size of the forward force needed from the engine to move the car at any speed. The smaller this force needs to be, the less fuel will be needed to drive the car at any speed.
- In nature, fish and sea creatures have streamlined shapes to enable them to move through water with the least possible water resistance.

Top Tip!

When identifying the forces acting on a moving object, don't forget about air resistance as well as other forces such as gravity and friction.

Did You Know?

Without a parachute to slow them down, sky divers accelerate at a rate of 9.8 m/s/s. This means that in each second their speed is almost 10 m/s faster than it was in the last second.

levels 5-6

Air resistance and unbalanced forces

- When a parachutist jumps out of a plane, the force of gravity (see page 42) makes him accelerate towards the ground, and air resistance acts upwards to slow him down. The forces on the parachutist are unbalanced as the air resistance is less than the force of gravity and this causes him to fall faster.
- When arrows are used in diagrams to represent forces, the direction of the arrow shows the direction of the force and the size of the arrow shows the size of the force.

level 6

Terminal velocity

- Eventually the parachutist will be moving so fast that the air resistance slowing him down will be as great as the force of his weight speeding him up. As the forces are then balanced, he will stop accelerating and continue to move at a **constant speed**. This speed is known as **terminal velocity**.
- The upward force from the air resistance is now the same as the downward force caused by the parachutist's weight. The arrows showing the two forces are now the same size.

level 6

Changing forces

- When the parachutist opens his parachute, the air resistance will become much greater. This will slow him down. As his speed reduces, the air resistance will then become less. Eventually the forces will balance again and he will stop slowing down and continue at a new – but slower – terminal velocity.

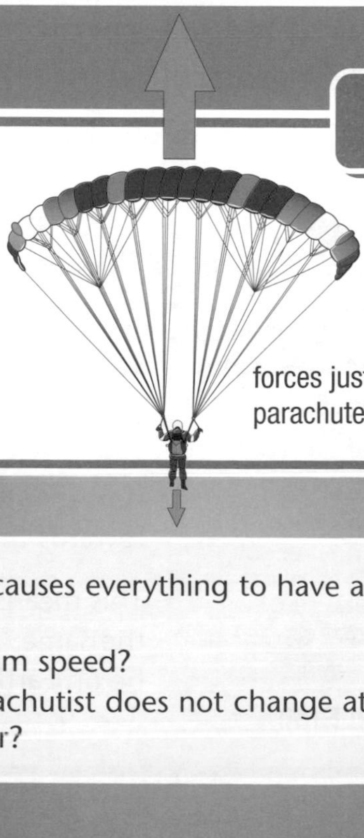

forces just after parachute opens

Spot Check

1. What is the name of the force that causes everything to have a maximum possible speed?
2. What name is given to that maximum speed?
3. Which of the forces acting on a parachutist does not change at any point as thcy fall through the air?

Gravity

level 3

Gravity, mass and weight

Like friction and air resistance, **gravity** is a force that is all around us.

- Any object that has a **mass** is subject to the force of gravity that causes a downward force called **weight**.

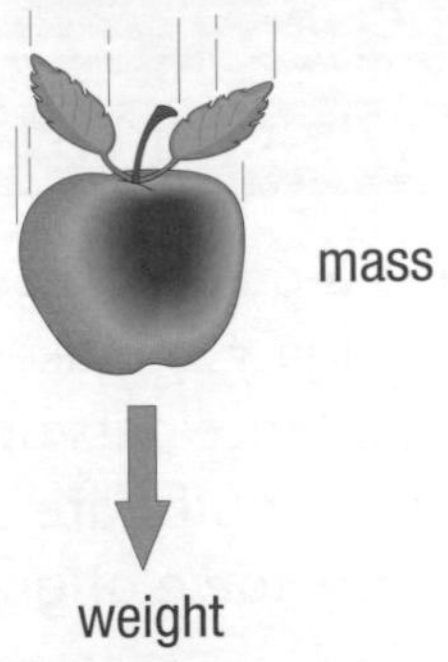

Top Tip!

Don't confuse mass and weight. Mass is the measure of how much there is of something (in kilograms). Weight is a force caused by gravity (in newtons).

level 4

Falling

- We think of things falling downwards, but in fact they are falling towards the centre of the Earth – otherwise, if people on the other side of the Earth dropped things they would float off into the sky!
- Wherever you are on the surface of the Earth, downwards always means towards the centre of the Earth.

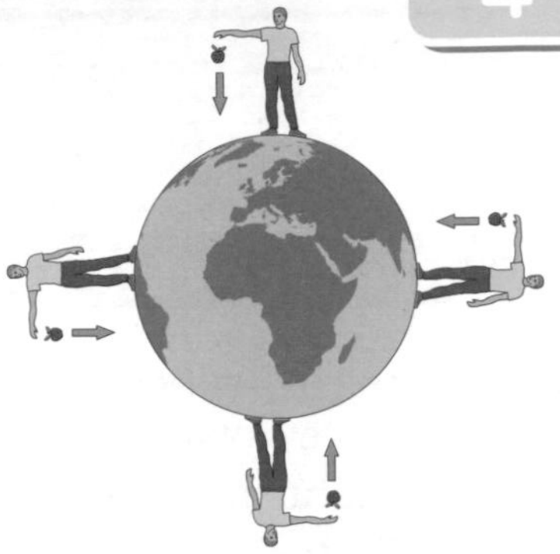

level 4

Gravitational pull

- Any two bodies exert a gravitational force on each other – but the effect of that gravitational pull depends on the mass of the body. This is why an apple falls towards the Earth – the Earth does not move towards the apple!
- On Earth a mass of 1 kg has a weight of 10 **newtons**.

level 5

Gravity and the Moon

On Earth

- The mass of the Moon is much less than the mass of the Earth. This makes the gravitational force pulling objects towards the centre of the Moon much less than the force pulling objects towards the centre of the Earth.
- This means that if we are on the Moon, although our mass is the same, our weight is less – about one-sixth of what it would be on Earth.

On Moon

level 5

Gravity on other planets

- On a planet with a bigger mass than the Earth, the gravitational pull is greater, so an object weighs more, but it still has the same mass.
- The amount of gravitational pull depends on the distance from the object as well as on the mass of the object. So if you travel in space, far from the planets, you will not be affected by the gravitational pull from any of them.

level 5

Newton and Galileo

- Forces are measured in units called newtons after Sir Isaac Newton, a scientist who lived from 1642 to 1727. He is said to have 'discovered' gravity when an apple fell on his head! Newton worked out how to calculate the gravity acting on objects – and used his ideas about gravity to predict how the planets moved around the Sun.
- Before Newton, an Italian scientist called Galileo Galilei did experiments on the force affecting falling objects. He thought that if he dropped objects of different masses from a great height, they would all reach the ground together. His theory was right, but the objects all hit the ground at different times because he did not take into account the air resistance acting on each object.
- Hundreds of years later Galileo's experiment was repeated on the Moon using a hammer and a feather. As there is no atmosphere on the Moon, there is no air resistance and so both objects hit the ground together.

Did You Know?

As well as his more famous scientific work, Isaac Newton invented the cat flap!

Spot Check

1 If a person has a mass of 70 kg what would their weight be: **a** on Earth; **b** on the Moon?

2 You want to show someone that Galileo was right – without going to the Moon. What other factors would you have to keep the same if you dropped a heavy object and a light object from the same height at the same time to show that they hit the ground together?

FORCES The Earth and beyond

level 3

The Earth and the Moon

Newton's ideas about gravity and forces help us to understand the motion of the **Moon** and the planets.

- The Moon **orbits** the Earth about once every 28 days – the Moon is kept on its path by the action of the Earth's gravitational field. The shape of the path is called an **ellipse** – rather like the shape of an egg.

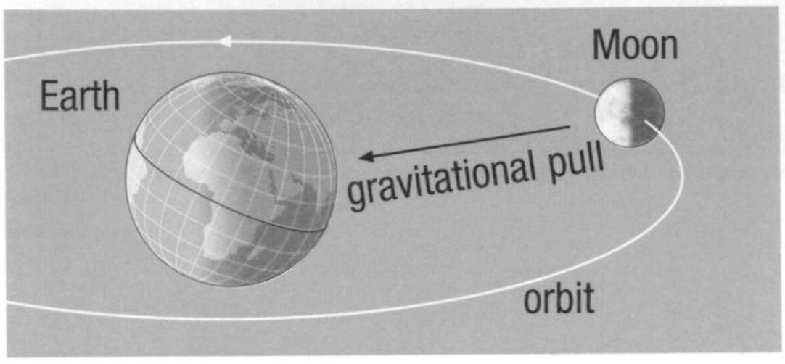

Did You Know?

Mercury, Venus, Mars, Jupiter and Saturn were discovered a very long time ago, Uranus in the 1780s, and Pluto and Neptune even more recently. But new smaller bodies are being discovered in space all the time. In 2003, astronomers discovered a tenth planet that they called Sedna.

- The Moon is much smaller than the **Earth**, the Earth is much smaller than the **Sun** – so the Moon is very, very much smaller than the Sun. When we look at the sky, the Moon and the Sun look about the same size. This is because the Sun is much further way. The Sun is about 400 times bigger than the Moon but it is about 400 times further away.
- The Moon does not give off its own light but reflects light from the Sun towards the Earth. The amount of the lit side of the Moon that is visible from Earth changes. When the Moon is between the Earth and the Sun, very little of the lit side of the Moon can be seen from Earth – this is a new moon. When the Moon is on the far side of the Earth from the Sun, the whole of the lit side can be seen – this is a full moon. In between, we see crescent moons and half moons.

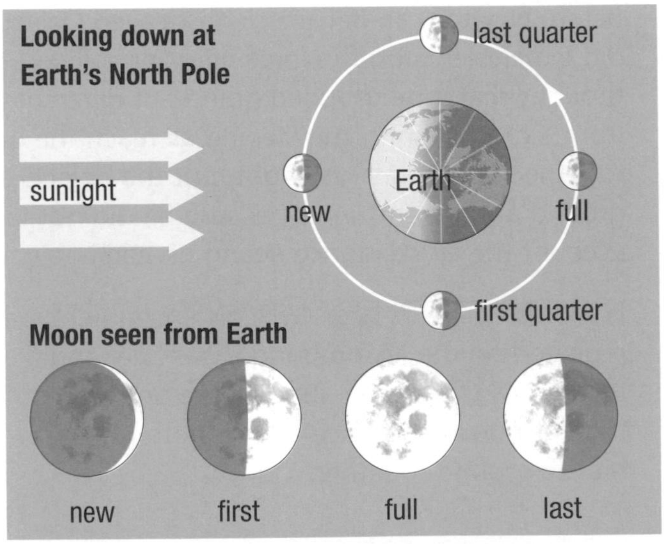

level 4

The Earth and the Sun

- The Earth orbits the Sun just as the Moon orbits the Earth. Long ago people thought the Earth was at the centre and the Sun and the other planets travelled around the Earth. Around 1500, a Polish astronomer called Copernicus was the first to suggest that the Sun was at the centre. Galileo agreed with this theory when he used an early telescope to observe the planets.

level 4

Day and night

- The Earth spins on its **axis** once in 24 hours – this gives us day and night.

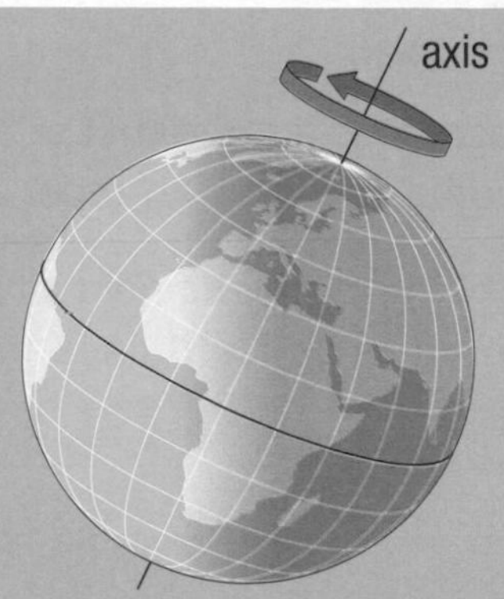

Top Tip!

Remember that the Earth spinning on its axis gives us day and night, but its orbit around the Sun determines our seasons.

level 4

Summer and winter

- The Earth orbits the Sun once in $365\frac{1}{4}$ days. The 365 days make one of our years and the $\frac{1}{4}$ days are added to give us an extra day in February every 4 years.
- During a year we have summer and winter because the Earth is tilted on its axis. When the northern **hemisphere** – where Britain is – is tilted towards the Sun, we have summer. When it is tilted away from the Sun, we have winter.

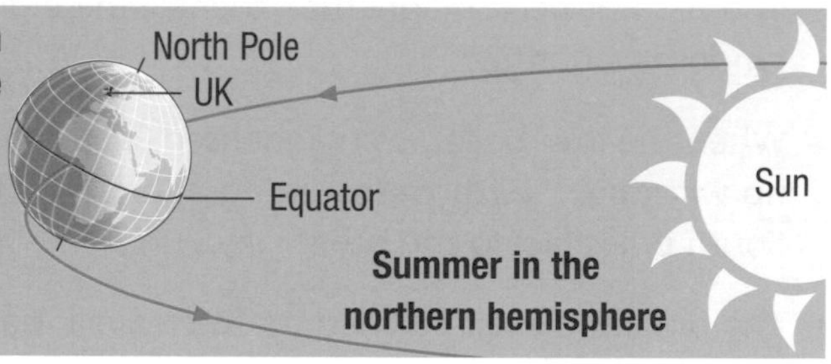

levels 4-5

The solar system

- The Earth is not the only planet to orbit the Sun. There are eight other planets in our **solar system** as well. It is important to remember the order of the planets.

Planets in order of distance from the Sun	MERCURY	VENUS	EARTH	MARS	JUPITER	SATURN	URANUS	NEPTUNE	PLUTO
A way of remembering	MY	VERY	EASY	METHOD	JUST	SPEEDS	UP	NAMING	PLANETS

Spot Check

1 How long does it take for:
a the Moon to orbit the Earth; **b** for the Earth to orbit the Sun?
2 Which **two** planets will have a shorter year than an Earth year and why?
3 Does the Moon give off its own light?

Magnetic forces

level 4

Magnetic fields

Like gravity, magnetism is a force that acts at a distance. Unlike gravity, magnetic forces can repel as well as attract.

- A bar **magnet** has a magnetic field all around it. Iron filings will follow the **magnetic field** lines and give a pattern around a magnet.

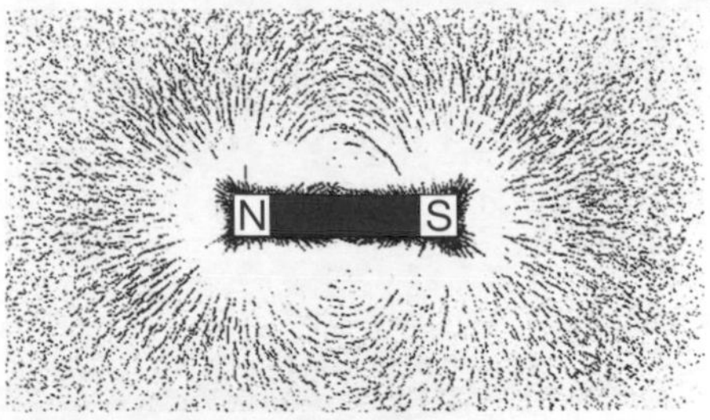

level 4

Dipoles

- Inside a piece of magnetic material such as iron, the atoms all behave like tiny magnets, which called dipoles. If the iron has not been magnetised then all these dipoles are randomly arranged.
- When the iron becomes magnetised, all the dipoles line up with their North **poles** facing in one direction and their South poles facing the other way.
- The dipoles can all be lined up to create a magnet by stroking the iron with an existing magnet or by using the magnetic field produced by an electric current (see page 47).

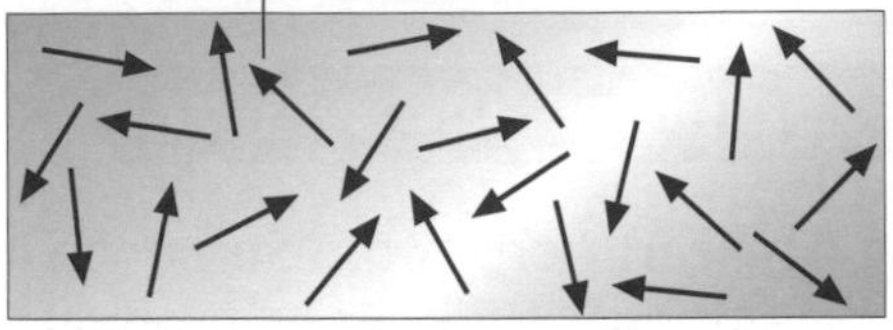

An unmagnetised piece of iron

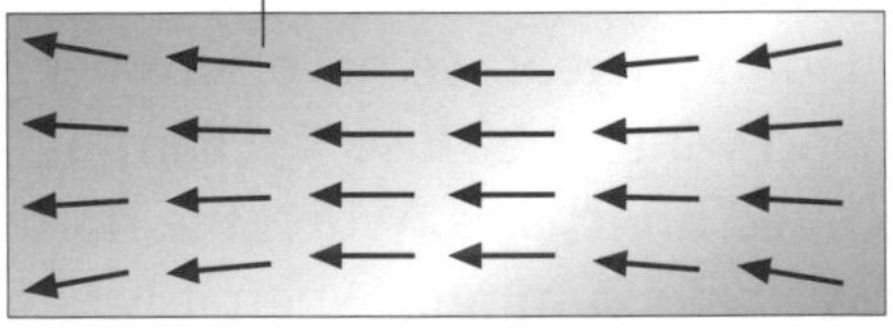

Magnet

Top Tip!

The only magnetic elements are iron, nickel and cobalt. Steel is magnetic because it is made mostly from iron.

levels 4-5

Repulsion and attraction

- If you put two magnets close to each other, and two like poles (North-North or South-South) are facing each other they will repel (this means push away). If two unlike poles (North-South) are together, they will attract.
- These two magnets will move away from each other …

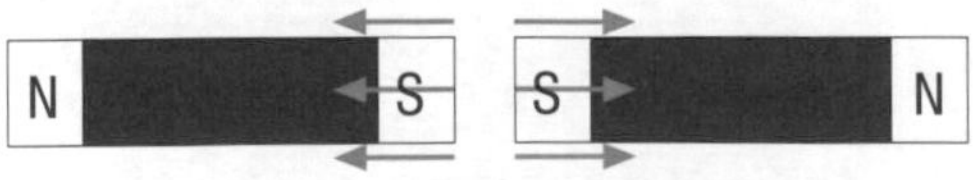

… but these two will move together.

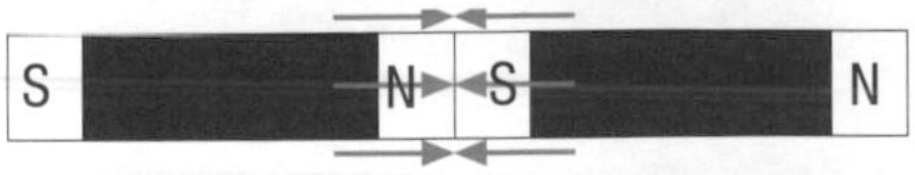

- A magnet will attract a piece of magnetic material, but only two magnets can repel each other.

Did You Know?

The strongest magnet in the world is an electromagnet in California which is 250 000 times stronger than the Earth's magnetic field.

The Earth's magnetic field

level 5

- The Earth has a magnetic field – in fact it behaves as if it has a giant bar magnet in its centre.
- The North-seeking pole of a magnet inside a plotting compass will point to magnetic North, which is not in quite the same position as the geographic North Pole.

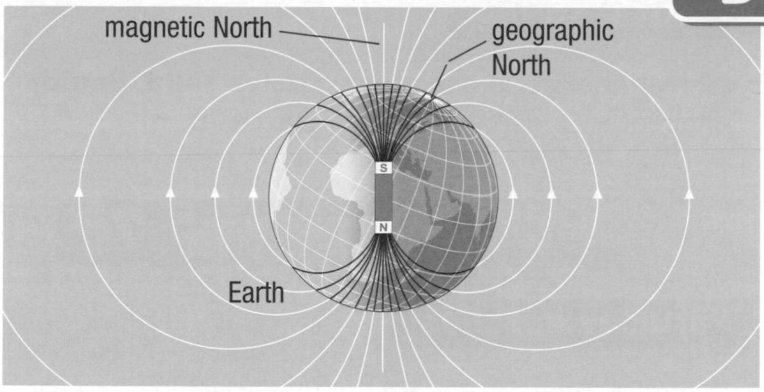

Electromagnets

levels 5-6

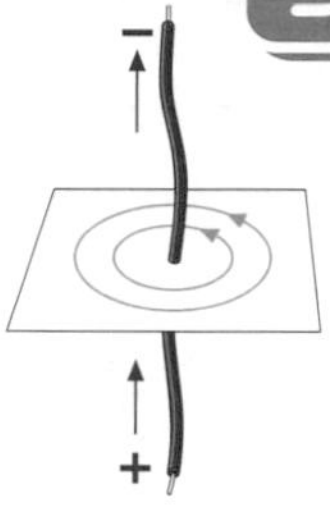

- Whenever a current flows in a wire it creates a magnetic field around it.
- This magnetic field can be used to magnetise an iron **core** – which will remain a magnet for as long as the current is flowing in the circuit. This gives us a magnet we can switch on and off, called an **electromagnet**.
- The nail acts as an iron core inside the coil of wire – this makes the magnetic field stronger than if it was just the field around the wire itself.
- You can also make the magnetic field stronger by having more turns on the coil or by having a larger current.
- Electromagnets differ from ordinary magnets because the magnet can be turned on and off by switching the current on and off.

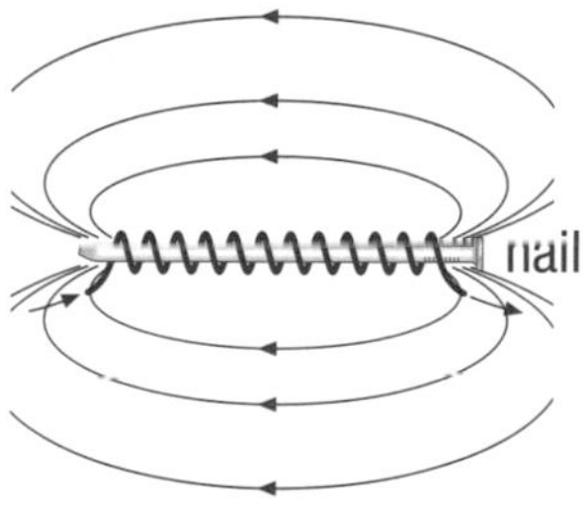

Using magnets and electromagnets

levels 5-6

- Simple applications include a cat flap that closes using magnets.
- Electromagnets are used in many everyday devices such as circuit breakers. They are also used in scrap yards to pick up or drop large quantities of steel from old cars. In hospitals, electromagnets are found in very delicate machines that remove metal splinters from eyes and wounds.
- A more complex application is a door bell that rings because it contains an electromagnet which can turn on and off very quickly, making a tiny hammer hit a bell many times a second to keep the bell ringing.

Spot Check

1. If you have a magnet and a piece of iron, how could you tell if the piece of iron was magnetised as well?
2. What **two** things can you change to make an electromagnet stronger?
3. What is the big difference between magnets and electromagnets?

PARTICLES Solids, liquids and gases

level 3

Particle states

- All matter exists in one of three states: **solid**, **liquid** or **gas**. These states of matter all have different arrangements of their **particles**.

level 4

Particles in solids

- In a solid, the particles are tightly packed in a regular lattice pattern. The bonds between the particles are strong and individual particles do not have enough energy to escape from the lattice. This is why solids have fixed shapes. The particles are not still – they vibrate within the lattice – but they cannot break free from it.
- It is important to draw the particles in a solid in this kind of regular, even, lattice structure.

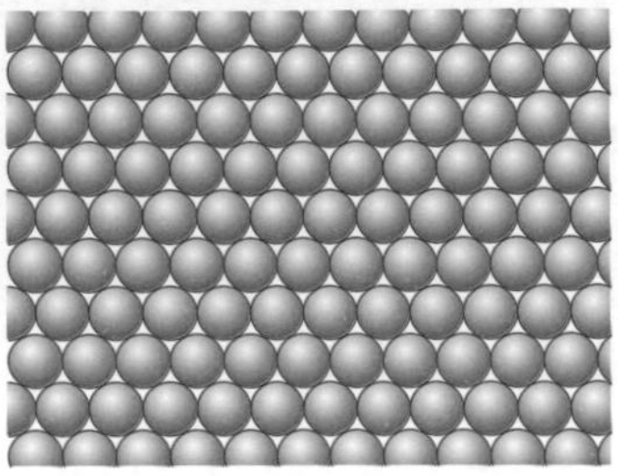

Solid

level 4

Particles in liquids

- When a substance is given more energy – usually by heating – the particles start to vibrate more and more until they have so much energy that the lattice structure starts to break down and the particles begin to slide over each other. The substance has then become a liquid. Liquids can flow and they take up the shape of their container because the particles are able to move more freely while still remaining in contact with one another. Liquids cannot be squashed.

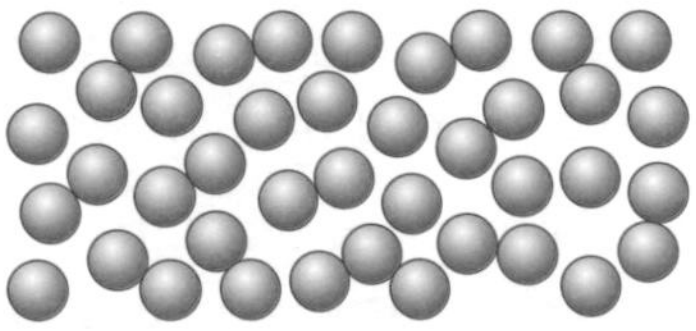

Liquid

- Particles in a liquid are the most difficult to draw. You must have two-thirds of the particles in contact with each other – but it must not be a regular pattern.

level 4

Particles in gases

- If even more thermal energy is put into the substance, then the particles move more and more freely until they can escape the bonds between them completely. The substance has then become a gas. Gases spread out to fill whatever space is available because the particles are free to move right away from each other. Gases can be squashed because there is so much space between the particles.

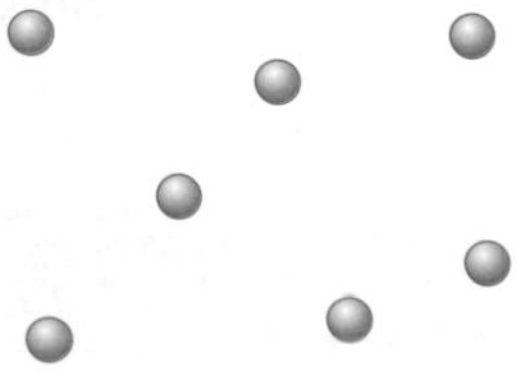

Gas

- Gases are the easiest to draw as there are only ever a few particles – well spaced out.

download, watch and listen to help you revise
www.collinseducation.com/revision

level 5

Changes of state

- A substance can change from a solid to a liquid, from a liquid to a gas, from a gas to a liquid or from a liquid to a solid. We describe this as a **change of state**.
- These changes are **physical changes**, NOT **chemical changes**. The substance remains the same – it is just in a different form – and these changes can be easily reversed.
- If you think of a beaker of hot water, it does let off steam but not all the water changes to steam at once. This is because the particles do not all have the same amount of energy. The most energetic particles will escape the liquid water as steam and the less energetic ones will remain as water.

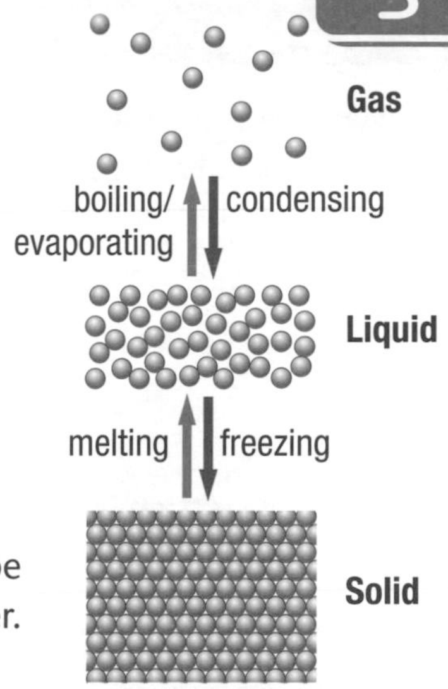

Top Tip!

Remember that water is a liquid, but water vapour is a gas.

level 4

More than one state

- Elements and compounds can all exist in more than one state of matter. Very cold oxygen and nitrogen will be liquids, as will very hot metals.
- The most familiar state for any substance will be its state at normal temperatures – oxygen as a gas and metals as solids – but they can exist in other forms.

Did You Know?

The temperature −273 °C is called Absolute Zero. It is thought that at this temperature everything would be solid – but no-one knows how to get any substance to this temperature.

level 4

Expansion and contraction

- When solids and liquids get hotter, they **expand** because the particles move further apart. When they cool, they **contract** because the particles become closer together. This is why, for example, railway lines are built in sections with small gaps in between to allow the rails to expand in hot weather.
- When solids and liquids expand, the particles move more and spread out more – the particles themselves do NOT get bigger. It is like living things growing because the cells divide and make more cells rather than the cells getting bigger.

Spot Check

1 What is the correct name for each of these changes of state: **a** from solid to liquid; **b** from gas to liquid?
2 How would you describe the arrangement of particles in a solid?
3 What are the particles in a liquid able to do that means a liquid can take on the shape of any container?

Solubility and separation

level 4

Solubility

- When a solid **dissolves** in a liquid, we say that the solid is **soluble** in that liquid. The liquid is called a **solvent** and the solid a **solute**. Together they make up a **solution**.
- Many solids will dissolve in some liquids but not in others. When a solid dissolves in a liquid, there is no chemical change – the solid substance is still there. It is may be less easy to see, but it has not gone away. You can demonstrate this quite easily:

Solvent

Solute

Solution

if you take 100 g of solvent ... and add 10 g of solute ... then you will have 110 g of solution.

The solid particles of the solute have spread out among the particles of the liquid solvent so you can no longer see them, but the increased mass of the liquid shows that they are still there.

- If a solid will not dissolve in a particular solvent, we say it is **insoluble** in that solvent.
- If you put sand into water, you can still see the sand because it is insoluble. If you put salt into water you cannot see it because it dissolves.

Top Tip!

Don't confuse the term solvent (the liquid) with the term solute (the solid), both of which make up the solution.

levels 4-5

Particles and solubility

- If a solid dissolves, it is because the particles are small enough to fit into the spaces between the particles of the liquid.
- If a solid does not dissolve, it is because the particles are too big. More solid can dissolve in a hot liquid as there is more space between the liquid particles when they have more thermal energy.
- This is important when we start to think about how to separate the dissolved particles from the liquid solvent.

Spot Check

1 Fill in the blanks in the passage by putting in the correct word from the list. You may need to use a word more than once.

solution insoluble solute solvent dissolve

To make a ...., take some .... and dissolve it in a .... If your solute will not .... in your solvent then it is .... Every solute will not dissolve in every ....

2 What method or methods of separation would you use to get sand and salt from water containing both these solids?

Did You Know?

Distillation has been around for a very long time – its first recorded use was the distillation of wine in the City of Bath in the 1200s.

Separating techniques

level 4

One difference between a mixture and a compound (see page 53) is that it is quite easy to get back the substances that went into a mixture and very difficult to get back the substances that reacted together to make a compound. There are several techniques that can be used to separate mixtures.

Filtration

level 4

- If you have a mixture of a liquid and a solid that has not dissolved, you can **separate** the liquid and solid by **filtering**.
- The mixture is poured through filter paper, which is full of tiny holes. The large, solid particles are too big to go through the holes and are left in the paper, but the smaller particles of liquid pass through – so the solid and liquid are separated.
- Filtering works for sand and water, but not salt and water because the tiny particles of dissolved salt go through the paper with the water.

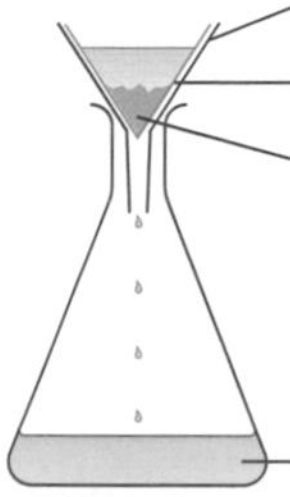

Filtration

Evaporation and distillation

levels 4-5

- To get pure water from sea water, you need to cool and condense the steam or water vapour produced when water boils, so that it turns back into liquid water. This process is known as **distillation**.

Evaporation

- Water boils at 100 °C and becomes steam. When you heat a solution of salt and water, all the water will evaporate leaving the salt behind. **Evaporation** is a good separation technique if you only want to get the salt from the solution and not the water.

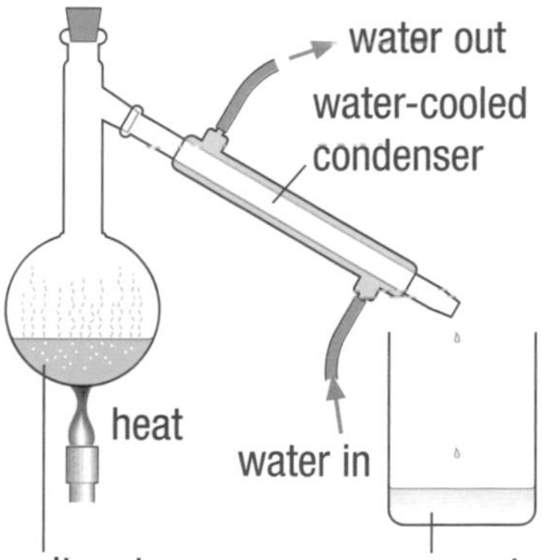

Distillation

Chromatography

levels 4-5

- When more than one solute is dissolved in a solvent, they can be separated using chromatography. In chromatography, the solutes, which all have different sized particles, move at different speeds across filter paper.
- Coloured inks are solutions made from several solutes with different colours (or pigments) dissolved in a single solvent. The different sized particles of the solutes can be separated by chromatography, creating a pattern of different coloured dots or lines on the filter paper.

Elements, compounds and mixtures

level 5

Elements

- An **element** is a pure substance. All the atoms in an element are of the same kind. For example, oxygen is made up of just oxygen **molecules**, and copper is made up of just copper **atoms**.

level 6

The Periodic Table

- All the known elements are listed in the **Periodic Table**. The elements are listed in order of how big their atoms are, and elements that are like each other are grouped together.
- All the metals are on the left-hand side and all the non-metals are on the right-hand side.
- The more reactive a metal is, the nearer it is to the left-hand side (see page 59 for more on reactivity). The elements in the last column on the right hardly react at all.
- In the Periodic Table, elements are represented by symbols. There are about 100 symbols. You do not need to know the whole of the Periodic Table, but you should know the names and symbols of the elements given below.

Element	Symbol	Element	Symbol	Element	Symbol
Hydrogen	H	Magnesium	Mg	Copper	Cu
Helium	He	Aluminium	Al	Zinc	Zn
Lithium	Li	Phosphorus	P	Lead	Pb
Neon	Ne	Sulphur	S	Gold	Au
Boron	B	Chlorine	Cl	Silver	Ag
Carbon	C	Argon	Ar	Sodium	Na
Nitrogen	N	Potassium	K	Nickel	Ni
Oxygen	O	Calcium	Ca	Iron	Fe

level 5

Combining elements

- Everything is made up of different combinations of the 100 or so elements. It is a bit like all the words in all the books in all the libraries being made up from the 26 letters of the alphabet!

- Just as letters go together differently to make up different words, so elements go together differently to make up different substances that we call compounds.
- Some molecules of some elements have only a single atom. But some elements, including hydrogen and oxygen, are made up of molecules which have two atoms each: H_2 and O_2.

Did You Know?

The Periodic Table was devised by a Russian scientist Dimitri Mendeleev in the late 1800s. He left spaces for elements that hadn't yet been discovered.

Compounds

level 5

- When two or more elements react together in a **chemical reaction**, a compound is formed. A **compound** is often very different from the elements that react together to make it – and it is very difficult, or impossible, to get the elements back.
- Sodium chloride, the salt that we eat, is a compound.

  The **formula** for sodium chloride is NaCl.

  NaCl is a white solid better known as salt. It is made from sodium, 

  which is a very reactive, soft, grey metal that reacts violently with water and chlorine, 

  which is a green poisonous gas that is used as a disinfectant in swimming pools.
- You might be asked to recognise the elements and atoms in a molecule of a compound. For example, a molecule of magnesium oxide MgO contains 1 magnesium atom and 1 oxygen atom. Something more complicated like ethanol C_2H_5OH has 2 carbon atoms, 6 hydrogen atoms and 1 oxygen atom.

Top Tip!

A mixture is a combination of substances that have NOT reacted with each other. A compound is a substance that is made when a chemical reaction takes place.

Mixtures

level 5

- Two or more elements, or compounds, can be mixed together in a way that does not include any chemical reaction. This is a **mixture**.
- The elements or compounds in the mixture do not change their nature and can be easily separated.
- An example of a mixture is sand and water. You can easily separate the two by just filtering off the water. As there has been no chemical reaction, the two compounds, water and sand, have not changed their nature.

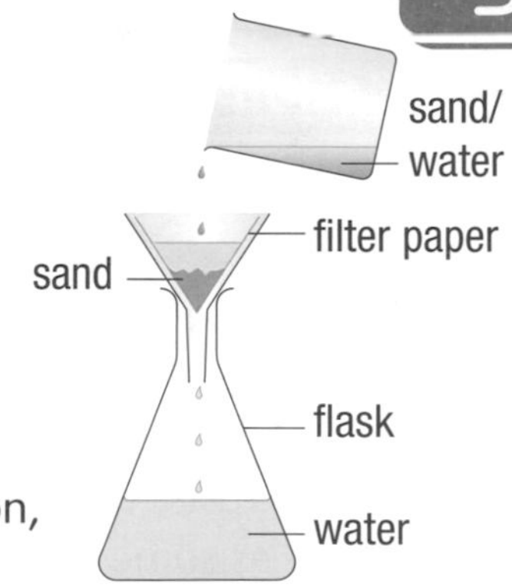

- Separating the elements from a compound is much harder – often impossible – because the elements have changed their nature in a chemical reaction.

Spot Check

1. What is the difference between a compound and a mixture?
2. Where in the Periodic Table would you find the elements that are metals?
3. What are the symbols for these elements:
   a oxygen; **b** sodium; **c** sulphur; **d** nitrogen; **e** nickel?

Chemical reactions

levels 4-5

Making new substances

- **Chemical reactions** between elements and compounds are how new substances are made. Chemical reactions can be complicated industrial processes or they can be everyday actions like cooking food and burning fuels.
- Chemical changes are different from physical changes of state in some important ways:
  - In a chemical change, new substances are formed.
  - In a physical change, the substance stays the same – it just exists in a different form.
  - Chemical changes are very hard – sometimes impossible – to reverse. You cannot 'uncook' a cake or 'unburn' a lump of coal.
  - Physical changes of state are quite easy to reverse. You can melt ice or condense steam to get the water back.

level 5

Energy changes in chemical reactions

- Chemical reactions always involve an energy change. Sometimes you have to put energy in to make the reaction happen – these are called **endothermic reactions**. In other reactions, like the burning of fuels, energy is given out – these are called **exothermic reactions**.

level 5

Oxidation

- **Oxidation** describes any reaction where another substance reacts with oxygen. For example:

  Magnesium + oxygen → magnesium oxide

- Many oxidation reactions occur in our everyday lives. If you leave an apple after you have taken a bite from it, the inside of the apple will go brown – this is oxidation. When iron rusts, we are seeing the formation of iron oxide – another oxidation reaction – as some metals can combine with the oxygen present in the air.

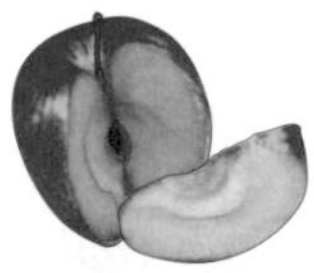

Top Tip!

When something burns in air, it is the oxygen present in the air that is used in the reaction.

level 5

Combustion

- **Combustion** describes the reaction that happens when any substance burns in oxygen. Combustion reactions such as the burning of fossil fuels give out a lot of heat.
- Not all oxidation reactions are examples of combustion, but burning always needs oxygen. This is why oxygen is one of the sides of the fire triangle which shows the three things that a fire needs to keep burning.

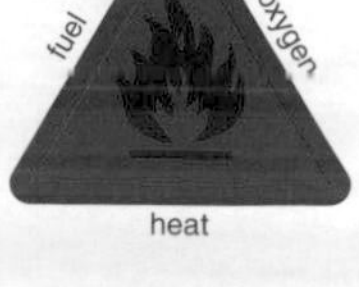

levels 5-6

Chemical equations

- **Chemical equations** are short-hand ways of describing chemical reactions.
- They can either be written as word equations or using **symbols** and **formulae**.

level 6

Examples of chemical equations

- The oxidation reaction that happens when magnesium burns in air can be written as:

  Magnesium + oxygen → magnesium oxide

  or as:

  $$2Mg + O_2 \rightarrow 2MgO$$

  As oxygen molecules have 2 atoms (O_2) and magnesium atoms exist on their own, we need 2 magnesium atoms, one for each oxygen atom, so that is why we write 2Mg.

- The same sort of equations describe the making of salt:

  Sodium + chlorine → sodium chloride

  $$2Na + Cl_2 \rightarrow 2NaCl$$

Did You Know?

The flame in a Bunsen Burner gets as hot as 1500 °C – so take care in school science lessons!

levels 4-5

Photosynthesis as an equation

- The word equation for photosynthesis is more complicated:

  Water + carbon dioxide $\xrightarrow[\text{sunlight}]{\text{chlorophyll}}$ glucose + oxygen

- The **reactants** are on the left of the arrow and the **products** on the right of the arrow. The things that have to be there for the reaction to happen, but do not actually react, are written above and below the arrow.

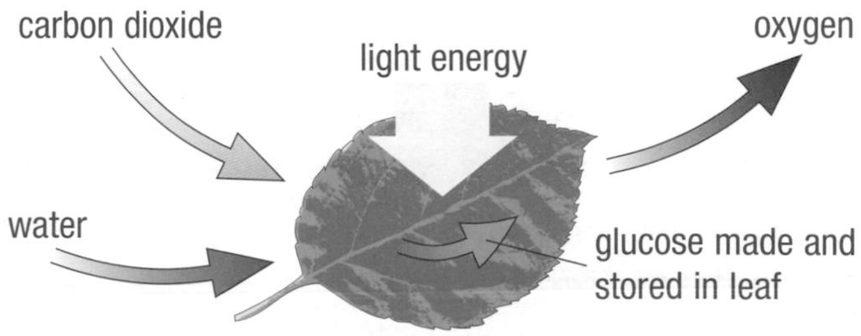

Spot Check

1. Give two differences between physical and chemical changes.
2. Write a word equation for the oxidation of magnesium.
3. Now write a word equation for the oxidation of zinc.

Acids and alkalis

level 4

Acid, alkali or neutral?

- When anything is dissolved in water, the solution it forms is either an **acid**, an **alkali** or **neutral**.

ACIDS: Everyday acids include fruit juices, vinegar and a lot of fizzy drinks!

ALKALIS: Soaps, toothpaste and detergents are generally alkaline solutions.

NEUTRAL: Pure water is neutral – a neutral solution is neither acidic nor alkaline.

levels 4-5

The pH scale

- The **pH** scale is a set of numbers from 1 to 14 that tells us not only whether a solution is acid or alkali but how strong it is. Very strong acids have low pH values from 1 to 3 or 4, weak acids are around 5 or 6, and neutral solutions are 7. A pH above 7 means the solution is alkaline, and the higher the number the more alkaline it is.

levels 4-5

Detecting acids and alkalis

- Looking at a solution does not tell us if it is an acid or an alkali. We need to use **indicators** to tell us the pH of the solution. Indicators are substances that turn different colours in acidic and alkaline solutions. A very simple indicator is **litmus** which turns red in acid and blue in alkali.
- **Universal indicator** has a range of colours to show the change in the pH of the solution in more detail.

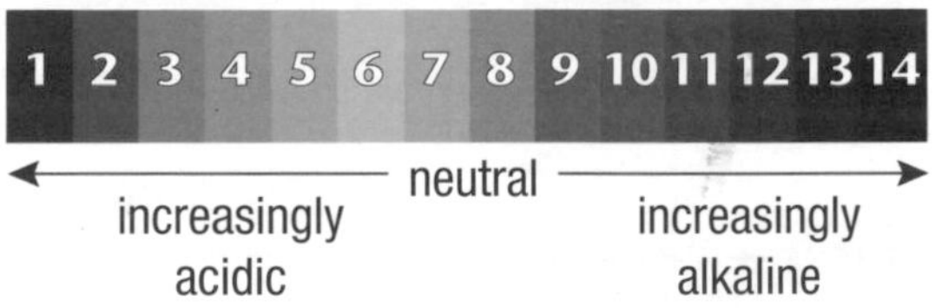

Top Tip!

Not all acids are dangerous. We eat and drink acidic substances every day.

level 5

Neutralisation

- When you mix an acid with an alkali, the resulting solution will be closer to neutral than either of the original ones. If you mix them in exactly the right amounts you will end up with a solution with a pH of exactly 7. Medicines to treat indigestion are alkalis designed to neutralise the excess stomach acid which causes the pain, but not all the acid as stomach acid is essential for digestion.

levels 5-6

Neutralisation reactions to produce a salt

- Neutralisation produces a **salt** and water. In this sense 'salt' means a group of compounds that are formed when acids and alkalis react. The word equation for this reaction is:

  Acid + alkali → salt + water

- The common salt that we eat, sodium chloride, is just one of this group of chemicals:

  Hydrochloric acid + sodium hydroxide → sodium chloride + water

  Other examples are:

  Sulphuric acid + potassium hydroxide → potassium sulphate + water

  Nitric acid + calcium hydroxide → calcium nitrate + water

- Sodium chloride, potassium sulphate and calcium nitrate are all salts.
- The type of acid is what controls the kind of salt produced:
  - hydrochloric acid gives **chloride** salts
  - sulphuric acid gives **sulphate** salts
  - nitric acid gives **nitrate** salts.

Did You Know?

Some fizzy drinks have the same pH as sulphuric acid – remember to brush your teeth!

level 6

Acids and metals

- Acids react with metals in a very similar way. This time the word equation is:

  Acid + metal → salt + hydrogen

- If the gas given off in a reaction is hydrogen, a lighted splint held close to the top of a test tube full of the gas will produce a 'pop'.

level 6

Acid rain

- Burning fossil fuels releases gases such as sulphur dioxide into the air. These gases dissolve and make the rain acidic. Acid rain falling into lakes and rivers changes the pH of the water and so affects the plants and animals that live there.

Trees affected by acid rain

Spot Check

1. What colour would you expect litmus paper to turn in lemon juice and why?
2. Complete these word equations for the reactions between an acid and an alkali and an acid and a metal:

   a Acid + alkali → **b** Acid + metal →
3. Which gas that is given off when fossil fuels are burned is mostly responsible for acid rain?

Metals and non-metals

level 4

Properties of metals and non-metals

- The elements in the Periodic Table are divided into **metals** and **non-metals**. Metals and non-metals have distinct **properties** (with some exceptions).

Properties of metals (such as copper, iron, zinc)	Properties of non-metals (such as wood, stone, glass)
All metals are good conductors of heat	Non-metals are generally poor conductors of heat
All metals conduct electricity	Non-metals do not conduct electricity – except graphite
Metals are all solids at normal temperature – except mercury which is a liquid	Non-metals can be solids, liquids or gases at normal temperature
Metals generally have a shiny appearance and are often grey	Non-metals have a wide variety of appearances

level 5

Properties and use

- The properties of metals and non-metals are linked to the things we use them for. For example, saucepans are made of metal because they **conduct** heat from the cooker to the food. But you stir the contents with a wooden spoon because it does not conduct heat – so your fingers will not get burnt.

Top Tip!

Metals feel cold to the touch because they conduct the heat away from your skin. Non-metals feel warm because they are poor conductors of heat.

level 5

Reactions of metals

- Metals react with oxygen to produce metal oxides:

Metal + oxygen → metal oxide

- This reaction is called **corrosion**. With some metals, like magnesium, aluminium and lead, this corrosion produces a thin layer of the metal oxide which makes the surface look dull instead of shiny. Corrosion is usually quite a slow reaction – some metals like gold and platinum, which are not very reactive, do not corrode at all.
- You need to know the properties of metals and how they are linked to their uses. However, not all metals are the same and cannot be put to the same uses. For example, you cannot make water pipes out of iron because it rusts – water pipes are normally made from copper which does not react with water.

Did You Know?

Gold jewellery found in the Pharaohs' tombs in Egypt was completely untarnished after thousands of years because gold does not react.

level 4

Rusting

- The corrosion of iron is called **rusting**. Rusting needs oxygen and water:

  Iron + oxygen + water → hydrated iron oxide (rust)

  You can show this in an experiment by putting iron nails into test tubes under different conditions.

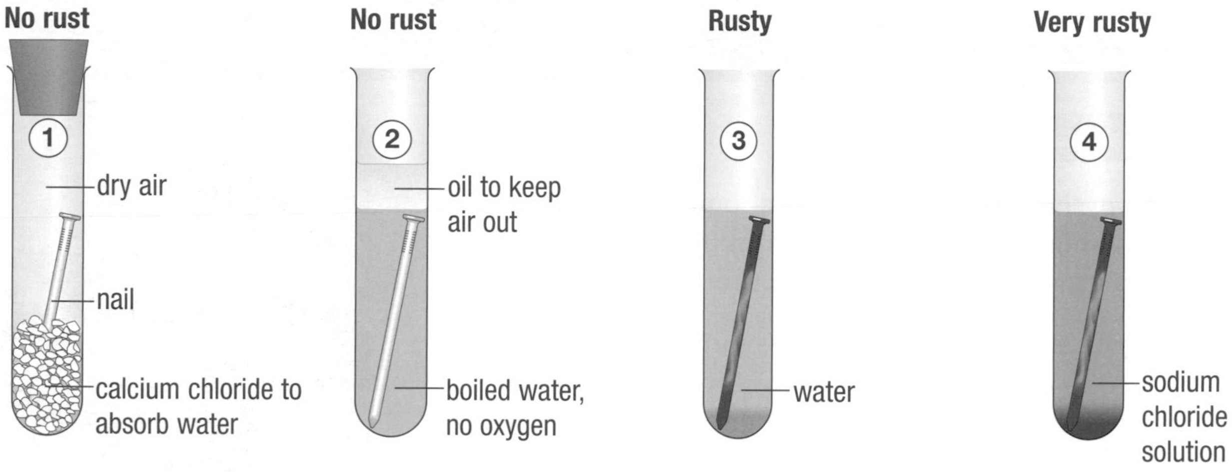

The nails in either the dry air (1), or in the water without oxygen (2), do not rust at all. The nail in ordinary water, containing oxygen (3), rusts a little. The nail in the water containing sodium chloride solution (salt) (4) becomes very rusty.

level 6

Reactivity series of metals

- Some metals react far more readily than others with water, steam and acids.

  Metal + water → metal hydroxide + hydrogen

  Metal + steam → metal oxide + hydrogen

  Metal + acid → salt + hydrogen

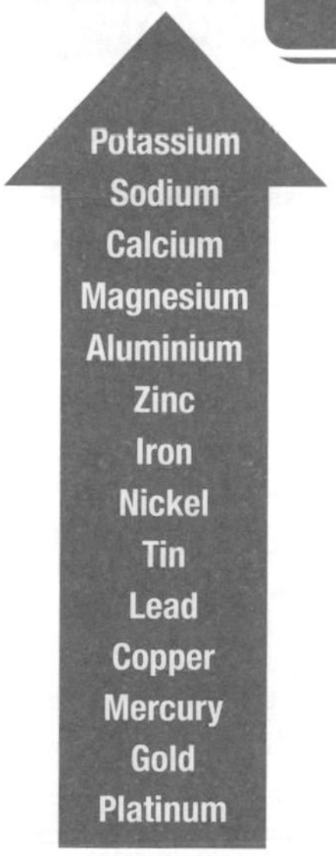

- The metals at the top of the list on the right react with cold water – at the very top they react quite violently. The metals in the middle do not react with cold water but they do react with steam. The ones at the bottom don't even react with steam.
- Metals as far down as copper and mercury also react with dilute acids.
- The nearer they are to the top, the more rapidly they react.

Spot Check

1. What two things does iron have to be protected from to stop it rusting?
2. Why are saucepans generally made of metal?
3. What is the word equation for the reaction of a metal with steam?

Rocks and the rock cycle

level 3

Types of rock

- There are three main groups of rock:

igneous **sedimentary** **metamorphic**

levels 4-5

Igneous rocks

- The inside of the Earth is very hot and some of the rock is molten. The molten rock is called **magma**. When magma cools it forms crystalline rocks called igneous rocks.
- If the magma escapes onto the Earth's surface through a volcano and then cools quickly, it forms rocks with small crystals. If it cools more slowly underground, then the crystals in the rock will be bigger.
- Granite is an example of an igneous rock with large crystals and basalt is an igneous rock with small crystals.

Granite rocks

Top Tip!

Heat, pressure, weathering and erosion are the main factors that change one type of rock to another.

levels 4-5

Sedimentary rocks

- When rainwater gets into rocks and then freezes and thaws, it can cause pieces of rock to break off. This is called **weathering**.

Rainwater collects in a crack.

The temperature falls below 0 °C. The water freezes and expands, making the crack bigger.

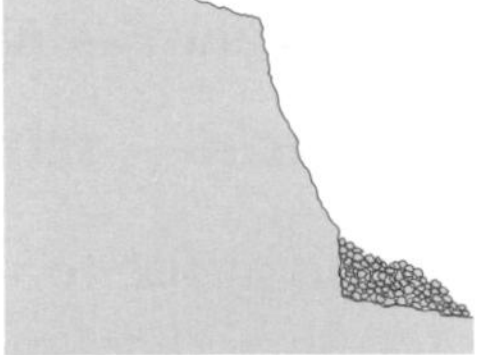

Eventually, after repeated freezing and thawing, the rock breaks off.

- The small pieces of rock are moved by rivers and glaciers and are gradually worn smooth. These pieces of different-sized rock sink to the bottom of the sea and over many, many years the sediment is stuck together and the water squeezed out, forming sedimentary rocks.
- Sandstone, chalk and limestone are examples of sedimentary rocks. Sometimes the remains of animals and plants are caught among the sediment and are preserved and compressed to form **fossils**.

Chalk rocks

levels 4-5

Metamorphic rocks

- The word metamorphic means 'changed', so rocks that have changed are called metamorphic rocks.
- Layers of sedimentary rocks are changed by underground heat or underground weight, or both. They have a layered or streaky appearance.

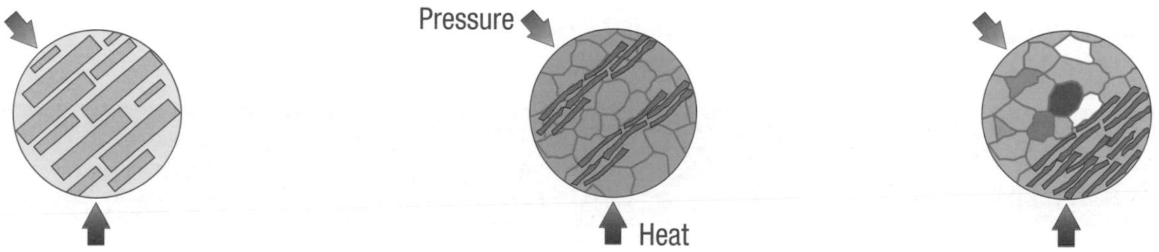

The fragments that make up sedimentary rocks are deposited in layers.

The rock is heated and squashed (compressed) and new layers start to form.

This heat and pressure cause new minerals to form, often crystals in layers.

- When limestone is heated and compressed it forms marble. Sandstone changes into a much harder rock called quartzite.

Did You Know?

One person in every 10 in the world lives within range of an active volcano.

level 5

The rock cycle

- The surface of the Earth is always changing and the three groups of rocks recycle from one kind to another.

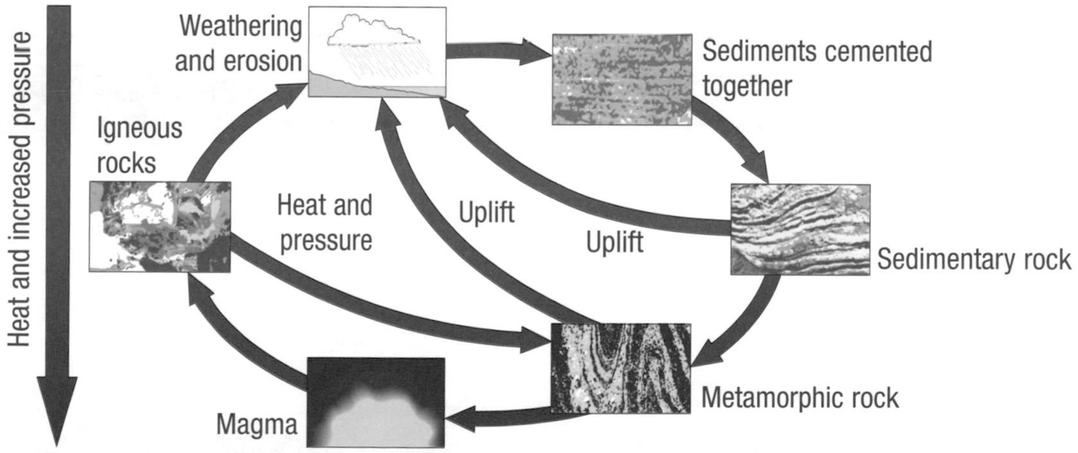

Spot Check

1. How can we tell by looking at an igneous rock how quickly the magma cooled to form this rock?
2. What is the name of the metamorphic rock that is formed from limestone?
3. In what kind of rock would you expect to find fossils?

INTERDEPENDENCE Food chains and food webs

level 3

Obtaining energy

- All living things need energy to enable them to carry out life processes.
- Plants are able to trap the energy of sunlight and make their own food.
- Animals have to eat plants or other animals to obtain the energy they need.

level 3

Food chains

- A green plant is always at the start of every food chain. These plants are called **producers**.
- Animals that eat plants are called **primary consumers**. They are **herbivores**.
- Animals that eat the primary consumers are called **secondary consumers**. They are **carnivores**.
- Then **tertiary consumers** may eat the secondary consumers. These are also carnivores.

PRODUCER → PRIMARY CONSUMER → SECONDARY CONSUMER → TERTIARY CONSUMER

GREEN PLANT → HERBIVORE → CARNIVORE → CARNIVORE

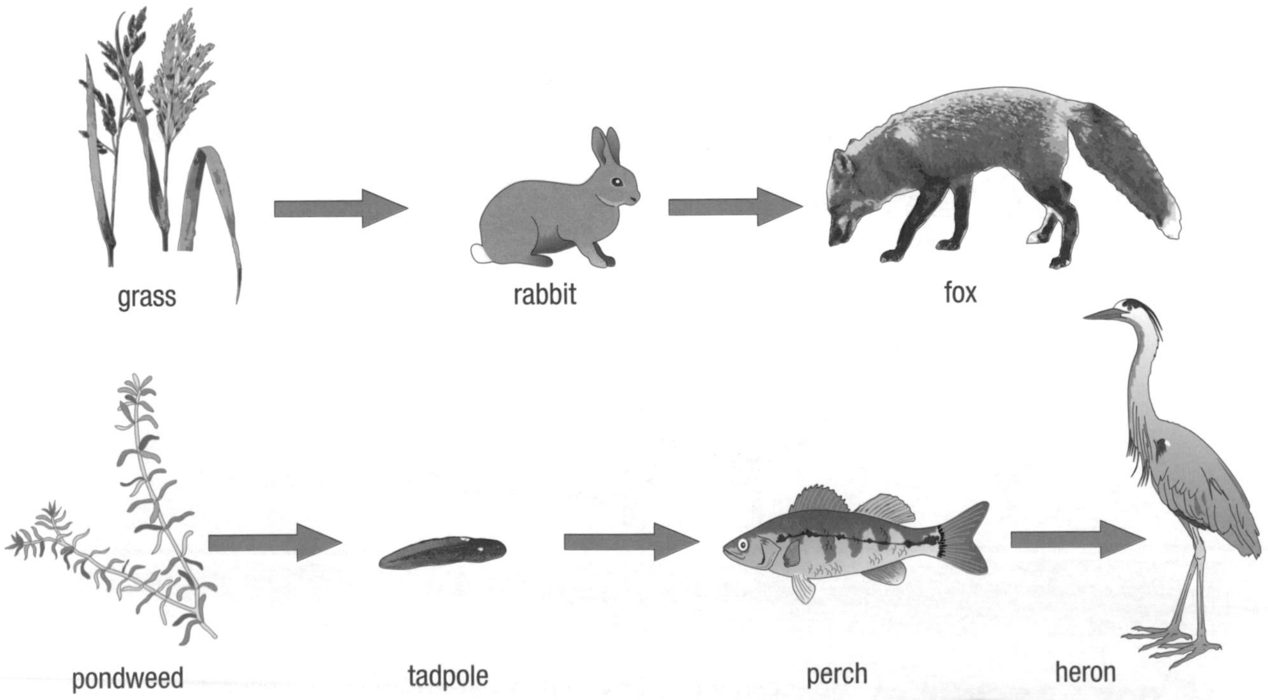

Top Tip!

The arrow in a food chain always goes from food to the creature that eats it. It shows the way in which the energy moves through the food chain.

Did You Know?

Owls can fly almost silently so that their prey will not hear them coming – but they have very sensitive ears themselves to help them find their prey at night.

Food webs

level 4

- In reality, many food chains are not as simple as this. For example, most humans are neither only herbivores nor only carnivores – they eat both plants and animals. They are called **omnivores**. This is less usual among other animals, though.
- In any habitat there will be several food chains connected together to make **food webs**.
- A woodland food web might look like this:

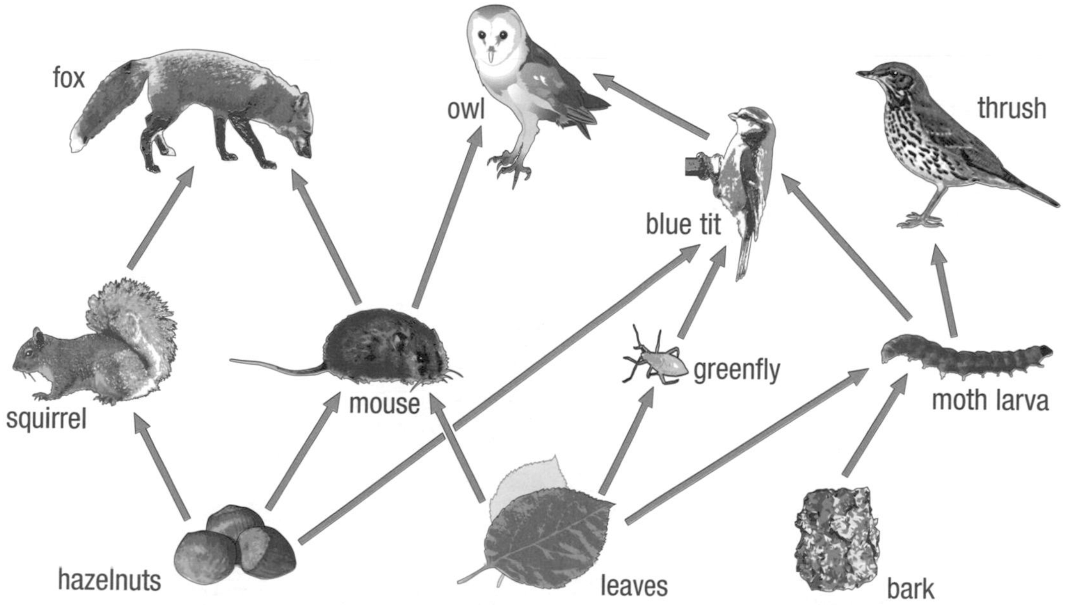

Pyramid of numbers

level 5

- There are not the same numbers of individuals at each stage – one blue tit will eat a lot of greenfly and one owl will eat several blue tits. We can show this in a **pyramid of numbers**.

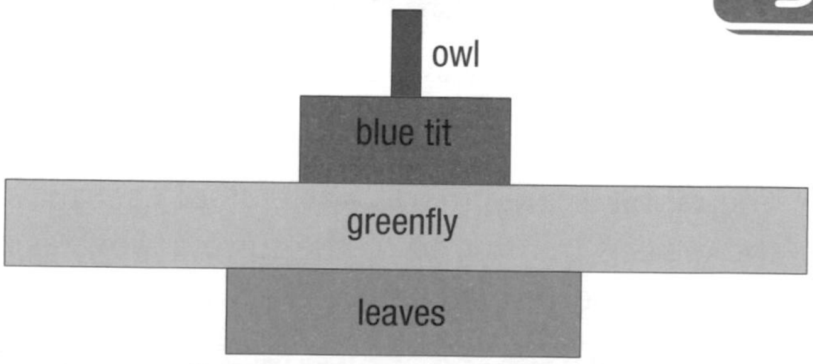

Spot Check

1. What kind of organism is a producer and why is there always one of these at the start of every food chain?
2. Draw a pyramid of numbers for this food chain:
   pondweed → tadpole → perch → heron
3. In a food chain, how would you describe the diet of the secondary consumer?

Energy transfers in food chains and food webs

level 6

Passing on energy

- Food chains and webs always have a green plant at the start because plants can trap the energy from sunlight. This energy is then passed up the food chain to the other organisms.
- Only a small amount of the energy taken in can be passed on up the food chain, the part of the energy the organism uses for growth. Think of the food chain on page 62:

  The fox is a **predator** that eats the rabbit that is its **prey**.

  GRASS → RABBIT → FOX

- One rabbit will feed on a lot more than one grass plant and a fox will expect to eat more than just one rabbit in its life! This gives us a pyramid of numbers, as we saw before:

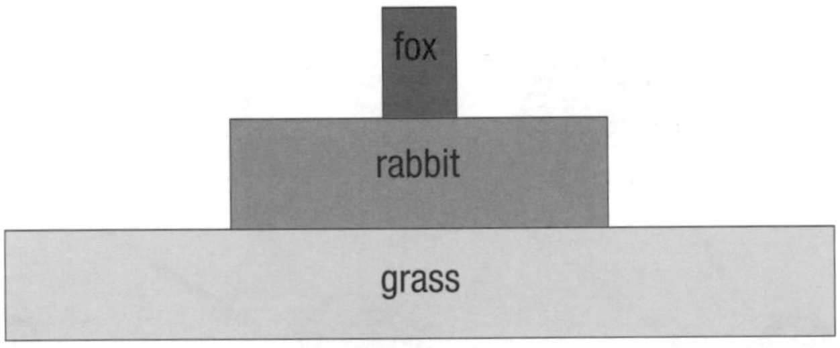

level 6

Using and losing energy

- If all the energy in all the grass were transferred to all the rabbits and all the energy in all the rabbits were transferred to all the foxes, then there would not be such a big change in the number of individuals between each level. However, grass plants don't just use the energy from the Sun to grow – they also use some of it for other life processes.
- The rabbit is even more 'wasteful' of energy. Some of the energy the rabbit takes in from the grass is transferred to the surroundings as heat, so that the rabbit can maintain its body temperature. Some of the energy is used as movement energy as the rabbit moves around.

Did You Know?

Humans are the most numerous mammals on Earth, closely followed by rats.

Top Tip!

Everything you know about energy transfers applies to energy transfers in food chains and webs – particularly the fact that energy is always lost as heat at each stage of the transfer.

level 6

Where does the energy go?

- The percentages in the picture below are approximate and vary between species, but the proportion of energy passed up the food chain to the next **trophic level** is never more than 10%. This is why food chains are very short. There is just too much energy lost at each stage for there to be more than one or two, or at the most three, **consumers** after the green plant **producer**.

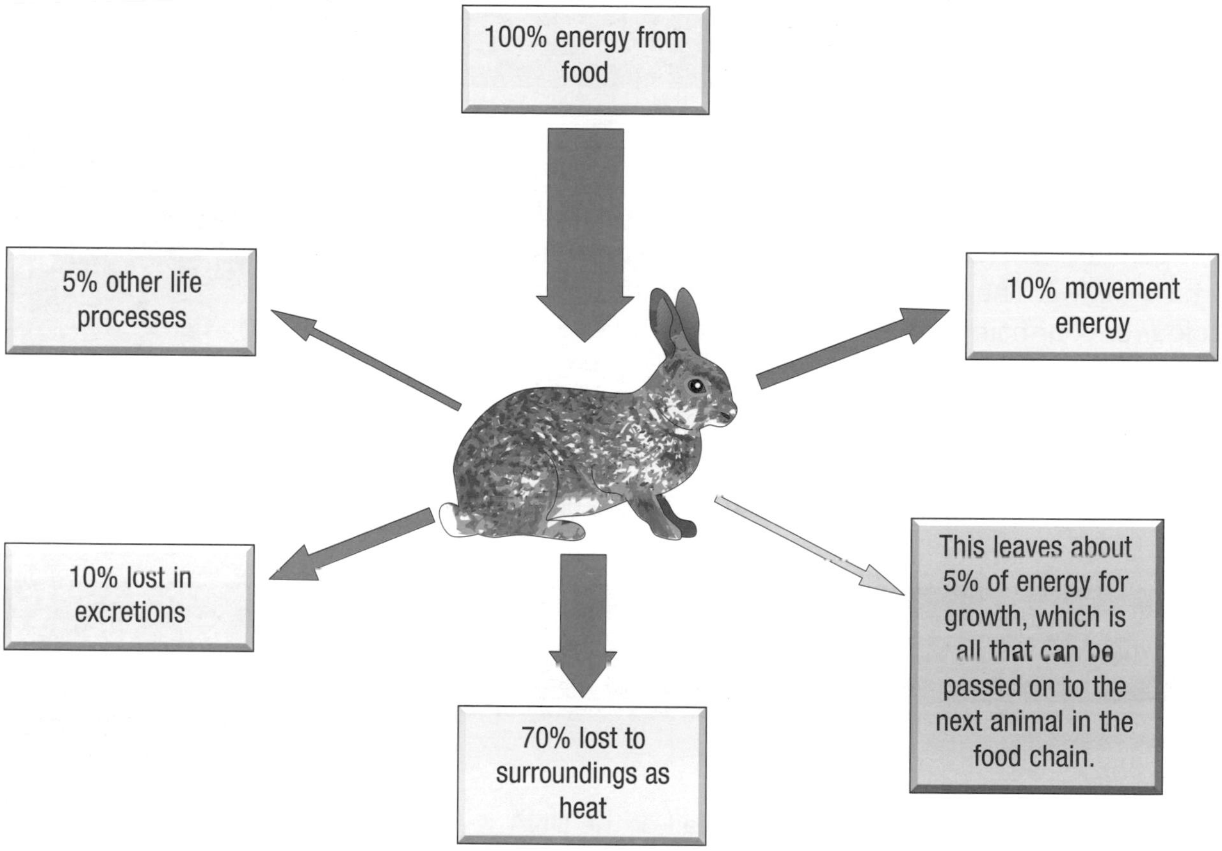

- Food webs can be spread out and be very complicated but there are never more than three consumers after the producer.

Spot Check

1 What names do we give to an animal that eats another animal, and to the animal that gets eaten?
2 Why is all the energy that a plant traps from sunlight not passed all the way along the food chain?
3 Approximately how much energy that an animal takes in is transferred to the next creature in the food chain?

INTERDEPENDENCE Variation and inheritance

level 4

Variation within species

- Members of the same species have a lot of things in common – but they have differences as well. Humans can have different eye, skin and hair colour. These differences are called **variations**.

levels 4-5

Inherited and environmental factors

- Most of our physical **characteristics** are **inherited** from our parents; others are affected by the **environment** in which we live. The colour of your eyes and the natural colour of your hair will be inherited, but if you choose to change the colour of your hair or put on weight, then these are environmental factors.

- Some things such as height are a mixture of inheritance and environment. We all inherit a maximum possible height but we will only reach that if we have the right diet when we are growing.

level 5

Inheritance

- A sperm and an egg cell each contain half of the DNA that is found in ordinary cells. When the sperm and egg cell join, these two halves of DNA fuse together to form a person who will get half their characteristics from each parent. Different combinations of the genes from each parent produce individuals with different characteristics.

- Identical twins have the same genes so they have the same inherited characteristics. This is because they are made when one fertilised egg divides in two.
- Other brothers and sisters often look quite different as it depends upon which characteristics they inherit from which parent. This includes non-identical twins who are made when two separate eggs are fertilised and implanted in the mother's uterus at the same time.

Top Tip!

Remember, our parents pass our inherited characteristics down to us, but some of our characteristics can be changed by our environment.

Did You Know?

Humans share 98% of their genetic material with chimpanzees and 50% with bananas.

level 4

Species characteristics

- Other **species** also show great variation within their members.
- Although dogs are members of the same species, they can have very different characteristics, as shown in this picture.

level 6

Selective breeding

- Members of the same species are those animals or plants that can breed together and produce offspring that can then breed in their turn.
- **Selective breeding** aims to produce more individuals with a characteristic that is thought to be valuable.
- Cattle breeders will select animals with the best milk production and maybe a natural resistance to some diseases in the hope that their offspring will have the same good qualities. Plant breeders go to great efforts to produce a plant with a flower of a particular colour, size or shape by carefully selecting parent plants with the desired characteristics.

level 5

Variation between species

- Usually there are great differences between members of different species. Some species, however, have things in common, for example, horses and donkeys or rats and mice, but they are still different species and there will be variations between them.
- These are all woodlice and may look very similar but they are actually different species and have variations.
- It is important to remember that if members of different species try to breed together, the offspring, if any, will not be able to breed.

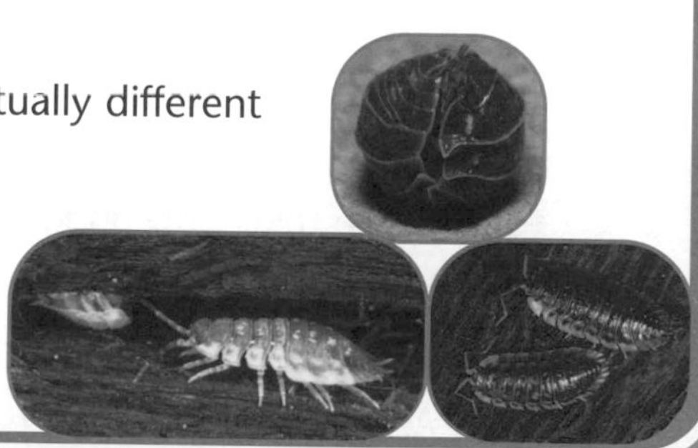

Spot Check

1 Which of these are inherited characteristics in humans?
eye colour **natural hair colour** **height** **weight** **ability to speak a foreign language**

2 If two members of different species breed together, what will be the drawback with the offspring?

3 What characteristics do you think people look for when breeding racehorses?

Adaptation

level 3

Fitting into the habitat

- For things to live successfully in their **habitat** they often need to be adapted to their surroundings.
- This **adaptation** has happened over many, many generations because the individuals that had the most useful characteristics were most able to survive and breed and so pass on these useful characteristics.

level 4

Adaptation in animals

Here are two examples of animals that have become adapted to their environments.

- Moles have the characteristics that they need to live underground:
  - a good sense of smell to detect their food
  - large front claws to dig through the earth
  - a streamlined shape to move efficiently through the tunnel created.

- Polar bears have the characteristics needed to live in the cold and snow:
  - a white coat to make them less easy for predators to see
  - thick fur to trap heat and keep them warm
  - sharp teeth for killing prey
  - plenty of fat for insulation and as a food store
  - strong legs for walking and swimming long distances in search of food
  - sharp claws and hair on the soles of their feet to improve their grip on icy surfaces.

Top Tip!

Adaptation is an everyday word, so make sure you understand and can use its scientific meaning correctly.

Adaptation in plants

level 4

- Many plant species have also adapted so that they can live successfully in particular habitats.
- Cactus plants, for example, have adapted to live in the hot, dry conditions of deserts. They have:
  - long roots to find water below the ground
  - swollen stems to store as much water as possible
  - small spines for leaves, which not only reduce water loss because the surface area is small but also deter animals from eating the plant.

Daily adaptations

level 4

Many species have adapted in ways that allow them to cope with changes in their environment.

- Daily adaptations include:
  - plants with flowers that open in the day to allow pollinating insects in and close at night for protection
  - animals that come out at night rather than during the day – owls hunt at night for other **nocturnal** creatures, using their excellent sense of hearing rather than sight.

Did You Know?

There is a tree-like cactus in desert regions of North America that has flowers 30 cm in diameter.

Seasonal adaptations

level 4

- Seasonal adaptations include:
  - deciduous trees losing their leaves before the winter when there will be little sunlight for photosynthesis
  - animals growing thicker coats in the winter and even changing colour between winter and summer for maximum camouflage
  - animals eating a lot in the autumn when there is plenty of food and then sleeping or **hibernating** in the winter when food supplies are short
  - birds flying away to warmer places in the winter where there is more food. This is called **migration**.

Spot Check

1. If you were going to design a mammal to live in a cold, wet climate with plenty of green plants and very large animals but not many small animals, what adaptations would this creature need to live there successfully?
2. Why do some animals hibernate in the winter? And what do they do to prepare for this?
3. Why do some plants have flowers that open in the day and close up at night?

Classification

Grouping things together

level 4

- When you go into a supermarket you can find the things you want to buy because similar things are all put together. If you want apples, you go to the fruit and vegetable section; if you want ice-cream you go to the freezer. It saves time and makes doing the shopping much easier than if everything were just put anywhere.

Classifying living things

level 4

- Classification of living things is much the same. It works on the basis that different species share common features and so can be put together. It also means that if we observe the characteristics of an unfamiliar organism, we can most probably tell something about it by working out its classification.
- There are over 800 000 species of animals on Earth so they have to be broken down into groups. The first division is **vertebrates** and **invertebrates** – vertebrates have backbones and invertebrates do not.
- The plant kingdom is also divided into groups and there are three other kingdoms: fungi, bacteria and protoctists.

Top Tip!

Not only mammals are animals – birds, fish, frogs, snakes and insects are all animals, and humans are too!

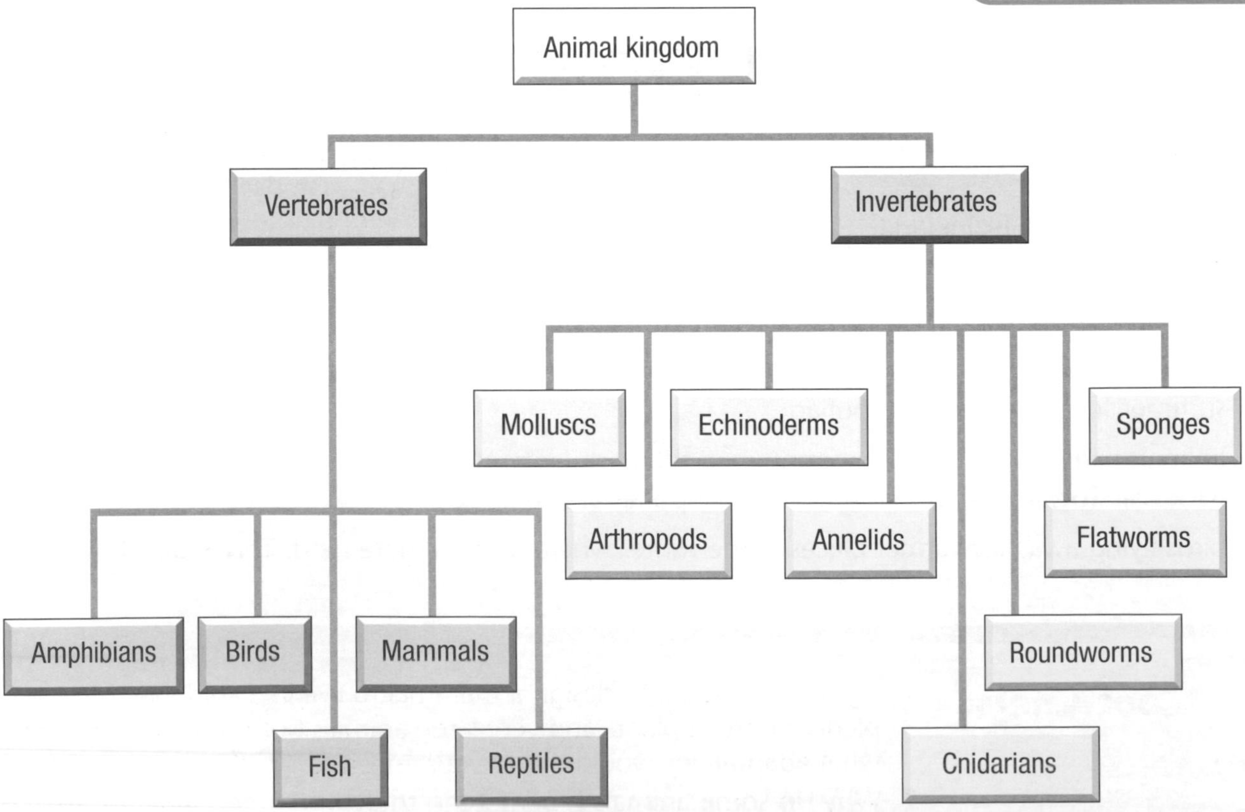

level 5

Characteristics of vertebrates

All vertebrates have a backbone, but their other characteristics are quite different.

- **Amphibians**
  - have moist skins
  - lay jelly-coated eggs in water
  - can live on land or under water.

- **Fish**
  - have streamlined shape
  - breathe through gills
  - live and lay eggs in water
  - have wet skin with scales.

- **Birds**
  - are warm-blooded
  - breathe through lungs
  - have feathers
  - lay eggs with hard shells.

- **Mammals**
  - are warm-blooded
  - develop the young inside the mother
  - feed their young on milk from the mother
  - breathe through lungs
  - have fur or hair.

- **Reptiles**
  - have dry scaly skin
  - breathe through lungs
  - lay eggs with a leathery skin on land.

Did You Know?

A large fossil discovered in South Africa is thought to be one of the first vertebrates. The eel-like creature called a Conodont evolved 520 million years ago which is 50 million years before the first fish.

level 5

Characteristics of invertebrates

Arthropods are the biggest group of invertebrates. They can be sub-divided into four groups:

- **Insects**, such as grasshoppers, dragonflies and wasps, have three-sectioned bodies and three pairs of legs.
- **Arachnids**, such as spiders and scorpions, have two parts to their bodies and four pairs of legs.
- **Crustaceans**, like crabs and lobsters, have two pairs of antennae, a chalky shell and up to seven pairs of legs.
- **Myriapods**, such as millipedes and centipedes, have long, thin, segmented bodies with a pair of legs on each segment.

Spot Check

1 In what way are mammals different from other vertebrates?
2 What are the four groups of arthropods called?
3 Name two characteristics of birds.

Using keys to identify living things

level 4

Types of key

- As there are so many species of living things, it would not be possible for anyone to remember the names of all of them. However, it is possible to find out which species any organism belongs to using something called a **key**.
- Keys may be either a set of questions and answers or a branching diagram. For example, you can use a simple question and answer key to distinguish between some of the 15 000 known species of butterfly. There are 6000 species in the family Nymphalidae alone!

These are pictures of five examples:

level 4

Using a question key

- Look carefully at the pictures and answer the questions below to name these five butterflies.

1 Does the butterfly have a yellow or white edge to its wings?
- If yes, it is the Camberwell Beauty (**C**).
- If no, go to question 2.

2 Does the butterfly have a noticeable amount of white on its wings but hardly any at the edges?
- If yes, it is the White Admiral (**A**).
- If no, go to question 3.

3 Does the butterfly have blue colouration anywhere on its wings?
- If yes, go to question 4.
- If no, it is the Comma butterfly (**B**).

4 Is the blue colour around the edge of the butterfly's wings?
- If yes, it is the Small Tortoiseshell (**E**).
- If no, it is the Peacock butterfly (**D**).

Top Tip!

Learn about how keys work so that you can apply the rules to anything – and don't be put off if the plants or animals you are asked to identify are unfamiliar.

Branching diagrams

- The other sort of key commonly used is a branching diagram which identifies species from their **characteristics**.
- In this example, a branching diagram is used to identify some types of wild flowers.

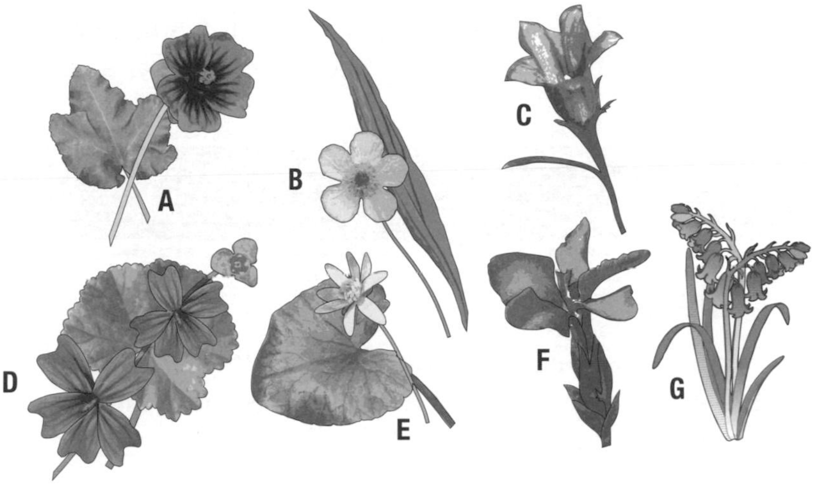

Did You Know?

The venus fly trap is a plant that traps and digests insects.

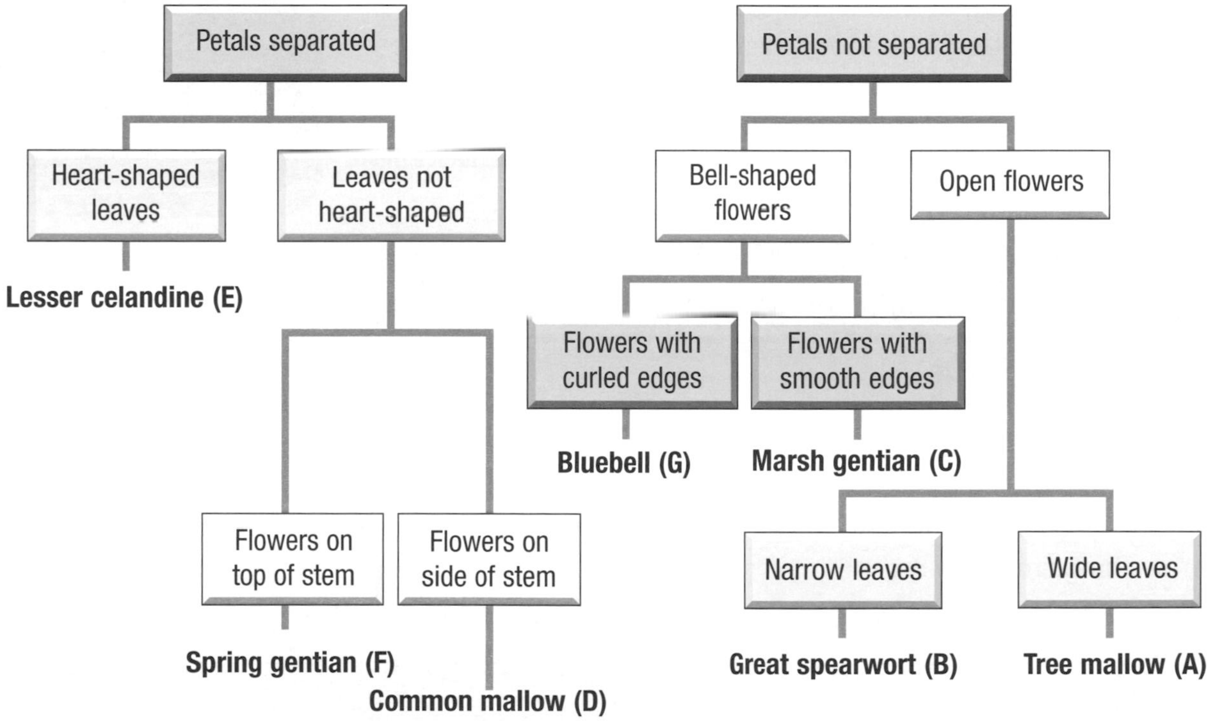

Spot Check

Use the keys on these pages to answer these questions.

1. Which butterfly has blue edges to its wings?
2. Which plant has separate petals and heart-shaped leaves?
3. Which plant has open flowers and wide leaves?

Competition among living things

level 4

Consequences of competition

- Over the centuries, many species of animals and plants have become **extinct**. This means that there are none of these animals or plants left. Many other species are **endangered** which means that there are so few individuals left that the species may become extinct.
- Sometimes the reduction in numbers is due to human impact on the environment (see page 76) and sometimes it is due to other species being better adapted to live in that habitat.

level 4

Woodlands

- In woodland, the trees will often block out the light and prevent plants nearer the ground from being able to make their own food by photosynthesis.
- In a tree, there is only room for a limited number of nest sites for birds, which means that birds have to compete for space as well as food. If there is not enough food, then the number of individuals will be reduced as some will starve.

The leaves of woodland trees block the light so fewer plants grow well under them.

level 5

Interdependence

- If the numbers, or **population**, of one species goes down, then it has an effect on other creatures that are part of the same food web. Look back at the food web on page 63 and think about the effect of a reduction in the population of greenfly. If there were fewer greenfly, then all of these things might happen:
  - The blue tits would eat more hazelnuts so there would be less for the squirrels and mice to eat.
  - This would in turn mean more competition so the population of all three species might go down.
  - There would be less leaf matter eaten by the greenfly so the mice who can eat leaves as well would be in a better position.
  - If there were fewer blue tits then the owl population might go down – or the owls might eat more mice and then there would be less for the foxes to eat.

Did You Know?

Another two species of animal become extinct in Britain alone each year.

level 5

Changes in population

- Take the simple food chain: **grass → rabbit → fox**. A reduction in the numbers of any one of these species would affect the size of the population of the other species.
- In a very hot dry summer, the grass would not grow at all well. This would mean more **competition** among rabbits – leading eventually to fewer rabbits, more competition among foxes and fewer foxes.

  A graph of the rabbit and fox populations might look like this:

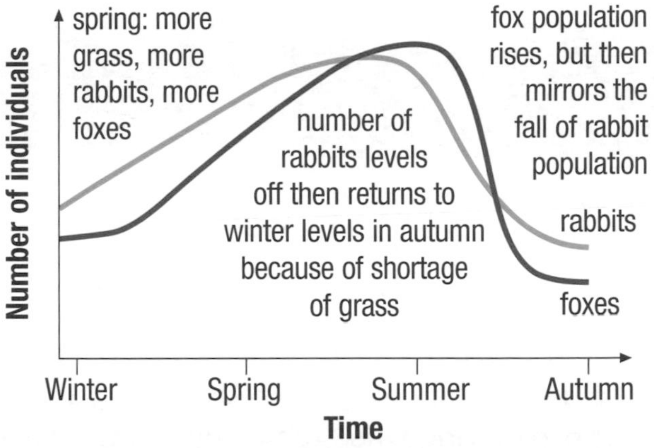

level 6

Other factors

- An outbreak of disease among rabbits would mean less for the foxes to eat so more competition for the remaining rabbits and eventually fewer foxes.
- However, it does not necessarily follow that an outbreak of disease among foxes will mean more rabbits. If some of the foxes died out, then at first the rabbit population would increase as there would be fewer foxes to eat them – but this would then mean that there was more competition for the grass and so rabbits would die of starvation instead of being eaten by foxes. The rabbit population would peak and then go down.

  The graph of the two populations might look like this:

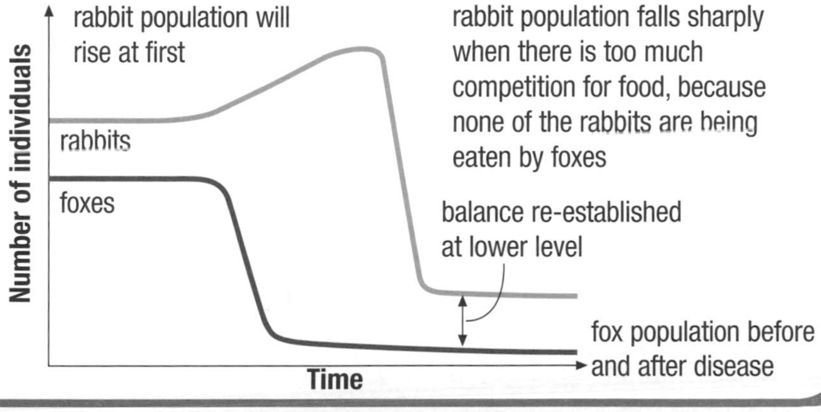

Top Tip!

Make sure you are able to correctly interpret information given in a graph.

Spot Check

1. In a woodland habitat, a very wet summer may mean fewer hazelnuts on the trees. What effect might this have on the fox population?
2. Plants like bluebells and primroses grow in woodland conditions. Why do they flower in early spring?
3. What do we mean if we say a species of plant or animal is endangered?

Human impact on the environment

Competition from humans

level 5

All the animals and plants that have become extinct have suffered too much **competition** from another species. One of the species that is most in competition with other living things is us – humans.

Competition for space

level 5

- As the human population increases, the effect we have on the environment increases too.
- We compete for space in some parts of the world. People cut down forests and woodlands to use the land to grow crops or for grazing. Competition for space can also take the form of overgrazing when too many animals have to graze on too small a piece of land.

Climate change

level 5

- We still get most of the energy we need to heat our homes and offices – and for transport – from burning fossil fuels. Burning these fossil fuels produces carbon dioxide. Cutting down forests reduces the trees available to take in carbon dioxide for photosynthesis.
- All of this leads to more carbon dioxide in the upper atmosphere. The carbon dioxide acts like a blanket insulating the Earth which leads to something called the **greenhouse effect**. So an increase of carbon dioxide could lead to the polar ice caps melting, as well as to changes in rainfall and wind patterns.

The greenhouse effect

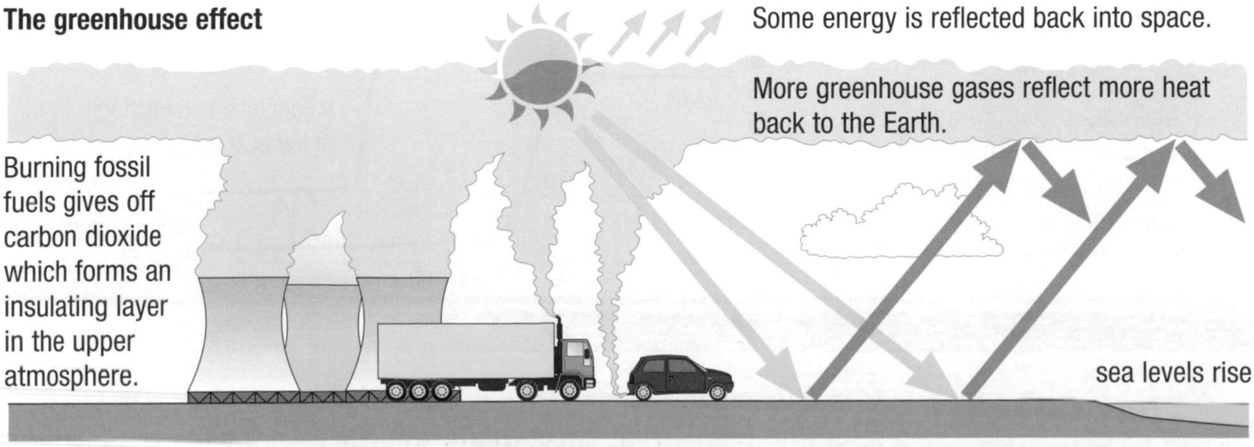

Did You Know?

There are about 4000 species of fish living on the Great Barrier Reef off the coast of Australia.

level 5

Acid rain

- Some of the other waste gases from burning fossil fuels dissolve in the water in the atmosphere and create **acid rain**. When this acid rain falls on lakes and rivers it makes the water more acidic.
- Many species of fish and plankton are not adapted to cope with acidic conditions. Unless something is done to **neutralise** the water, they die. In this picture, limestone is being sprayed onto a river in Sweden to neutralise the acidity in the water.

level 6

Pesticides

- **Pesticides** are chemicals used to kill insects and pests (e.g. slugs) in the garden and on farms. They do not easily break down and so they are passed up the food chain. At each level in the food chain, the organisms eat more than one of those in the level below, so the amount of pesticide builds up. This means that the pesticide kills creatures other than the ones it is targeted at, for example the birds that eat the pests and insects.

level 6

The ozone layer

- High up in the atmosphere, a layer of a gas called **ozone** protects the Earth from damaging radiation from the Sun. A group of chemicals called CFCs, which used to be used in aerosols and fridges, can damage this protective layer and let the dangerous radiation through. This can cause skin cancers in humans as well as harming other species.

Top Tip!

Don't confuse the greenhouse effect and global warming with damage to the ozone layer. Check you know the causes and effects of each.

Spot Check

1. Which gas is responsible for the greenhouse effect and what is the biggest source of this gas?
2. If acid rain has made a lake more acidic how can this be neutralised?
3. What is the name of the gas that makes up the protective layer in the upper atmosphere?

Asking questions and making predictions

level 5

Asking clear questions

- Before you start on any **experiment** it is important to be very clear what the question is that you are **investigating**.
- For example, it is not enough to say that we want to investigate the effect of sunlight on plants; or of acids on alkalis; or of forces on motion.
- The question must explain exactly what you want to find out, what you are going to change and what you are going to measure.
- For example, you could ask:

A Does the amount of sunlight that a plant receives affect the rate of photosynthesis, as shown by the amount of growth?

B What quantity of different alkalis will be needed to neutralise 100 ml of hydrochloric acid?

A

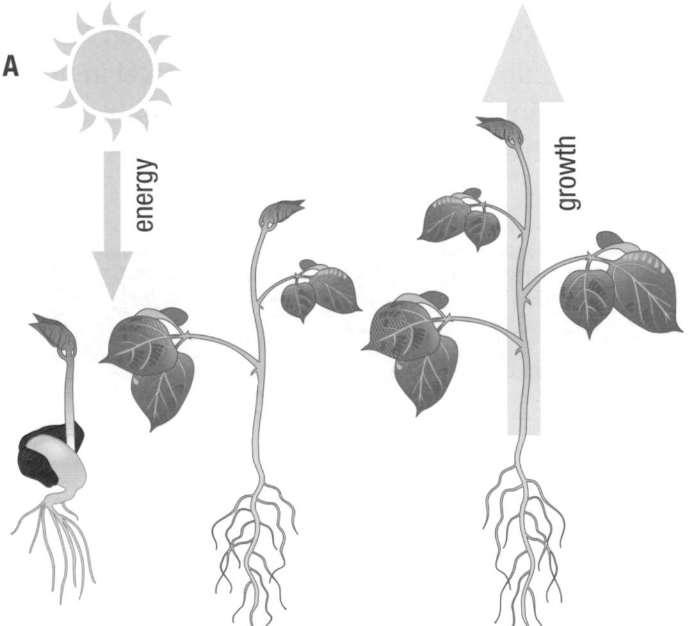

B

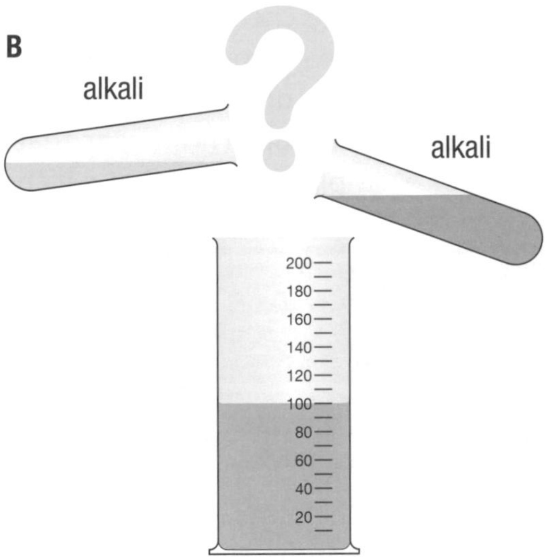

Did You Know?

The word hypothesis comes from two Greek words – 'hypo' meaning under and 'thesis' meaning study. So a hypothesis is an idea 'under study' or one being tested by experiment and observation.

Top Tip!

The theoretical science you learn has all been confirmed by someone doing an experiment. That is what science is. Think about all the science you know while planning and carrying out experiments.

level 5

Making predictions

When you have decided on a clear question, it becomes much easier to make a prediction. Another word for prediction is **hypothesis**.

- Your prediction must explain what you think will happen and *why* you think it will happen.
- The 'why' must be based on good science. Even if the prediction turns out not to be correct when you do the experiment, this is less important than the quality of your prediction.
- Predictions for the examples on the opposite page could be:

A If the plant gets more hours of sunlight, it will be able to make more food and grow more. This is because light is essential to the chemical reaction of photosynthesis which is how plants make food for growth.

B The stronger the alkali, the less of it will be needed to neutralise the acid. When you mix substances with different pH values, the resulting solution has a pH value that lies between the two original values. An alkali with a high pH (12) will have more neutralising effect than the same quantity of an alkali with a lower pH (8). A neutral solution has a pH of 7.

A

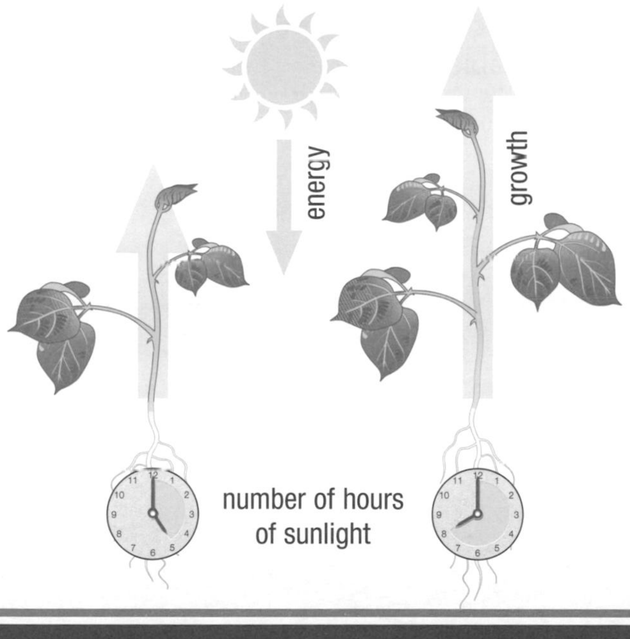

B

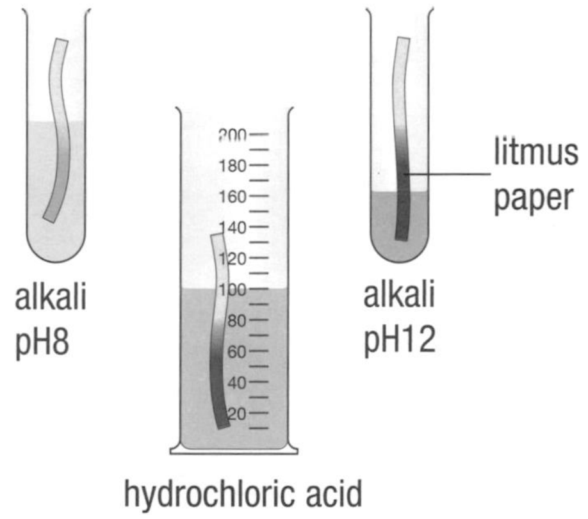

Spot Check

1 Write a suitable question for an enquiry into the effect of temperature on the solubility of salt.
2 Write a hypothesis or prediction for this question.
3 Some students wanted to know which kitchen towel was the most absorbent. Their question was – are blue paper towels more absorbent than white ones? Can you help them to write a better question?

Variables and fair tests

level 4

What is a variable?

- A variable in an experiment is anything that you can change and the effect of which can be measured.
- There are two kinds of variables: **continuous** and **discontinuous variables**. It is important to know the difference between them.

level 4

Continuous and discontinuous variables

- A continuous variable can have any value at all, sometimes within a given range (a range is the difference between the highest and lowest value).
- A discontinuous variable has only certain specific values.
- To get an idea of a continuous and a discontinuous variable, think about the difference between the length of your foot and your shoe size. If you measure your foot in centimetres with a ruler, it could have any value at all – but if you go into a shop to buy a pair of shoes you cannot ask for a pair of 27.832 cm shoes, you have to ask for a size such as 5, $5\frac{1}{2}$, or 6. The centimetre value is a continuous variable; shoe size is a discontinuous variable.
- The sort of variable that you put into your experiment will affect the way in which you show your results in a graph (see page 83).

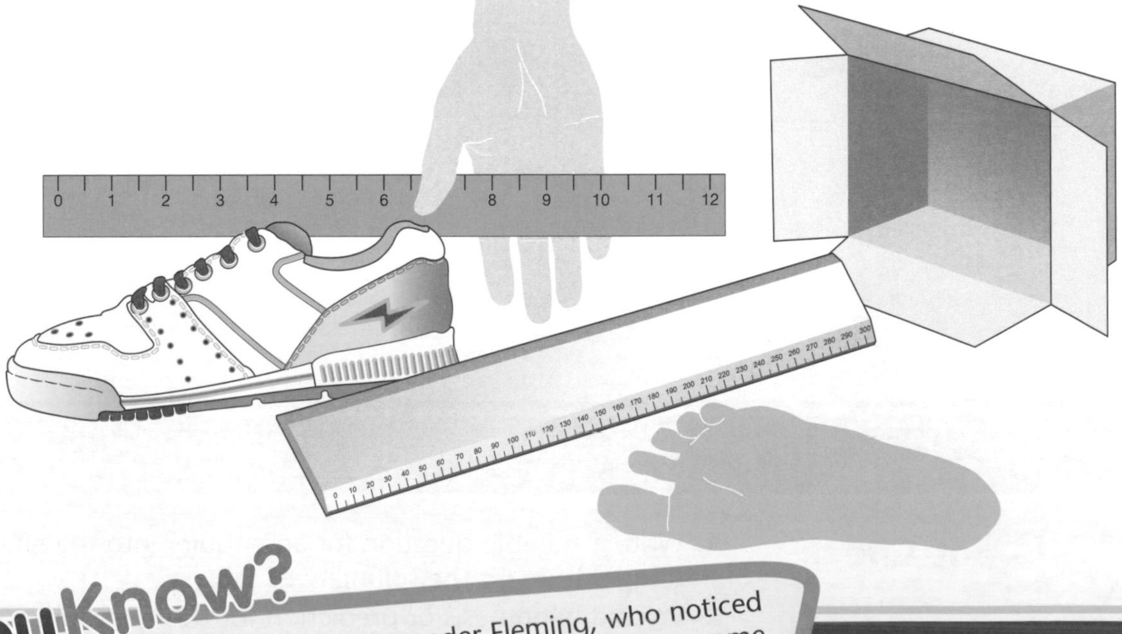

Did You Know?

Penicillin was first observed by Alexander Fleming, who noticed that some bacteria in his lab stopped growing when they came into contact with mould. Good scientists observe what is around them and then carry out experiments to test their ideas.

level 4

Variables in experiments

- In any experiment there is the variable you can change. This is sometimes called the input variable, but the correct term is the **independent variable**.
- There is also the variable that you can measure to see if it changes as a result of changing the independent variable. This is sometimes called the outcome variable, but its correct term is the **dependent variable**.

Top Tip!

Always use the correct scientific vocabulary and talk about factors and variables not 'things' or 'it'.

level 4

Fair tests

- In any experiment, you can only be sure of the effect of your independent variable on your dependent variable if you make sure you only have one independent variable.
- In other words, you must only change one thing if you are to be sure that the results of your experiment tell you about that variable and its effects. Everything else must be kept the same.
- Often the things that are kept the same could be changed – they are variables themselves – but because they are kept the same they are called **control variables**.
- For example, if you wanted to find out about the amount of energy stored in a particular food by burning it to heat water, then the independent variable would be the kind of food – this is a discontinuous variable. The rise in the temperature of the water would be the dependent variable. All the other factors such as the amount and temperature of the water at the start, the mass of the food used and the distance of the food from the test tube of water would be the control variables.

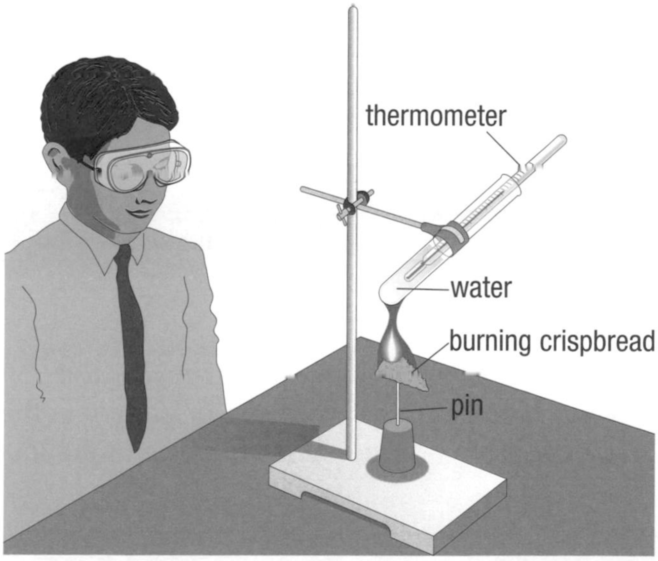

Spot Check

1 Is hand span a continuous or discontinuous variable?
2 In an experiment to test how much friction different shoes exerted on the ground by seeing how much force is needed to pull the shoe along, what would be the independent variable?
3 In the same investigation, what would be the dependant variable?

Presenting results and drawing graphs

level 5

Using tables to present results

- At the end of any experiment, you should always present your results in a **table** which shows the values of your independent variable and the values of your dependent variable. It might look like this:

Type of food	Start temperature	End temperature	Increase in temperature
(100 g mass)	of 50 ml of water in °C	of 50 ml of water in °C	of 50 ml of water in °C
the independent variable	one control variable	the measurement of the dependent variable	(end temperature minus start temperature) the calculation of the dependent variable

- The table should include as much information as possible about quantities and units and have room for the **calculation** if there needs to be one. In this example, the calculation is the difference between the start and end temperatures of the water.
- By just looking at this table you can find out quite a lot about the experiment, including some of the control variables such as the start temperature of the water and the quantities of food and water. If the start temperature of the water is not always the same, then you can immediately see a possible error in the experiment – which will help when you come to evaluate it.

Top Tip!
Always show your units in a table.

level 4

Drawing graphs

- The results table is one way of showing the results of an experiment – but you need to read it very carefully to see any trend or pattern in the results. If you take the same information and plot a **graph**, then these trends or patterns are much easier to see.

levels 5-6

Choosing the right graph or chart

- If you carried out a survey to show how many pupils travel to school in a particular way, then a pie chart might be an excellent way to show your results.
- This would show you at a glance what proportion or percentage of pupils travel by each means. (See page 86 for help with understanding this pie chart.)

Bar charts for discontinuous independent variables

levels 5-6

- However, this would not be a good way to show the results of the food-burning experiment (on page 81). When the independent variable is discontinuous then the most suitable way to show the results is in a bar chart.

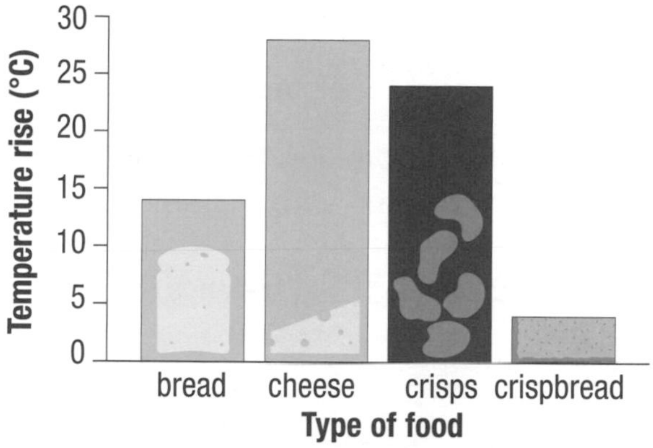

Graphs for continuous independent variables

levels 5-6

- If the independent variable is a continuous variable then you must plot a line graph. For example, if you heated a beaker containing ice until it became boiling water and took the temperature every minute (60 seconds), then you would have a graph that looks like the one below.
- Usually the independent variable goes on the *x*-axis (along the bottom) and the dependent variable goes on the *y*-axis (up the side).

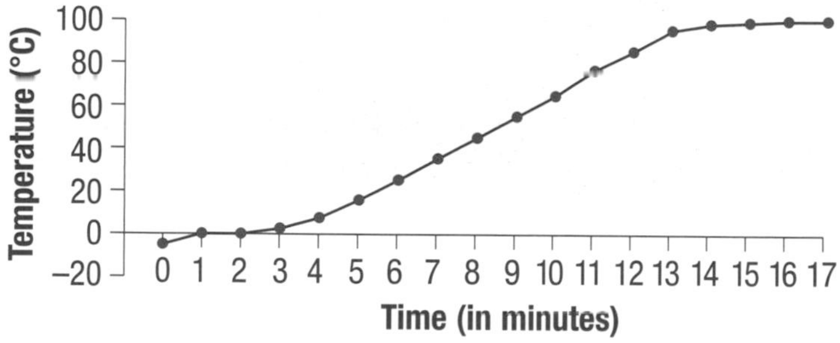

Did You Know?

The metre was originally calculated to be one ten-millionth of the length of a line drawn from the North Pole to the equator through Paris.

Spot Check

1 In an experiment to find out the friction between different kinds of shoe and the ground in the playground, the floor in the classroom and the grass on the football pitch, what headings would you need to have in your results table?

2 If you wanted to compare the amount of force needed to move the same shoe on the three different surfaces what kind of graph or chart would you use and why?

3 If the experiment was to see if increasing the mass of the shoe made the friction between the shoe and the ground greater, what sort of graph or chart should be used and why?

Patterns and relationships

level 4

Seeing patterns in results

- In any experiment we can only test some of the possible values for our chosen variable BUT if we can see a **pattern** in these results, we can use that pattern to predict what would happen with other values.
- To make it easier to see the pattern in our results we can alter the way we display them in a table.
- Take the planets orbiting the Sun in our solar system – we can compare the distance of each planet from the Sun with the time taken to orbit the Sun by putting this information into a table:

Name of planet	Distance from the Sun (millions of km)	Time to orbit the Sun (years)
Mars	228	1.9
Jupiter	778	11.9
Pluto	5900	248
Saturn	1427	29.5
Mercury	58	0.2
Uranus	2870	84
Earth	150	1
Neptune	4479	165
Venus	108	0.6

- By comparing each line individually, we begin to see a pattern emerging.
- BUT if we use our knowledge of the order of the planets (see page 45) …

Top Tip!

Remember that in science disproving a theory is just as valid as proving one – not finding patterns or relationships in your data doesn't mean your experiment didn't work.

… and put the planets into the same table in their correct order …

Name of planet	Distance from the Sun (millions of km)	Time to orbit the Sun (years)
Mercury	58	0.2
Venus	108	0.6
Earth	150	1
Mars	228	1.9
Jupiter	778	11.9
Saturn	1427	29.5
Uranus	2870	84
Neptune	4479	165
Pluto	5900	248

… THEN it is easy to see that as the distance from the Sun increases, the length of time taken to orbit the Sun also increases. When two variables change together in this way we call this a **relationship**.

Did You Know?

Edmund Halley observed a comet in 1682. From the pattern of sightings of the same comet made in 1456, 1531 and 1607, he correctly predicted that it would be seen again in 1758. Unfortunately Halley died in 1742, but using his formula we can predict when this comet (now known as Halley's comet) will be sighted again.

levels 4-5

Relationships between variables

- When we carry out an experiment or collect information (usually called data), we must present the data so that it shows if there is a relationship between two variables.
- For example, if you look at a group of students that are about the same age, they will have many variables that differ, such as height, weight, hair and eye colour, and shoe size.
- Sarah put the information she had collected about six students into a table to see if there were any relationships between the variables. First she decided how to make her list based on the question she wanted to ask. She wanted to investigate the relationship between eye colour and birthday, so she used one of those variables (birthday) to order the list like this:

Name	Height (cm)	Mass (kg)	Hand span (cm)	Eye colour	Birthday
James	161	51	19	green	January
Sarah	152	48	17	blue	January
Tom	170	58	21	brown	March
Safina	155	45	16	brown	June
Peter	158	49	20	brown	August
Jenna	145	50	17	blue	November

- As eye colour is an inherited characteristic (see page 66) and has nothing to do with our month of birth, there isn't a relationship. There is a pattern – all the brown-eyed students were born in spring and summer, but Sarah's sample size was too small to support an hypothesis.
- Sarah then decided to see if there was a relationship between height and mass. She listed the students in height order to see if this gave a pattern.

Name	Height (cm)	Mass (kg)	Hand span (cm)	Eye colour	Birthday
Tom	170	58	21	brown	March
James	161	51	19	green	January
Peter	158	49	20	brown	August
Safina	155	45	16	brown	June
Sarah	152	48	17	blue	January
Jenna	145	50	17	blue	November

- There is no direct relationship, but there is a pattern – the tallest people are generally heavier than the shortest people – but it is not true that the taller you are the more you will weigh.

Spot Check

1. What would you expect the relationship to be between the distance of a planet from the Sun and the temperature on the surface of that planet?
2. It takes 5 g of salt 10 min to dissolve in water and 10 g takes 20 min to dissolve in the same volume of water at the same temperature. Is there a relationship?
3. Would it be possible from this to predict how long it would take for 20 g of salt to dissolve?

SCIENTIFIC ENQUIRY

Interpreting results and reading graphs

level 4

Reading bar charts and pie charts

- Being able to plot the correct graph or choose the correct type of chart to use is very important. But it is also essential to be able to read or **interpret** graphs and charts as this tells us what has happened in the experiment.

level 4

Pie charts

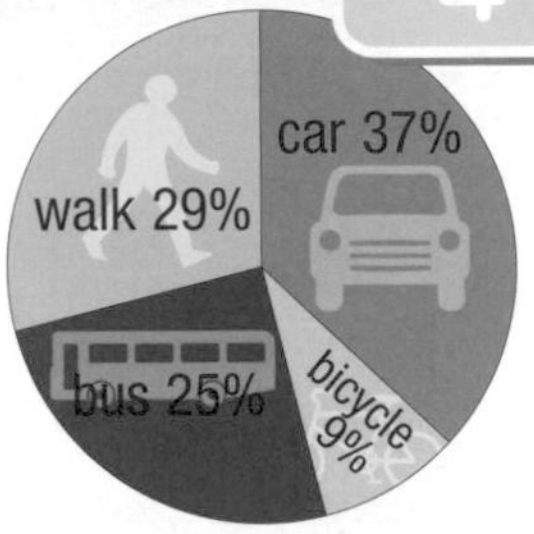

- Pie charts are easy to read – the bigger the slice of pie, the more there is of that group or quantity.
- In a travel survey carried out by a school, a lot of the students travel by car and many walk, nearly as many come by bus, but very few cycle.

level 4

Bar charts

- Similarly, in this bar chart – showing the results of a food-burning experiment – the taller the bar, the more energy there is.
- The water is heated most by the cheese and crisps, a bit less by the bread and a lot less by the crispbread – so we can see which food released the most energy when it was burned.

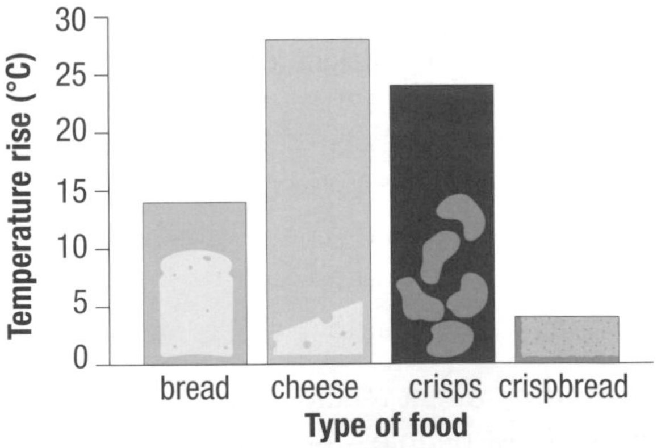

Did You Know?

Edward Jenner (1749–1823) noticed that people who caught cowpox didn't get smallpox. From this observation, he developed the idea of using cowpox as a vaccination against smallpox. Vaccinated people developed a mild form of cowpox, which stopped them getting the more serious smallpox. Jenner's idea is used for present-day vaccinations against many diseases.

> **Top Tip!**
> If your independent variable is discontinuous, then a bar chart is probably fine. Continuous variables need line graphs – with a line joining the points (see page 88 for lines of best fit).

level 5

Interpreting line graphs

- Pie charts and bar charts give a picture – but line graphs can tell a story over time and can show how one thing can change in response to the change of another. In the graph of temperature and time, we see how the temperature of the water changes over time, levelling off when the ice was melting and again when the water was boiling.

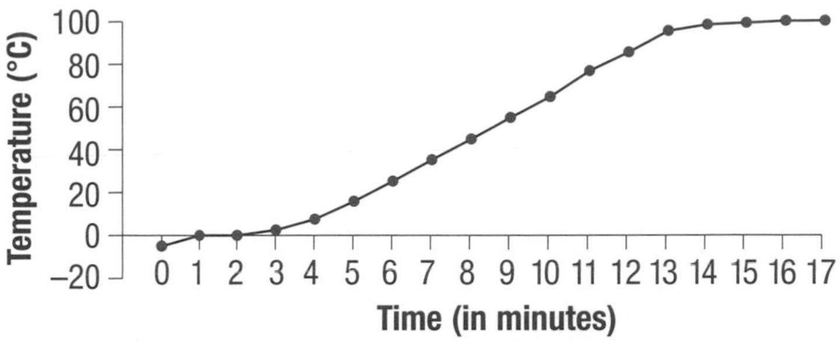

level 5

Giving a scientific explanation

- You always need to give a scientific explanation for what you discover. For the temperature and time graph, the temperature levels off because changes of state use up most of the energy being supplied, so little is left to raise the temperature at these points.
- In the same way, a graph of speed against time can tell us the story of a journey.
- The person doing this journey starts by accelerating until a speed is reached at B, which stays steady until C. She then slows down to a new steady speed which is maintained from D to E. At E she starts to accelerate again and reaches the highest speed of the journey at F. She holds this speed until G when she slows down very quickly to stop at H. She remains still until I, accelerates to J, then slows down again to K, where she stops at her destination.

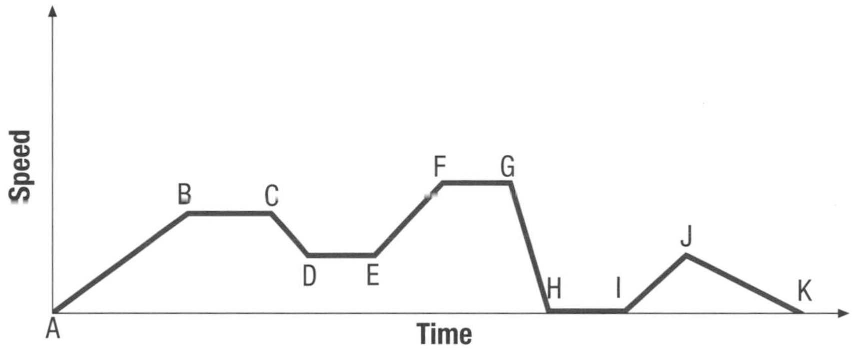

Spot Check

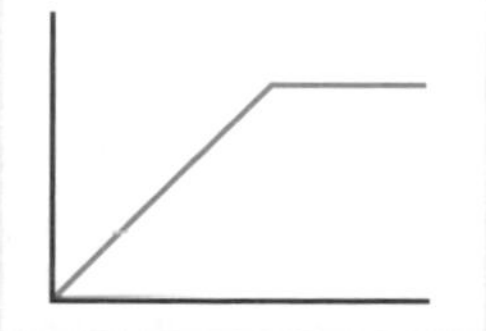

Look at the graph and answer the **three** questions below.
The graph shows how much a spring extends when masses are added to it.

1 What variable should be on the *x*-axis?
2 What should be on the *y*-axis?
3 What do you think has happened at the point where the graph stops going up and becomes a flat straight line?

Evidence and conclusions

level 5

Conclusions

- The results of an experiment can help us to draw **conclusions** about the effect of one variable on another.
- When the results of an experiment show a clear trend or pattern, we can express this as a conclusion. We can conclude from the temperature and time graph on page 87 that if you heat ice, the temperature of the water rises most of the time when it is above 0 °C and below 100 °C, but at 0 °C and 100 °C the temperature levels off.
- The explanation for this is that the changes of state use up most of the energy being supplied so there is little energy left to raise the temperature at these points.

level 5

Lines of best fit

- When our results give a graph that is not a smooth curve or a straight line, any trend will not be as clear. For these graphs, we often draw a **line of best fit** – the line follows the trend of the graph without joining up every point.

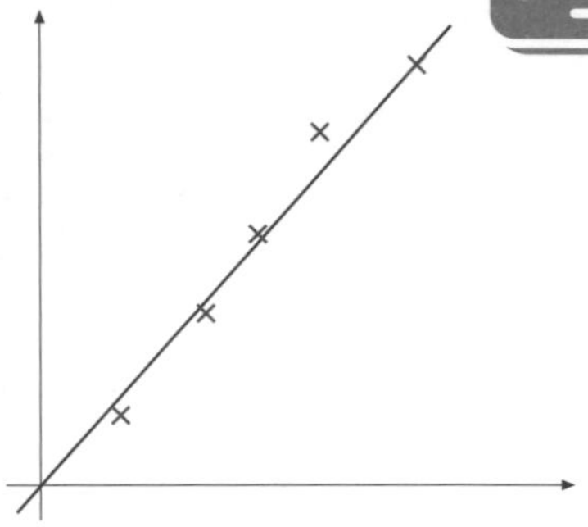

level 5

Evidence

- Results from experiments are examples of **evidence**.
- It is important when drawing conclusions to only use the evidence that is there – not to draw on other things that we might know but which are not shown by the results.
- Evidence leads to the development of scientific theories, but the conclusions from one experiment would not be enough for the development of a new theory. It may support a theory or show an area where the theory was weak and more evidence needs to be gathered.

level 5

Opinions and evidence

- It is important to understand the difference between what someone thinks (their opinion) and evidence. To say that smoking is bad for you is an opinion. To be able to show that the number of smokers developing lung cancer is much higher than the number of non-smokers developing lung cancer is evidence to support that view.

Did You Know?

Sir Isaac Newton described how his work built on that of earlier scientists saying: 'If I have seen further than other men it is because I have stood on the shoulders of giants'.

level 6

Development of scientific ideas

- Scientific **ideas** and **theories** are NOT completely fixed and unchanging.
- All the scientific ideas that we have today have been developed over time – sometimes over hundreds of years – as scientists have done more experiments and thought more about the results of experiments done in the past.

level 6

Developing the laws of motion and gravity

- Look back to page 43 where we examined what affects the speed of falling objects.
- A man called Aristotle, who lived more than 2000 years ago in Greece, decided that heavier objects would fall faster. But about 500 years ago, in Italy, Galileo Galilei did some experiments, dropping light and heavy objects from a high building. He concluded that the mass of an object did not affect the speed at which it fell to the ground. His evidence changed people's ideas away from what Aristotle had thought before.
- Sir Isaac Newton, who lived just after Galileo, did more experiments and more work, and developed the laws of motion and gravity that we use today. His work built on what Galileo had done before.
- This is how scientific ideas and theories develop. Scientists challenge or develop the work that others have done before them.

Galileo Galilei

Sir Isaac Newton

Top Tip!

Remember that scientific ideas develop over time. What we know now is based on work from the past – and the work being done now will shape the ideas of the future.

Spot Check

1 In a survey of 25 people, none of the males had naturally blond hair. Is this evidence to support the statement that no men have blond hair?

2 The number of children catching measles each year throughout Great Britain is recorded. If this number went down a great deal in the year that a vaccination was introduced and given to all children, and stayed down – would this be evidence that the vaccination was effective?

3 Where was Galileo's hypothesis finally proved right?

Evaluating experiments

level 6

Reliability and evaluation

- If experiments can be used as evidence to change scientific ideas, then it is important that the conclusions are **reliable**.
- Working out how reliable the conclusions are from an experiment is called **evaluation**.
- Evaluation involves looking at how good an experiment has been – there is no such thing as a perfect experiment. Evaluation sometimes gives ideas as to what further work could be done to check and develop those conclusions.
- When you are evaluating your own work – or in a Test evaluating an experiment that has been described to you – there are some things you need to ask yourself.

level 5

Was the test really a fair test?

- Was it possible to control all the control variables completely?
  - Sometimes it isn't possible to do this.
  - For example, in any experiment that involves people, or most other living things, it can be very hard to control all the variables.
  - When an experiment involves working in the dark – how dark is dark?

Top Tip!

Experiments can always be improved. It doesn't mean you got it wrong if you can see faults in your experiment. It means you are well on the way to becoming a real scientist.

level 5

How easy was it to take accurate measurements?

- Was the thing that you were trying to measure easy or difficult to work on?
  - Measuring something that stays still is easy, but when something is moving it is much harder. Measuring a regular shape is much easier than measuring an irregular one.

level 5

How easy was it to take accurate readings?

- Was it possible to take readings that were **accurate**?
  - Did your measuring instrument enable you to take readings that showed up differences in your dependent variable? If you were measuring very small weights with a Newton meter accurate to only 1 N, or small changes in temperature with a thermometer that only measured to 1 °C, would you be able to notice small differences?

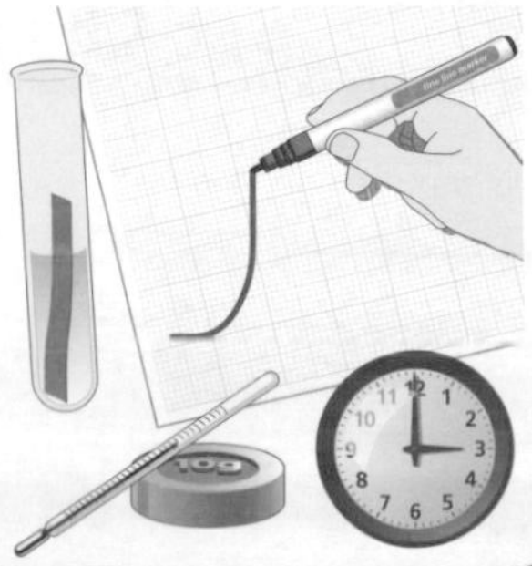

download, watch and listen to help you revise
www.collinseducation.com/revision

Did You Know?

Some experiments have to be done deep underground at the bottom of disused mines so that nothing on the surface of Earth can interfere with the results.

level 5

Did you take enough readings?

- If you only took two or three readings, then can you really see a trend or pattern or plot a meaningful graph?
- If you took repeat readings, were they close together and, if not, can you see why not? This will tell you about the reliability of your results.

level 5

Did you ask the right question in the first place?

- Was your question appropriate, taking into account the variables that you identified and measured?
- The best evaluations will often lead to further planning and more investigation – and more questions that need to be answered.

level 6

Evaluating real-life experiments

- Evaluation is important in large-scale projects, as well as those that take place in a laboratory.
- A farmer who grows a genetically modified crop will need to ask some questions when the crop has been harvested. Those questions might include:
  - Was the yield (the amount of produce) per acre more or less than in a similar field with a non-GM crop, or than in the same field last year?
  - How much did the crop cost in terms of fertilisers and pesticides and, again, how did this compare with the non-GM crop?
  - Was this crop in any way easier or harder to manage than a non-GM crop?
- All of these answers will include the effect of factors that are not possible to control, such as the weather.

Spot Check

1 In what sorts of experiments can it be difficult to make sure you have controlled all the variables?
2 How can you make sure that experimental readings are as accurate as possible?
3 How can you check to see if your results are reliable?

Answers to Spot Check questions

CELLS

Cell structure pages 4–5

1 Cell membrane; nucleus; cytoplasm.
2 Cell wall.
3 Cell membrane.

Specialist cells pages 6–7

1 Because their job is to allow the plant to draw water from the soil. They are not in the sunlight and so do not photosynthesise.
2 Red blood cells, to absorb and carry the most oxygen possible.
3 Nerve cells need to be very long and thin to go all over the body and carry messages from the brain.

Tissues and organs pages 8–9

1 They divide.
2 The brain, the nerves and the sensing organs such as eyes, ears and skin.
3 The skeletal system.

The digestive system pages 10–11

1 For growth, for movement and for warmth.
2 Saliva.
3 Large intestine.

The reproductive system pages 12–13

1 Fertilisation.
2 The placenta.
3 Ovulation.

The circulation system pages 14–15

1 Left ventricle, right ventricle, left atrium, right atrium.
2 Artery.
3 Carbon dioxide.

Photosynthesis pages 16–17

1 Because only green plants can make their own food.
2 Carbon dioxide.
3 Variegated leaves are ones where part of the leaf is green and part is white. Photosynthesis only takes place in the green parts of the leaf where there are chloroplasts.

ENERGY

Energy resources pages 18–19

1 Coal, oil and natural gas.
2 Carbon dioxide.
3 Because they took millions of years to produce so it is not possible to make any more.

Generating and using electricity pages 20–21

1 The steam in a power station turns the turbine which then turns the generator which makes the electricity.
2 There is no combustion (burning), the turbine is turned directly.
3 Loft insulation, double glazing, shutting doors and windows; also cavity wall insulation and draft excluders.

Electrical circuits pages 22–23

1 A series circuit.
2 It is always the same at any point.
3 The other bulbs will stay alight.

Energy transformation pages 24–25

1 Stored energies are called potential energy.
2 Heat or thermal energy.
3 The transfer of light energy does not need particles but the transfer of sound energy does.

Energy transfer pages 26–27

1 Heat or thermal energy.
2 Convection.
3 The heated particles get more energy and so move more quickly and collide with other particles and so pass the energy on.

Energy from food pages 28–29

1 Glucose + oxygen → carbon dioxide + water + energy
2 By burning the same amount of a number of different foods and using the energy to heat the same amount of water each time and measuring the increase in the temperature of the water.
3 Protein.

Sound and light pages 30–31

1 Amplitude.
2 It will be a high pitched sound.
3 Luminous.

Reflection, refraction and seeing colour pages 32–33

1 A periscope.
2 Refraction.
3 All the light that falls on it is absorbed and none is reflected.

FORCES

Balanced and unbalanced forces pages 34–35

1 Speed, direction and shape.
2 It will continue to move at the same speed in the same direction for as long as the forces are balanced.
3 By making the surface area smaller.

Speed and motion pages 36–37

1 Speed = distance ÷ time
= 150 miles ÷ 3 hours
= 50 mph (don't forget the units)
2 No this is the average speed, the speed of the train will have been different at different parts of the journey. Sometimes it will have been going much faster than 50 mph and at other times much more slowly.
3 metres per second (m/s)

Friction pages 38–39

1 All except **b**.
2 The push force will be greater than the friction force when the block starts to move.

Streamlining and air resistance pages 40–41

1 Air resistance.
2 Terminal velocity.
3 Weight (or gravity).

Gravity pages 42–43

1 **a** 700 N; **b** 117 N.
2 The shape and size of the two objects so that one did not have more air resistance than the other.

The Earth and beyond pages 44–45

1 **a** 28 days; **b** 365 days (or $365\frac{1}{4}$).
2 Mercury and Venus because they are closer to the Sun, so it takes less time for them to complete an orbit, so the year is shorter.
3 No, we can see the moon because it reflects the light from the Sun.

Magnetic forces pages 46–47

1 If there is a force of repulsion. A magnet can attract an un-magnetised piece of iron but only another magnet can repel.
2 The size of the current and the number of turns on the coil.
3 With an electromagnet, the magnetism can be turned on and off by switching the current on and off.

PARTICLES

Solids, liquids and gases pages 48–49

1 **a** Melting; **b** condensation.
2 It is a fixed regular lattice with particles only able to vibrate around fixed points.
3 The particles in a liquid are more free to move than in a solid but not so spread out as in a gas. They can slide over each other and move quite freely but still remain in contact with each other.

Solubility and separation pages 50–51

1 To make a **solution**, take some **solute** and dissolve it in a **solvent**. If your solute will not **dissolve** in your solvent then it is **insoluble**. Every solute will not dissolve in every **solvent**.
2 First filter the solution to get the sand and then evaporate off the water to leave the salt.

Elements, compounds and mixtures pages 52–53

1 In a compound the atoms have reacted together to make a new substance. In a mixture there has been no chemical reaction and the original substances are all still there.
2 On the left-hand side.
3 **a** O; **b** Na; **c** S; **d** N; **e** Ni.

Chemical reactions pages 54–55

1 In a chemical change a new substance is formed and it is hard to get the original substances back again. In a physical change of state no new substance is formed and it is easy to reverse the change.
2 Magnesium + oxygen → magnesium oxide.
3 Zinc + oxygen → zinc oxide.

Acids and alkalis pages 56–57

1 Red because lemon juice is acid.
2 a Acid + alkali → salt + water.
b Acid + metal → salt + hydrogen.
3 Sulphur dioxide.

Metals and non-metals pages 58–59

1 Water and oxygen.
2 Because metals conduct heat which cooks the food.
3 Metal + steam → metal oxide + hydrogen.

Rocks and the rock cycle pages 60–61

1 If the crystals are large then the rock has been formed by magma cooling slowly. If they are small, the magma has cooled quickly.
2 Marble.
3 Sedimentary rock.

INTERDEPENDENCE

Food chains and food webs pages 62–63

1 A producer is always a green plant – there is always one at the start of a food chain because only green plants can make their own food using the energy from sunlight.
2

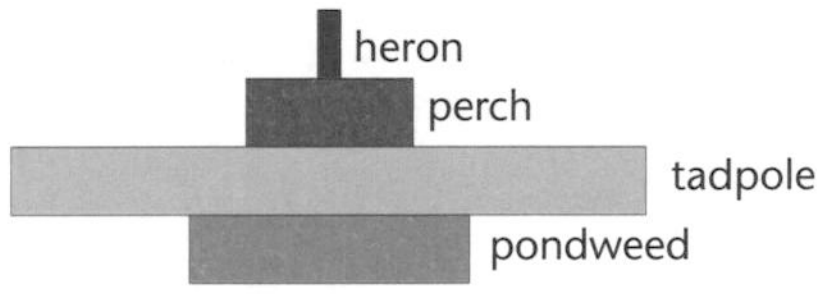

3 The secondary consumers are probably carnivores.

Energy transfers in food chains and food webs pages 64–65

1 An animal that eats another is a predator and the animal it eats is its prey.
2 Because at each level some energy is used by the organism for other life processes. In animals to maintain body temperature and for movement.
3 About 5%.

Variation and inheritance pages 66–67

1 Eye colour and natural hair colour are completely inherited characteristics; height is partly so, as although we inherit a maximum possible height we will only reach that in the right conditions; weight depends on what we eat and how much exercise we take and anyone can choose to learn a foreign language – these are not inherited.
2 They would not be able to produce any offspring themselves.
3 The ability to gallop very fast and maybe stamina to enable them to go on for a long time.

Adaptation pages 68–69

1 Thick coat with waterproof fur/a greenish-brown colour for camouflage/a herbivore/powerful legs for running away from predators, etc., etc.
2 Because there is little food in winter, they eat a lot in the autumn when there is plenty of food.
3 Because in the daytime there will be insects about who will pollinate the plant. At night by closing the flower the plant is protected from the cold.

Classification pages 70–71

1 The young develop inside the mother and are fed on milk from the mother after birth.
2 Insects, arachnids, crustaceans, myriapods.
3 Any two from: warm-blooded, breathe through lungs, feathers, lay eggs with hard shells.

Using keys to identify living things pages 72–73

1 Small Tortoiseshell.
2 Lesser celandine.
3 Tree mallow.

Competition among living things pages 74–75

1 If there were fewer hazelnuts then there would be less for the squirrels and mice to eat, which might mean less food for the foxes, so fewer foxes.
2 Bluebells and primroses flower in early spring before the leaves are all out on the trees, so there is more light at ground level than there would be later on when the trees are fully out.
3 There are so few individuals of that species left that it may soon become extinct.

Human impact on the environment pages 76–77

1 Carbon dioxide which is released by burning fossil fuels.
2 By dropping limestone into the water.
3 Ozone.

SCIENTIFIC ENQUIRY

Asking questions and making predictions pages 78–79

1 Does the temperature of water affect the time taken for a given amount of salt to dissolve?
2 If the water is at a higher temperature the same amount of salt will take less time to dissolve as the particles will all have more energy and be able to move about more.
3 What volume of water can be absorbed by a 30 cm square (or any size as long as it's the same for each) of different kinds of kitchen towel?

Variables and fair tests pages 80–81

1 Hand span is a continuous variable.
2 The type of shoe.
3 The force needed to move the shoe.

Presenting results and drawing graphs pages 82–83

1 Type of shoe/Mass of shoe (kg)/Surface/Force needed for shoes to move (N)
2 A bar chart because the type of surface is a discontinuous variable.
3 A line graph, because the increasing mass is a continuous variable.

Patterns and relationships pages 84–85

1 The nearer a planet is to the Sun, the hotter its surface will be.
2 From these the results it looks as if the relationship is that a greater mass of salt takes longer to dissolve.
3 A good prediction would be that 20 g of salt would take 40 min to dissolve – but it would be best to do an experiment to measure this.

Interpreting results and reading graphs pages 86–87

1 Mass added to the spring in grams.
2 The length of the spring or the amount of extension.
3 The spring has stretched so far that it is no longer a spring – adding more and more mass will not make it any longer.

Evidence and conclusions pages 88–89

1 No, because not enough people were asked.
2 Yes, because the sample size is very large and there has been a clear change – the introduction of the vaccine had a clear effect – the reduction in the number of cases of measles.
3 From the top of a tall building.

Evaluating experiments pages 90–91

1 Experiments involving living things.
2 By making sure that you use the correct measuring instrument.
3 By repeating them to see if you get the same result each time or if they are quite different.

Glossary

accuracy the quality of the measurements taken in an experiment

acid rain rain containing dissolved gases such as sulphur dioxide, which are produced when fossil fuels are burnt

air resistance the force that slows down objects moving through the air

ammeter a device for measuring electrical current

amplitude the height of a sound wave

arteries thick-walled blood vessels that carry blood away from the heart

average speed the total distance travelled divided by the total time

balanced forces when the forces acting on an object do not cause it to change its speed or direction

breathing taking in air, rich in oxygen, from the surroundings and expelling air, rich in carbon dioxide, from the body

capillaries tiny blood vessels with walls one cell thick

carbohydrate the food needed for energy

carnivore an animal that eats only other animals

cell membrane found in plant and animal cells and controls what goes into and out of the cell

cell wall rigid structure made of cellulose outside the cell membrane that gives plant cells support

chlorophyll the green pigment needed for photosynthesis that is found in the chloroplasts of plant cells

chloroplast contains the green pigment chlorophyll in plant cells

chromatography a method of separating different solutes from one solvent where the particles of the solutes are of different sizes

chromosomes structures containing DNA found in the nucleus of cells

competition trying to obtain the resources needed to survive at the same time as others

compound a substance formed when two or more elements react together chemically

conduction thermal energy transfer through solids

conductor thermal conductor – a material through which heat flows easily; electrical conductor – a material through which electrical current flows easily

control variable the quantity in an experiment that is kept the same to make sure that the effect of the independent variable is measured

convection thermal energy transfer through liquids and gases

corrosion the reaction of a metal with oxygen to form an oxide

dependent variable the quantity in an experiment that is measured to see the effect of the independent variable

digestion the process of breaking food down into simple substances that are used for growth and to provide energy

digestive system the organs that work together to break down the food an animal eats

distillation a method of separating liquids which have different boiling points

electromagnet a material that has a magnetic field only when an electric current is flowing through it

element a pure substance made entirely of one type of atom

embryo a ball of cells formed when a sperm fertilises an egg and which becomes implanted in the uterus

evaluation an assessment of how accurate and reliable an experiment has been, and how that experiment could be improved

evidence facts and factors that can be measured to prove or dispute a theory or an idea

filtration a method of separating large particles from small ones – used to separate a solid from a liquid

foetus the unborn baby, older than 8 weeks, developing in the uterus

food chain a series of organisms, always starting with a plant, each one feeding on the next one down the chain to obtain the energy needed for life processes

food web the interaction of several food chains reflecting the variety found in natural situations

formula the name of a compound written using chemical symbols

fossil fuels coal, oil and natural gas

frequency the number of sound waves passing a particular point in a second

friction the force that acts to oppose movement

gas a substance whose particles are free to move around and fill all the available space

global warming the increase in the temperature of the Earth's atmosphere caused by the greenhouse effect

gravity the attraction force between any two objects due to their mass

greenhouse effect the insulation effect of the layer of carbon dioxide in the upper atmosphere

habitat the place where plants and animals live

heart the muscular pump that moves blood around the body

herbivore an animal that eats only green plants

hibernation an inactive state that allows animals to survive in winter

independent variable the quantity in an experiment that is changed to study its effect

joule the unit used for measuring energy

kilocalories the unit used to measure the energy stored in food

kinetic energy the energy of movement

lava molten rock above ground

liquid a substance that is able to flow and fill the bottom of a container – the particles remain in contact but are able to move past each other

loudness related to the amplitude of a sound wave

luminous objects that give off their own light

magma molten rock underground

mass how much there is of something, measured in grams

menstrual cycle a 28-day cycle for receiving a fertilised egg in the uterus

menstruation (period) the breakdown and loss of the uterus lining through the vagina

migration the movement of animals to another place where conditions for survival are more favourable

mixture two or more elements or compounds that can be easily separated because they have not undergone any chemical change

molecule two or more atoms joined together

neutralisation the reaction of an acid with an alkali to produce a salt plus water

newton the unit of force – named after Sir Isaac Newton

nocturnal animals that are active at night-time

nucleus the part of a cell that contains the genetic information and controls the chemical activity of the cell

opaque a material that light does not pass through, so it cannot be seen through

organ a group of different tissues joined together to carry out a role within a plant or animal, such as a leaf or root, the heart or stomach

ozone layer a layer of ozone gas high in the atmosphere that protects the Earth from the damaging radiation of the Sun

parallel circuit an electrical circuit in which there are two or more possible routes for the current to flow along

Periodic Table a table of all the elements arranged according to the size of their atoms and their chemical properties

photosynthesis the process by which plants make their own food from carbon dioxide and water by trapping the energy from the Sun

pitch related to the frequency of a sound wave

potential energy stored energy

predator an animal that eats other animals

prediction a statement about the possible outcome of an experiment based on scientific knowledge

pressure the relationship between the force acting on an object and the surface area over which the force is applied

prey an animal that is eaten by other animals

producer the first organism in a food chain, which is always a green plant

protein the type of food needed for the growth and repair of our bodies

radiation thermal energy transfer from an object that is warmer than its surroundings

reactivity series metals placed in order of how reactive they are with water, steam and acids

reflection the way in which light rays bounce off objects, which enables us to see them

refraction the way in which light rays bend when they move from one medium to another

reliability how easy it would be to obtain the same results if an experiment was repeated

renewable energy sources types of energy resources such as wind and tidal power which will not run out in the way that fossil fuels will

reproduction the process by which living things produce new organisms like themselves

reproductive system the organs used by a plant or an animal to reproduce

respiration the chemical reaction that takes place in every cell to release energy from the products of digested food

rusting the corrosion of iron

salt a chemical formed when an acid reacts with an alkali

series circuit an electrical circuit in which all the components are on one continuous wire

solid a substance with a fixed shape in which the particles are in a rigid lattice structure

solute a solid material that can be dissolved in a liquid

solution a liquid containing dissolved particles of a solid

solvent a liquid in which a solid material can be dissolved

species animals, or plants, that can reproduce to give offspring that are capable of reproduction

spectrum the seven colours produced when white light is split up using a prism

speed the distance an object travels in a particular time

terminal velocity the maximum speed that any object can reach

thermal energy the proper way of describing heat

tissue a group of similar cells in a plant or an animal

translucent a material that light can pass through

trophic level the steps in a food chain

unbalanced forces when a force in one direction is greater than the forces in other directions, which causes the object to change its speed or direction

vacuole bag-like structure in the centre of a plant cell that helps to keep it rigid

variable a quantity in an experiment that can be changed, measured or controlled

veins vessels with valves that carry blood back to the heart

weathering the breakdown of rock by rain and wind

weight a downward force, measured in newtons, caused by gravity acting on an object

Index

Collins

Collins Revision KS3 Science Workbook Levels 3–6

Patricia Miller

Cell structure

level 3

1 Label the diagrams of plant and animal cells.

Plant cell

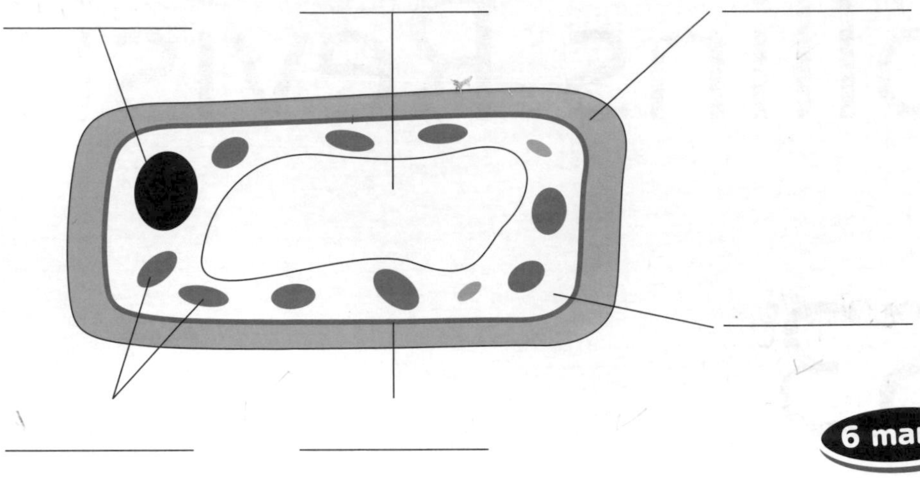

6 marks

Animal cell

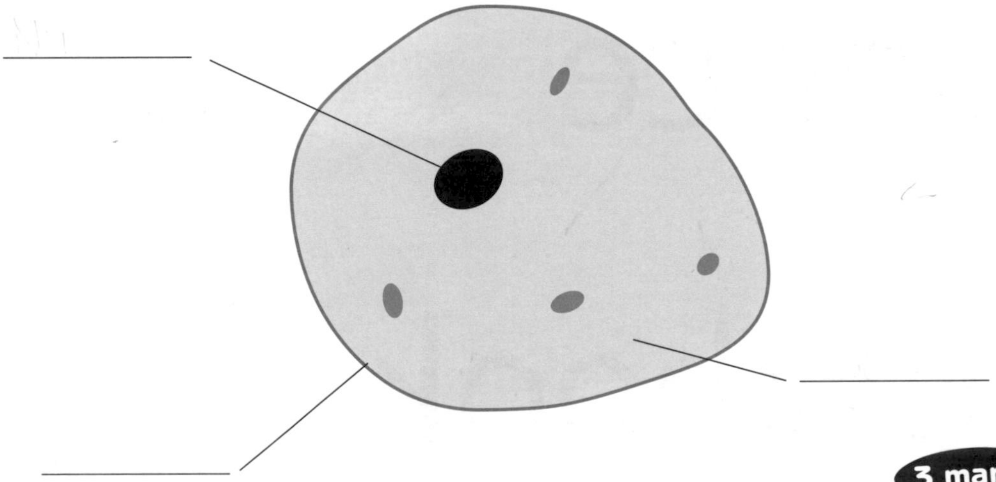

3 marks

2 Which **three** structures do both plant and animal cells have?

a ______________________

b ______________________

c ______________________

3 marks

3 Which **three** structures do only plant cells have?

a ______________________

b ______________________

c ______________________

3 marks

level 3

4 Match the part of the cell to its function.

Part of the cell	Function
Nucleus	Helps keep plant rigid
Cell wall	Matter that makes up most of the cell and where chemical reactions take place
Vacuole	Controls what goes in and out of cell
Cell membrane	Contains green pigment chlorophyll
Chloroplast	Controls chemical reactions in cell
Cytoplasm	Holds water to keep cytoplasm up against cell wall

5 marks

5 Why do only plant cells have chloroplasts?

____

____

1 mark

6 Why do all cells need a cell membrane?

____

____

1 mark

Specialist cells

levels 4-5

1 The diagrams show two different types of plant cell.

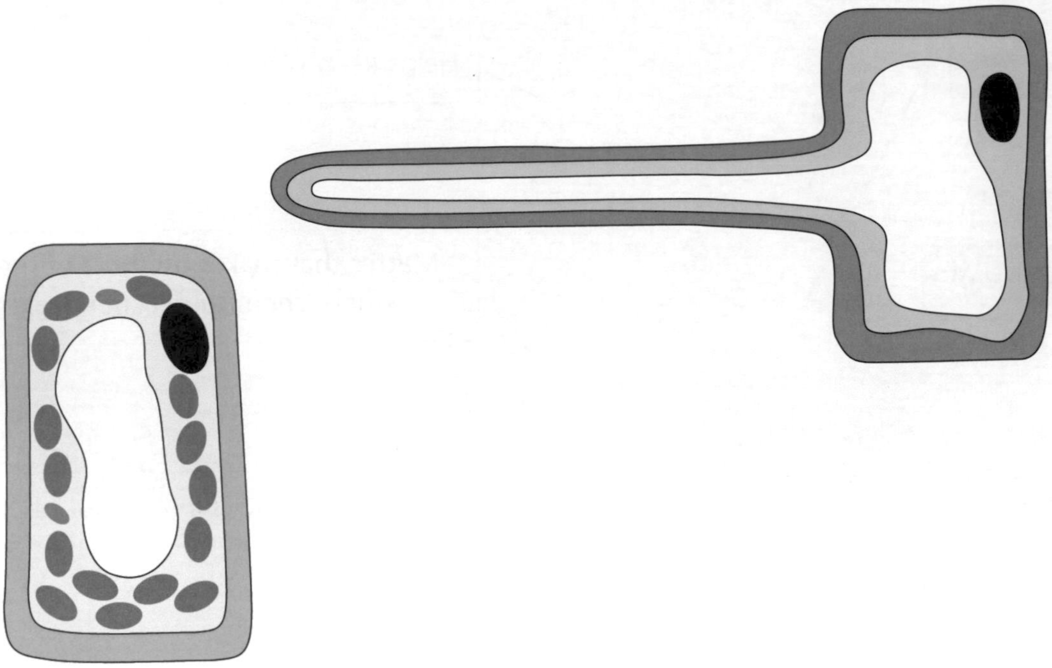

a Which structure is missing from the root hair cell?

______________________________ **1 mark**

b Why do root hair cells not need these structures?

______________________________ **2 marks**

c In what other way is a root hair cell adapted to its function?

______________________________ **1 mark**

2 These cells have adaptations to help them carry out their function.

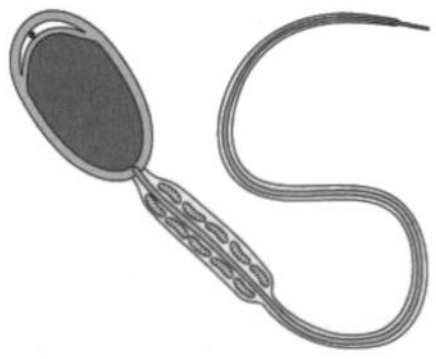

Sperm cell

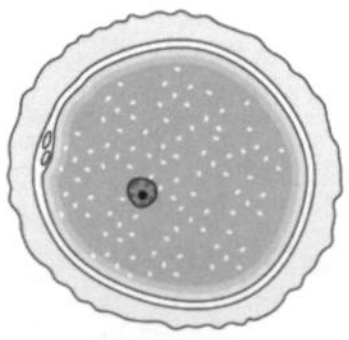

Egg cell (ovum)

a Name **one** adaptation that both cells have.

____

b Name **one** adaptation that only an egg cell has.

______________________________ **2 marks**

level 5

3 These cells both have unusual shapes that help them to carry out their function.

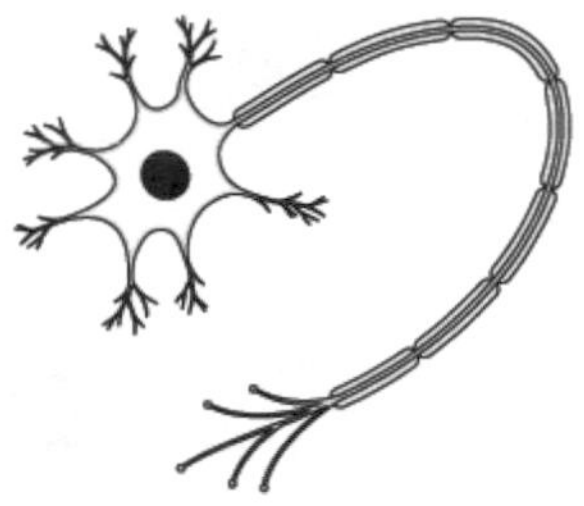

Cell A

Cell B

a Which types of cells are these?

Cell A ______________________

Cell B ______________________

2 marks

b For cell A

i In what way is its shape unusual?

____

____

1 mark

ii How does this shape make it better at carrying out its function?

____

____

1 mark

c For cell B

i In what way is its shape unusual?

____

____

1 mark

ii How does this shape make it better at carrying out its function?

____

____

1 mark

CELLS

Tissues and organs

levels 4-5

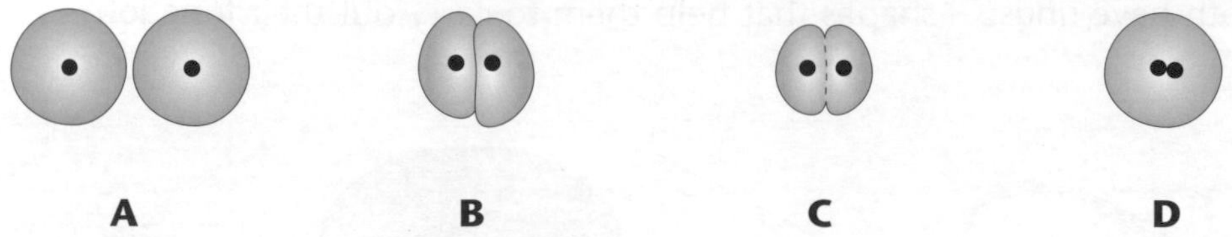

1 a Put the diagrams into the correct order for showing cell division.

4 marks

b When a group of similar cells join together, what do they form?

1 mark

2 a What are the **seven** characteristics of living things?

7 marks

b Which of these characteristics takes place in all systems in the body?

1 mark

c Name **one** organ that is needed to allow each of these characteristics to be carried out in humans.

Excretion __________

Nutrition __________

2 marks

d **i** Which organ in plants allows them to make their own food?

1 mark

ii Which characteristic of living things are plants showing by doing this?

1 mark

levels 4-5

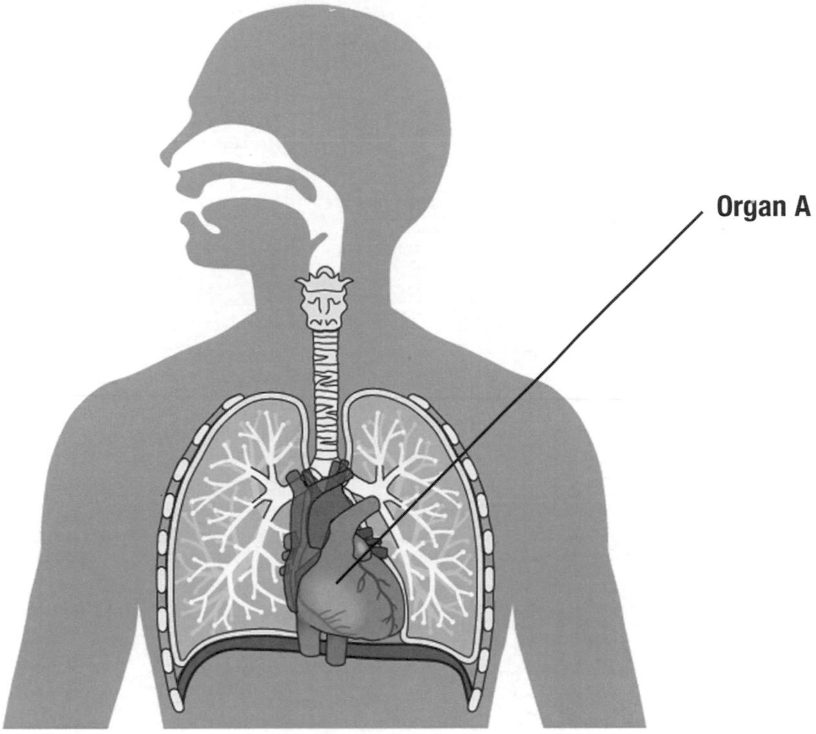

3 **a** This organ is essential to which characteristic?

____

____

1 mark

b What kinds of tissue make up this organ?

____

____

2 marks

c What do we call a group of organs working together to carry out a particular function?

____

1 mark

The digestive system

levels 3-6

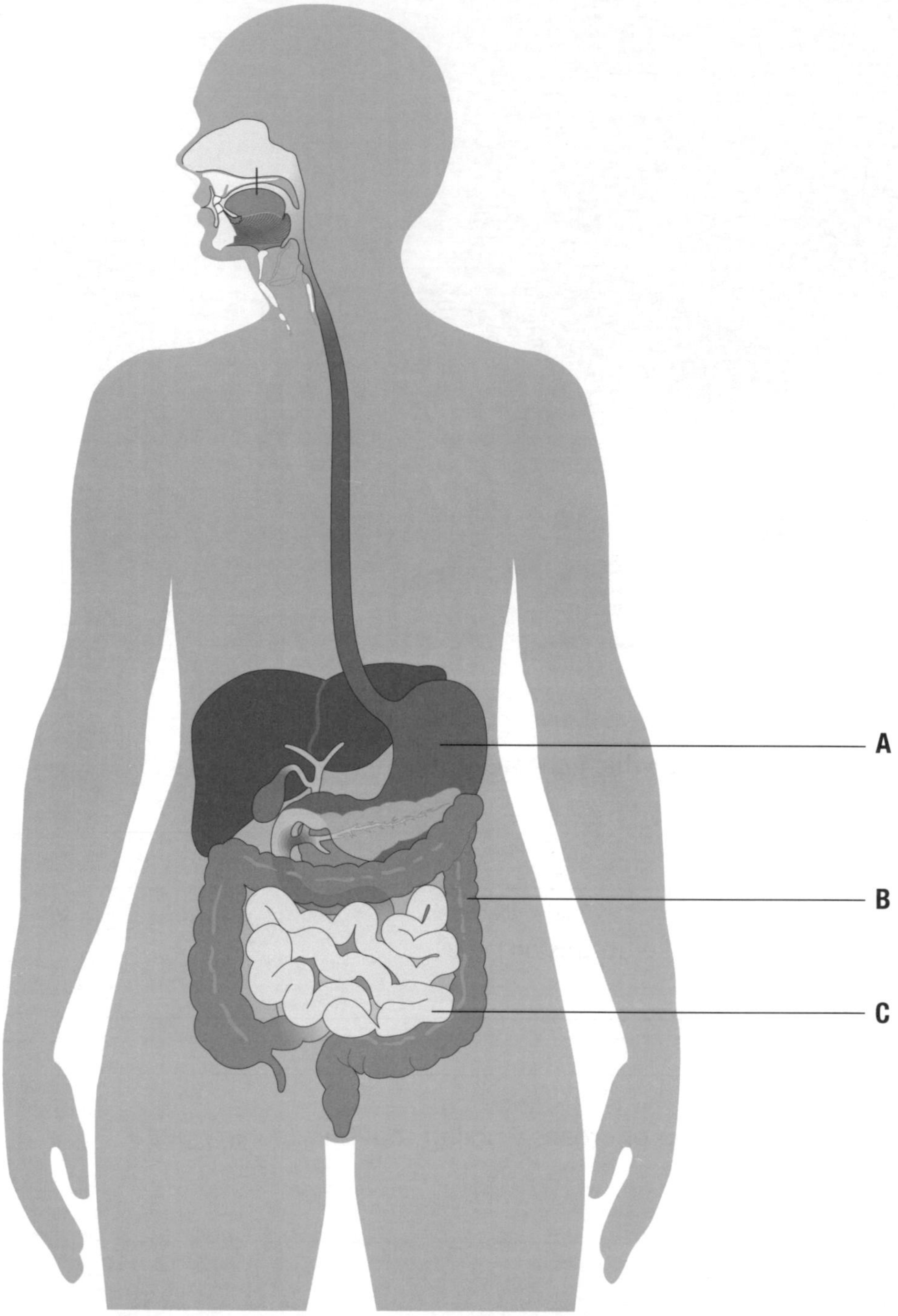

levels 3-6

1 a What are the names of organs A, B and C?

____

____

____

3 marks

b Put the correct letter next to the function of each organ given below.

i The food being digested is broken down into small molecules that can pass through the wall of this organ into the bloodstream.

Organ ______________________________

ii This organ has muscular walls to churn up the food.

Organ ______________________________

iii This organ is where the final stage of digestion happens and water is absorbed back into the body.

Organ ______________________________

3 marks

2 a The body produces chemicals to help break down food.
What are they called?

____

1 mark

b Another one of these chemicals is produced by glands in the mouth.
What is the name of the fluid that contains this chemical?

____

1 mark

3 a The body uses the energy from digestion in **three** ways – what are they?

____

____

____

3 marks

b Protein is particularly important for **one** of these uses.
Which is it?

____

1 mark

The reproductive system

levels 4-5

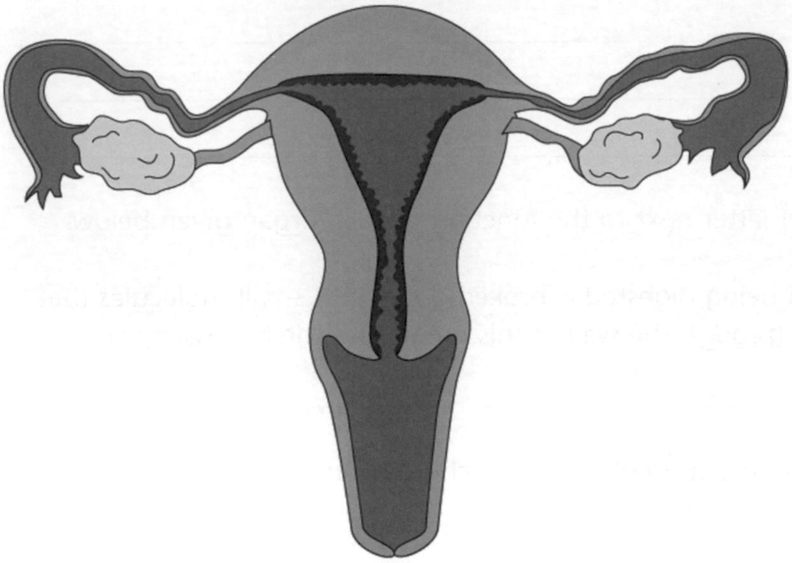

1 a On the diagram above, label the organ in which a foetus grows. **1 mark**

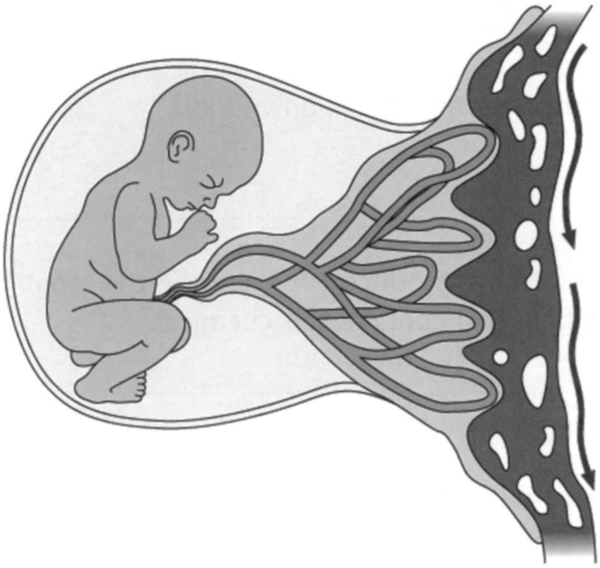

b On the diagram above, label the organ through which the mother passes nutrients to the unborn baby. **1 mark**

c Why should a pregnant woman not smoke cigarettes or drink alcohol?

____

____

____ **2 marks**

levels 5-6

2 a How often does an adult female release an ovum from one of her ovaries?

____

1 mark

b What is the correct term for the release of an ovum?

____

1 mark

c What happens before this to prepare the uterus for a fertilised ovum?

____

____

____

1 mark

d What happens if fertilisation does not take place?

____

____

____

2 marks

e All the above are stages in a cycle – what is the name of that cycle?

____

1 mark

f In what way is an ovum adapted to carry out its special role?

____

____

____

1 mark

g How long does a human foetus remain in its mother's body before it is ready to be born?

____

1 mark

The circulation system

levels 4-5

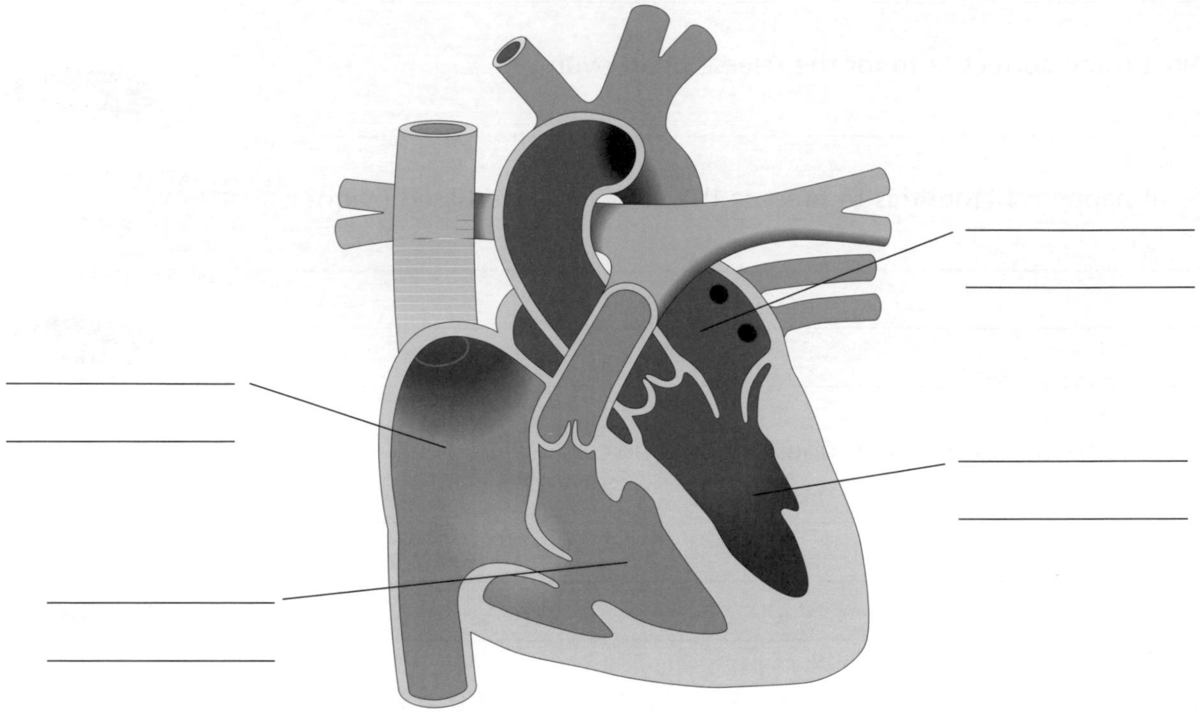

1 a Label the diagram of the heart. **4 marks**

b Show with an arrow on the diagram which side of the heart sends blood to the lungs. **1 mark**

c In which side of the heart would you find oxygenated blood? **1 mark**

____

d Explain your answer.

____

____

______________________________ **2 marks**

2 a Which type of blood vessel carries blood away from the heart? **1 mark**

____

b How is this vessel adapted to this function?

____

____

______________________________ **2 marks**

levels 5-6

3 Put these terms in the correct order to show how an animal or plant is made up.

tissue	**organism**	**cell**	**system**	**organ**

____

____

____

____

____

5 marks

4 **a** Explain the difference between respiration and breathing.

____

____

____

____

____

____

4 marks

b Explain why your heart beats faster when you exercise.

____

____

____

____

3 marks

CELLS

Photosynthesis

level 4

1 Explain why there is a green plant at the start of every food chain.

2 marks

2

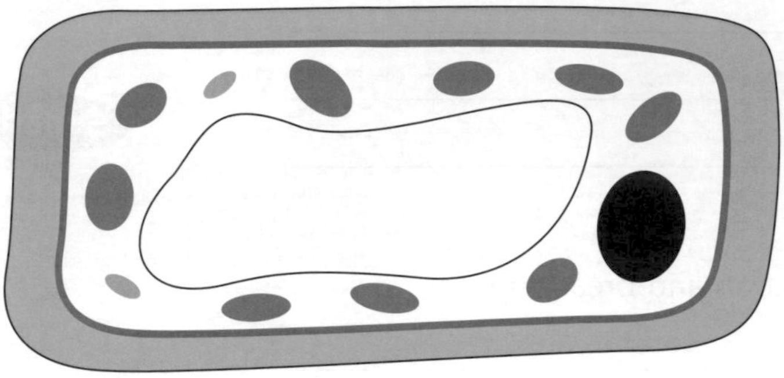

a In the diagram of a cell in the leaf of a plant, label the part of the cell needed for photosynthesis.

1 mark

b What sort of plant cells will not contain this structure?

1 mark

c Explain your answer.

1 mark

3 a What **two** chemicals does a plant need to take in for photosynthesis?

2 marks

b What gas is released as a result of photosynthesis?

1 mark

c Write the chemical reaction for photosynthesis as a word equation.

3 marks

levels 5-6

4 A gardener planted some shrubs that grew to be very dense with lots of leaves on the branches. As they grew bigger he noticed that there was a patch of bare earth under each one where there used to be grass. Explain what had happened.

____

____

____

2 marks

5 Explain why plants give out carbon dioxide in the dark and release oxygen in the light.

____

____

____

____

3 marks

Energy resources

level 4

1 a Tick the correct boxes to show which of these are fossil fuels.

Coal ☐

Biomass ☐

Uranium ☐

Oil ☐

Natural gas ☐

Solar power ☐

3 marks

b Are fossil fuels renewable or non-renewable?

____

1 mark

c Explain your answer.

____

____

____

2 marks

2 a Which gases are released into the environment when fossil fuels are burned?

____

____

2 marks

b What harm does each of these gases do?

____

____

____

____

2 marks

c Which gas that is released when fossil fuels are burned is also given off when biomass is burned?

____

1 mark

level 4

4 Put the following statements into the correct boxes in the table.

A Will one day run out and it is not possible to make more.

B Supplies can be fairly easily replaced.

C Can be used anywhere and when burned gives off a large amount of heat.

D Although not a fossil fuel, still gives off greenhouse gases.

E Can only be used where the conditions are right.

F Is clean to use and renewable.

Energy source	**Advantage**	**Disadvantage**
Coal		
Wind power		
Biomass		

6 marks

5 a What is the ultimate source of the Earth's energy?

____

1 mark

b How can this energy source be used directly?

____

____

____

1 mark

c What is the disadvantage of using this direct energy source?

____

____

____

1 mark

ENERGY

Generating and using electricity

levels 4-5

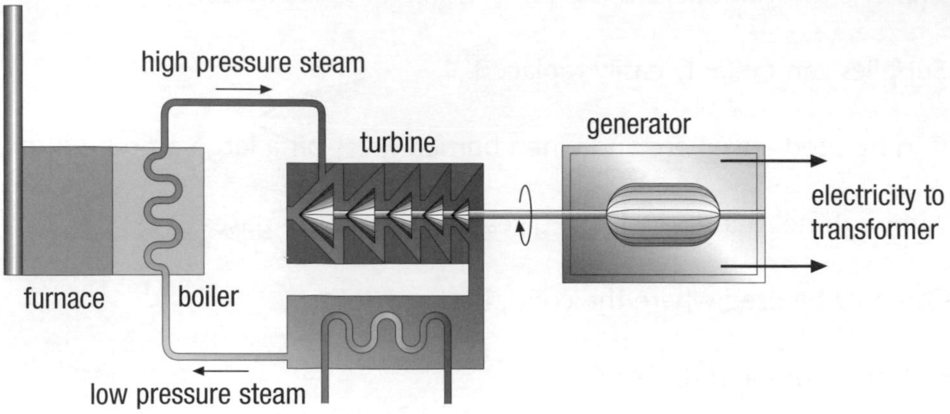

1 a Put these statements into the correct boxes to complete the flow chart to describe the process of generating electricity using a fossil fuel.

A The steam turns a turbine.

B Fuel is burned in a furnace to release energy in the form of heat.

C The turbine turns a magnet inside a generator which produces the electricity.

D The heat from the furnace heats the water in the boiler which creates steam.

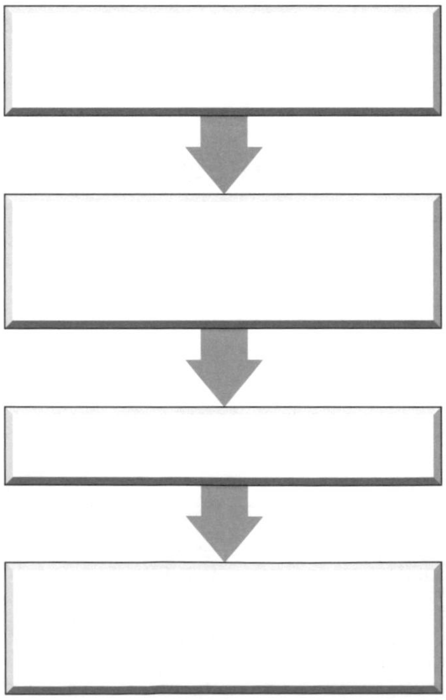

4 marks

b Which part of this process is not needed to generate electricity using wind or wave power?

1 mark

____

2

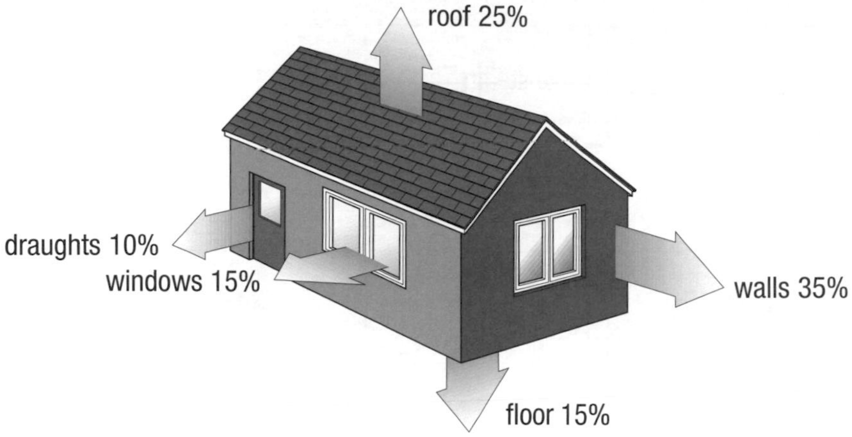

a Draw a bar chart to show how much heat is lost from this house in each way.

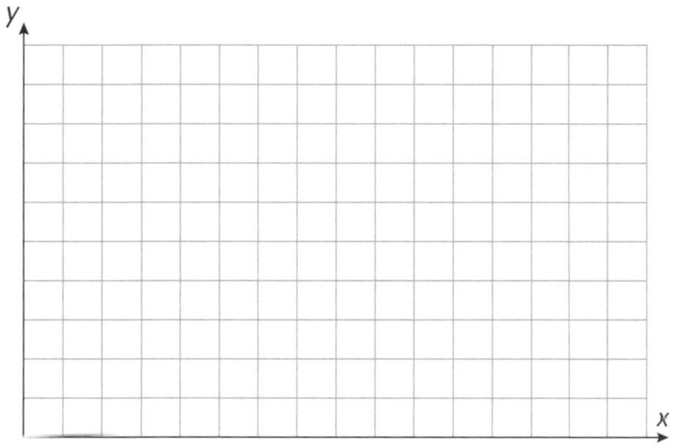

6 marks

b Choose **three** ways in which we can reduce the heat lost from our homes by deciding whether these statements are true or false:

i We can reduce heat loss from our homes by having a shower not a bath. **TRUE/FALSE**

ii Double glazed windows will reduce the heat lost from our homes. **TRUE/FALSE**

iii Loft insulation will reduce heat lost from our homes. **TRUE/FALSE**

iv We can reduce heat loss from our homes by only boiling the amount of water we need in a kettle. **TRUE/FALSE**

v Using energy efficient light bulbs will reduce the heat lost from our homes. **TRUE/FALSE**

vi We can reduce the heat lost from our homes by insulating the cavity walls with foam. **TRUE/FALSE**

6 marks

c The statements which are FALSE are all examples of:

A Money saving tips?

B Ways to cut down on our use of energy?

C Ways to make our homes safer?

1 mark

Electrical circuits

levels 3-5

1 Match the symbol to the name of the component.

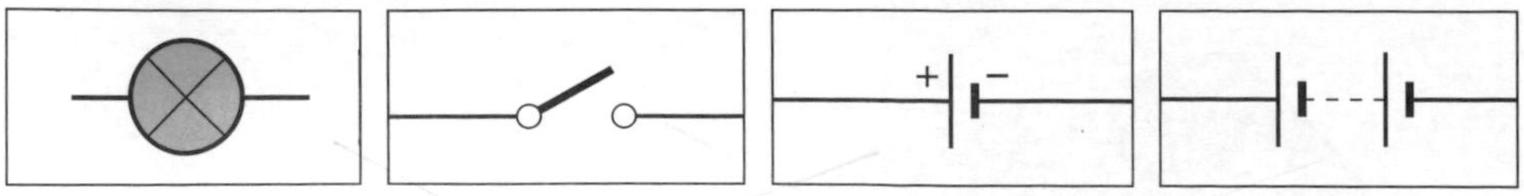

cell	battery	bulb	switch

4 marks

2

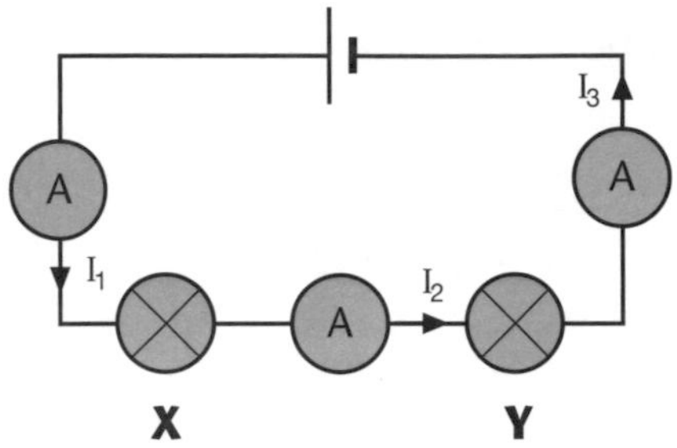

a What do you know about the current at each point in this circuit?

1 mark

b What would happen to bulb X if bulb Y went out?

1 mark

3

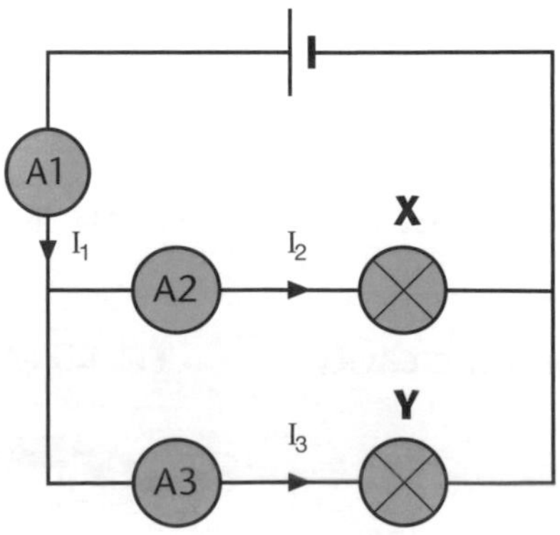

a Which **two** ammeters would have the same reading?

1 mark

levels 3-5

b What would the reading on the third ammeter be?

____

1 mark

c What would happen to bulb X in this circuit if bulb Y went out?

____

____

____

1 mark

4 In each of these circuits there is no current – the ammeter reading is zero.

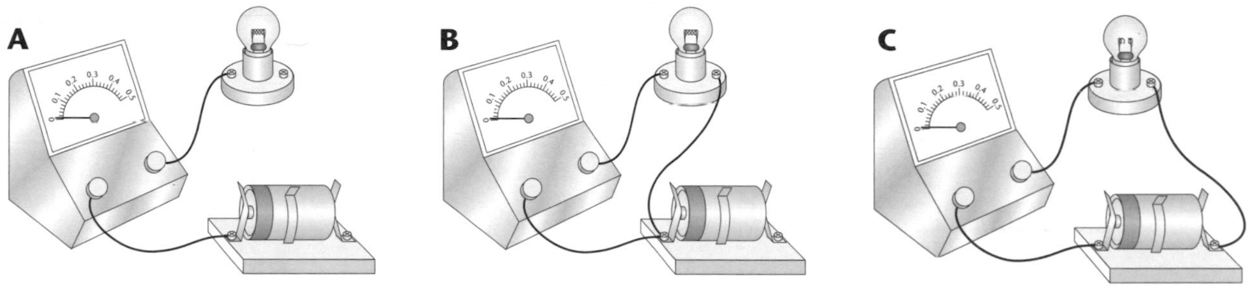

a What is wrong with each of the circuits?

A ____

B ____

C ____

3 marks

b Draw a circuit diagram for a circuit containing these components that would allow the current to flow.

3 marks

Energy transformation

levels 4-6

1 What sort of energy is always present during energy transfers?

____

1 mark

2 Why can sound energy not travel through a vacuum?

____

____

1 mark

3

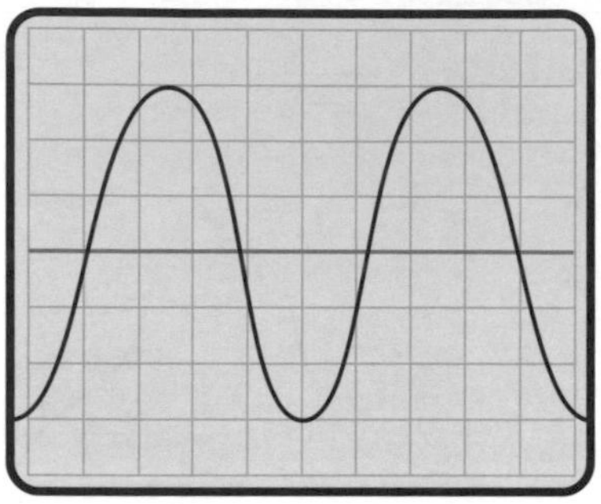

a Draw a wave to show a sound with the same pitch that is much quieter.

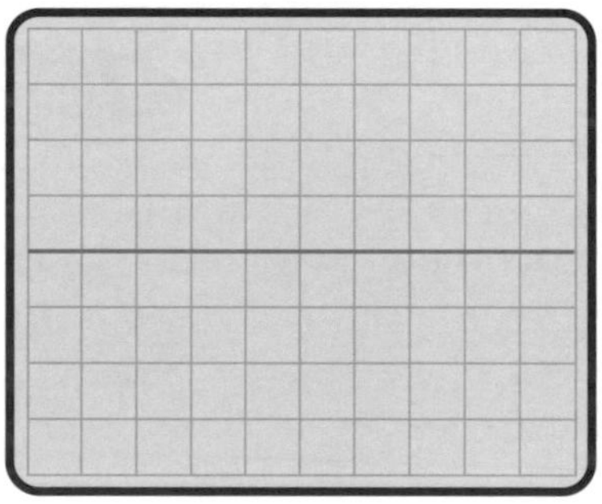

1 mark

b Draw a wave to show a sound that is just as loud but with a lower pitch.

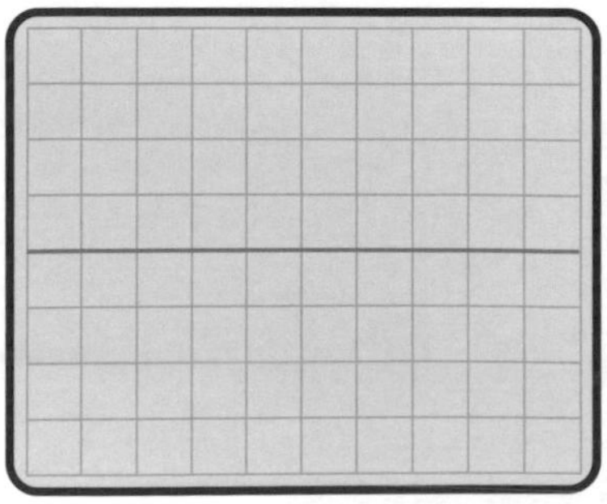

1 mark

levels 4-6

4

a What form of stored energy does this book have while it is still on the high shelf?

____ **1 mark**

b What form of energy will it have if it falls?

____ **1 mark**

c What forms of energy will this become when the book hits the ground?

____

____ **1 mark**

5 a Which of these stores of energy is the odd one out?

A Food we eat ☐

B Petrol for the car ☐

C The string in a bow and arrow ☐

D The wax of a candle ☐

1 mark

b What form of potential energy is stored in the others?

____ **1 mark**

Energy transfer

levels 5-6

1 A TV set takes in electrical energy from the mains supply.

a What does it transfer this energy as?

____

____

____

3 marks

b Which form of energy is the one that is not wanted?

1 mark

____

2 a Which of these materials would you choose to make a saucepan from?

wood	**glass**	**aluminium**	**plastic**	**copper**

____________________ and ____________________

2 marks

b Explain your answer.

____

____

____

2 marks

c Explain why you should always stir a pan of hot liquid with a wooden spoon not a metal one.

____

____

____

2 marks

levels 5-6

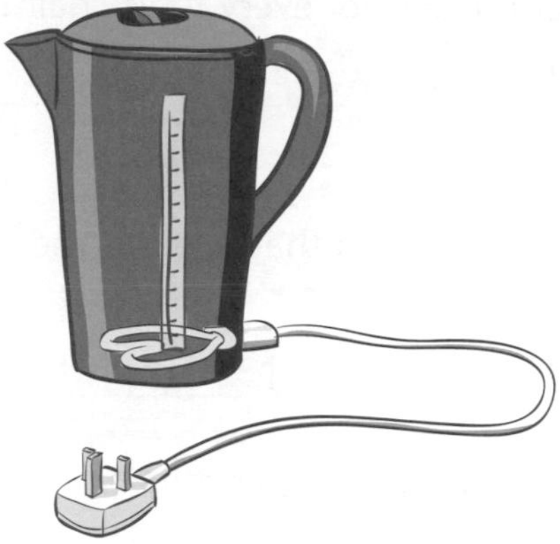

3 a Why do kettles have the heating element at the bottom? (You should use the word convection in your answer.)

____

____

____

2 marks

b By what method is thermal energy transferred through a vacuum?

____

1 mark

c When a hot cup of tea cools down, how is the heat from the tea transferred to the surroundings?

____

____

____

3 marks

4 Which of these statements about energy are true and which are false?

a Energy is not created or destroyed, it is just transferred from place to place. **TRUE/FALSE**

b Energy is sometimes used up, such as when a battery runs out. **TRUE/FALSE**

c When energy is transferred, it is not always in the form that we want. **TRUE/FALSE**

d Most of the energy transferred by a light bulb goes into lighting the surroundings. **TRUE/FALSE**

e Energy is measured in units called joules – this unit is named after a person. **TRUE/FALSE**

5 marks

Energy from food

levels 4-5

1 What sort of organism is always at the start of every food chain?

1 mark

2 a What is the name of the chemical reaction that releases the energy from our food?

1 mark

b Write a word equation for the chemical reaction.

3 marks

c What do our bodies use that energy for?

3 marks

3

A

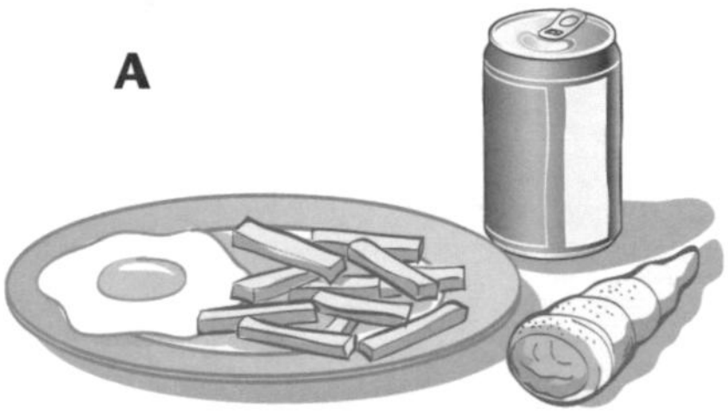

B

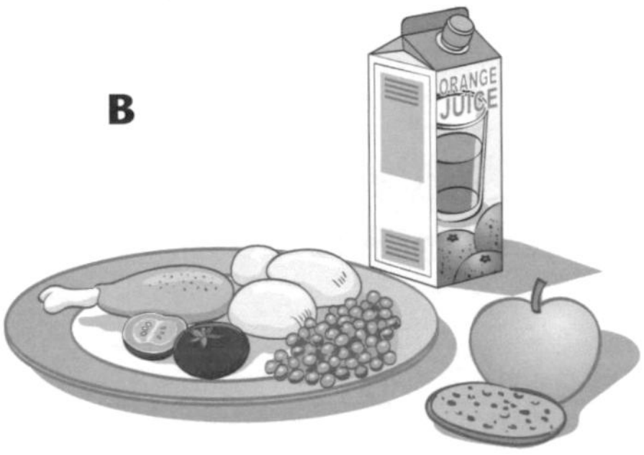

Look at the two meals A and B above.

a Which one is higher in fat?

1 mark

b Which one is higher in carbohydrate?

1 mark

c Which one is higher in sugar?

1 mark

d Which one is higher in vitamins and minerals?

1 mark

e Which of these meals would you recommend to someone wanting to follow a healthy balanced diet?

1 mark

levels 4-5

f Explain your answer.

____

____

____

____

2 marks

4 Choose the most suitable intake of energy from food for each person from the box below.

4000 kcal	**3000 kcal**	**1500 kcal**	**2000 kcal**

Person	**Energy intake**
a An adult female with an office job who sits at a desk all day.	
b An adult male who works at a hard manual job.	
c A pregnant woman who leads a busy active life.	
d A 10-year-old boy who plays a lot of sport.	

4 marks

5 Labels on food always show the energy content per 100 g. Explain why energy values are shown in this way.

____

____

____

1 mark

Sound and light

levels 4-5

1 Complete these sentences using words from the box.

frequency	**loud**	**pitch**	**amplitude**	**high**

It is possible to tell what a sound will be like by looking at the wave.

If the wave has a high ____________________ then the sound will have a ____________________ pitch. The ____________________ of the wave tells us whether it will be loud or quiet.

3 marks

2 a Which of these sounds would have a higher pitch…

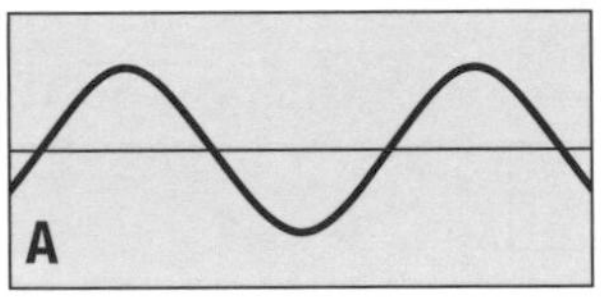

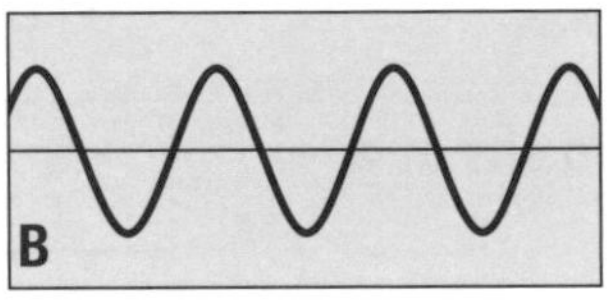

A or B?

____

1 mark

b …and which of these sounds would be louder…

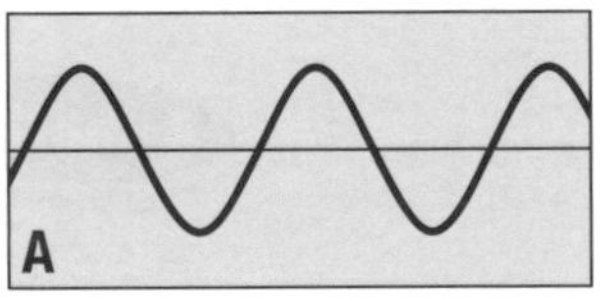

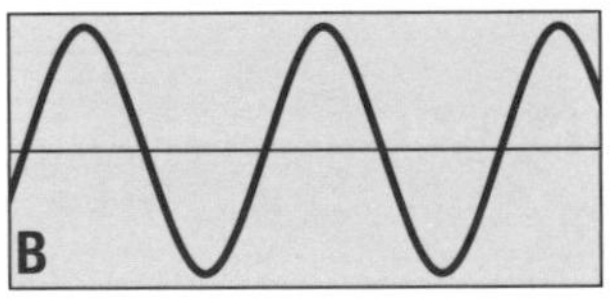

A or B?

____

1 mark

3 a What name do we give to objects that give off their own light?

____

1 mark

b Draw lines to match the name to the definition.

Translucent	Lets all the light through
Transparent	Lets no light through at all
Opaque	Lets some light through

3 marks

levels 4-5

4

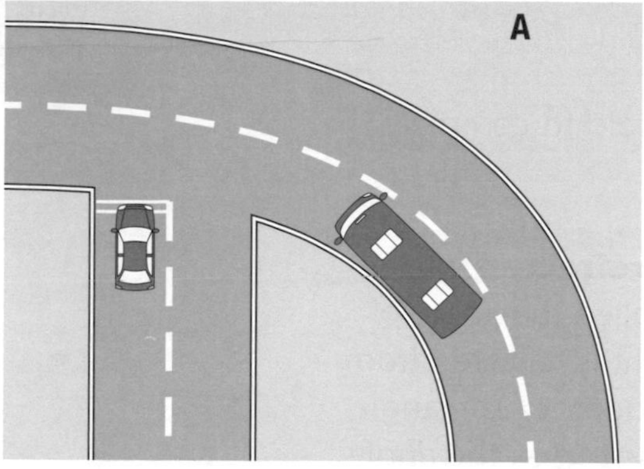

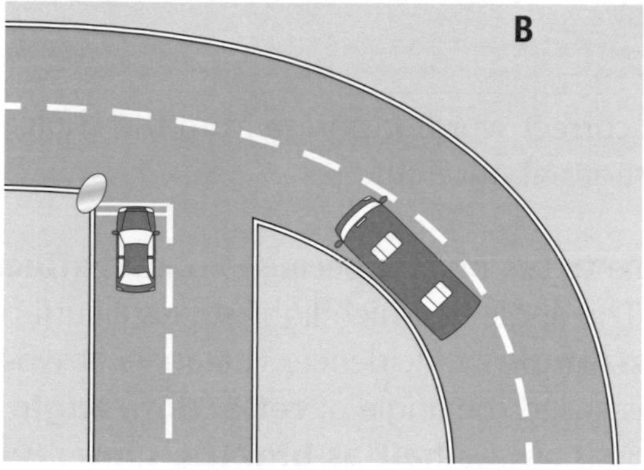

a Mark on diagram A the point when the driver of the car would be able to see the bus coming along the road without the mirror. **1 mark**

b Mark on diagram B the point when the car driver can see the bus coming with the mirror in place. **1 mark**

5 Which of these statements about sound and light are true and which are false?

a Sound and light both need a substance to travel through. **TRUE/FALSE**

b Light travels about a million times faster than sound. **TRUE/FALSE**

c Light and sound both travel as waves, moving energy from place to place. **TRUE/FALSE**

d Older people are better at hearing high-pitched sounds than younger people. **TRUE/FALSE**

e The Moon gives off its own light. **TRUE/FALSE**

f We see objects when light from them is reflected into our eyes. **TRUE/FALSE**

6 marks

6 Explain why astronauts on the Moon need radios to talk to each other.

____

____

____

2 marks

ENERGY

Reflection, refraction and seeing colour

levels 4-6

1 Circle the correct word or phrase from the choices in bold to complete these passages about light.

We are able to see objects because light is **reflected/refracted** into our eyes. The angle at which light strikes a surface is called the angle of **reflection/angle** of incidence. The angle at which light is reflected from a surface is called the angle of **reflection/angle** of incidence. The angle of reflection is always **half as big/the same/twice as big** as the angle of incidence.

White light is a mixture of **three/seven/ten** colours and objects that look white reflect **all/some/none** of these colours. Objects that look black reflect **all/some/none** of the colours of the spectrum and objects that look coloured reflect **all/some/none** of the colours. Although light always travels in straight lines, it will change direction at the boundary between two substances. This is called **reflection/refraction**. This can make water look **deeper/shallower** than it really is.

10 marks

2 Put the colours of the spectrum into the correct order. The first one has been done for you.

GREEN **RED** **VIOLET** **ORANGE**

BLUE **YELLOW** **INDIGO**

1 RED ____________________

2 ____________________

3 ____________________

4 ____________________

5 ____________________

6 ____________________

7 ____________________

3 marks

levels 4-6

3 What makes a red traffic light look red?

____

____

3 marks

4 Complete the diagrams to show how the ray of light behaves in each one.

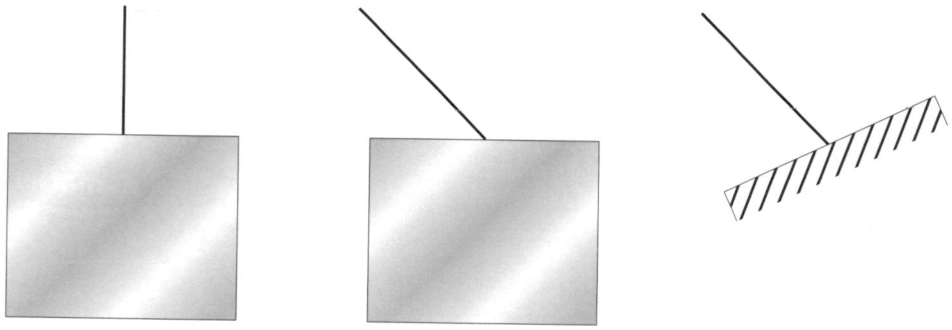

3 marks

5 Which colours of light are being reflected by these objects when viewed in white light?

a A white shirt

____

1 mark

b A black coat

____

1 mark

c A red car

____

1 mark

Balanced and unbalanced forces

levels 3-5

1 Which of these statements about forces are true and which are false?

a When the forces on an object are balanced, the object will always be stationary. **TRUE/FALSE**

b Forces can make things change shape, speed or direction. **TRUE/FALSE**

c If an object is moving and the forces on it are balanced, it will continue to move at the same speed in the same direction. **TRUE/FALSE**

d Pressure is greater if the force acts over a greater surface area. **TRUE/FALSE**

e Tractors have wide tyres to stop them sinking into the ground. **TRUE/FALSE**

5 marks

2

This person is pushing down on the chair with a force of 650 N.
What other force is acting to make this balanced?

1 mark

____

levels 3-5

3

A speeding up

B steady speed

C slowing down

a Give the letter of the car on which the force from the engine is greater than the friction and air resistance.

____

1 mark

b Give the letter of the car on which the forces are balanced.

____

1 mark

4

a If a person wanted to reduce the pressure they exerted on the floor, which of these shoes should they wear?

____

1 mark

b Explain your answer.

____

____

____

2 marks

Speed and motion

levels 4-5

1

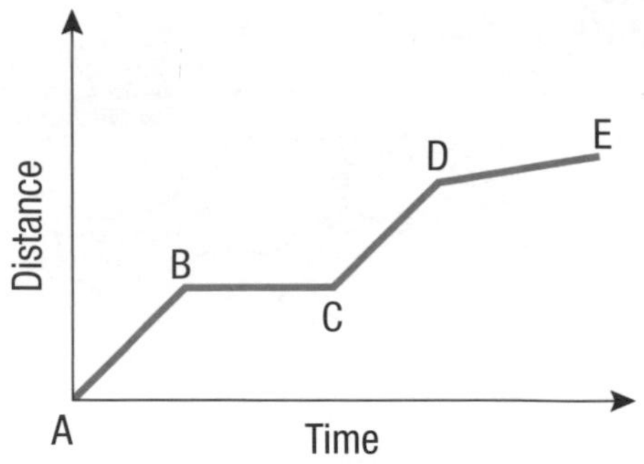

This is a graph of distance against time for a train journey.

a Between which **two** points was the train standing still in a station?

1 mark

____

b At point E, the train arrives at its destination station. On the graph, continue the line for the next unit of time.

1 mark

2 Sarah set off to walk to school. This is how her journey went:

A For 5 minutes she walked quite quickly to get to the corner, where she met her friends.

B One friend was late so the others chatted and waited for 3 minutes for her to arrive.

C They then set off together and walked quite slowly as there was a lot to talk about.

D After 10 minutes Sarah looked at her watch and saw that they were going to be late. They walked very quickly for the last 5 minutes.

E At the school gate they saw they were not late after all so they walked slowly to their classroom, which took another 2 minutes.

levels 5-6

On the axes below, sketch the graph of Sarah's journey.

5 marks

3 Choose values from the box to complete the table below.

100 s	**9000 m**	**50 km/h**

Speed	**Distance**	**Time**
	250 km	5 h
15 m/s	1500 m	
30 m/s		300 s

1 mark

1 mark

1 mark

4 a If a car travels 20 miles in 40 minutes, what is its average speed?

____

____

____

2 marks

b If the car then continues at the same average speed for another 60 minutes, how far will it travel in that time?

____

____

____

2 marks

FORCES Friction

levels 5-6

1

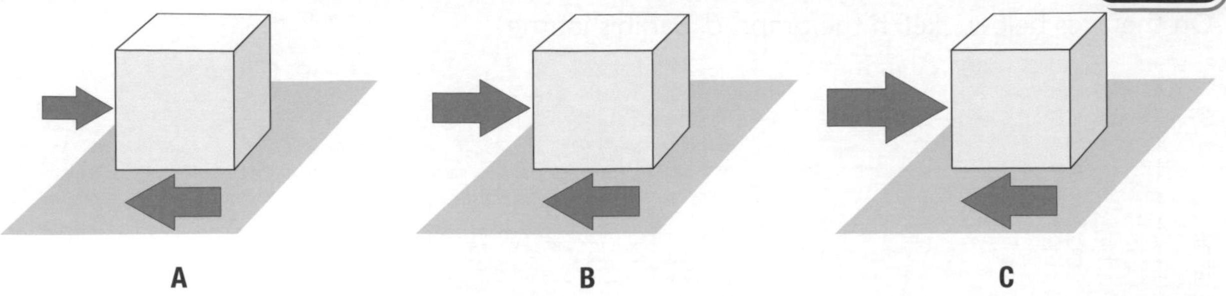

a Which of these boxes would start to move?

2 marks

b In which directions would they move?

2 marks

c Explain your answer.

1 mark

2

a From the picture above, identify **one** place where friction is useful.

1 mark

b Identify **one** place where friction will need to be overcome.

1 mark

levels 5-6

3 Suggest why all cars have oil put into their engines.

____

____

____

2 marks

4 When Shelley Rudman won her Olympic medal in the bobsleigh skeleton, suggest **three** things she would have done to make sure she went as fast as possible.

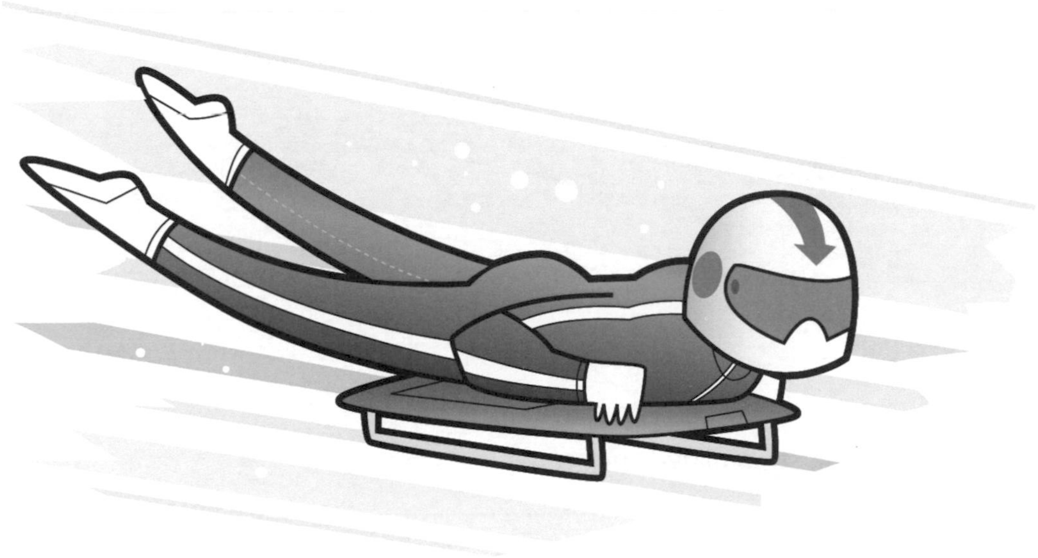

1 ____ **1 mark**

2 ____ **1 mark**

3 ____ **1 mark**

FORCES

Streamlining and air resistance

levels 5-6

1 What happens to air resistance as you move faster?

____

____

1 mark

2 a Why do dolphins have a streamlined shape?

____

____

____

1 mark

b What are the **two** effects of increasing the streamlining of a car?

1 ____

2 ____

2 marks

levels 5-6

3 a What happens to the air resistance when a skydiver opens their parachute?

____

1 mark

b Draw arrows on these four diagrams to show how the forces on a skydiver change as she falls to the ground.

A Just after she has jumped from the plane

1 mark

B Just before she opens her parachute

1 mark

C Just after she opens her parachute

1 mark

D just before she reaches the ground.

1 mark

4 What is the name given to the fastest speed that anything can travel at because air resistance has become as great as the forward force?

____

1 mark

Gravity

levels 3-5

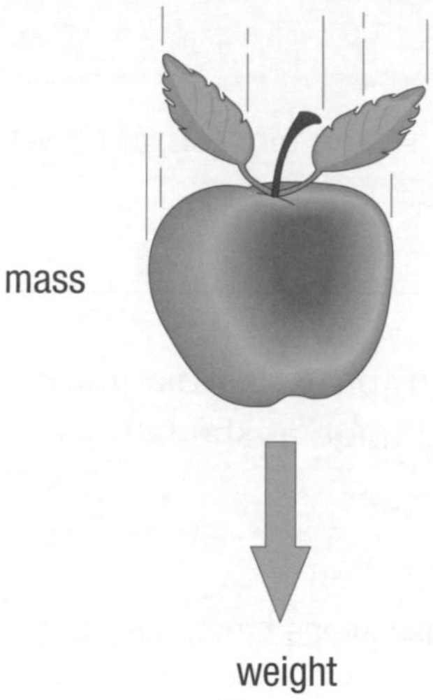

1 If an apple has a mass of 100 g, what is its weight?

____

1 mark

2 In which direction does gravitational force apply?

____

1 mark

3 Choose the correct numbers and units to complete the table about the mass and weight of an astronaut.

50 kg	**500 N**	**150 N**	**250 N**	**0 N**	**800 N**	**75 kg**
1000 N	**80 kg**	**15 kg**	**800 kg**	**900 kg**	**900 N**	
90 kg	**150 kg**	**15 N**				

	On Earth	**In deep space**	**On the Moon**
Mass			90 kg
Weight			

5 marks

levels 3-5

4 Jupiter is a much larger planet than the Earth.

a Suggest what would happen to the weight of an astronaut who travelled to Jupiter.

____

1 mark

b Explain your answer.

____

____

____

2 marks

5 Tick the box for the right combination of two factors that affect the size of the gravitational pull between two objects.

A Density and distance apart ☐

B Mass and weight ☐

C Mass and distance apart ☐

D Density and weight ☐

E Weight and speed of movement ☐

1 mark

6 a Which force did Galileo not take into account in his experiments on falling objects?

____

1 mark

b Where was Galileo's experiment repeated and why could it be done properly there?

____

____

2 marks

The Earth and beyond

levels 3-4

1 Circle the right word or phrase from the choices in bold to complete these passages about the Earth, the Moon and the Sun.

The Moon orbits the Earth approximately once every **24 hours/7 days/ 28 days/365 days**. The Moon is a **luminous/non-luminous** object which we can see because it reflects the light from the Sun which is a **luminous/non-luminous** object.

The Earth orbits the Sun approximately once every **24 hours/7 days/ 28 days/365 days**. This length of time gives us our **day and night/ week/month/year**. The Earth is tilted on its axis so different parts of the Earth's surface face towards it at different times in its orbit around the Sun. This is what gives us **day and night/summer and winter**. The Earth also rotates on its own axis once every **24 hours/7 days/ 28 days/365 days** and this is what gives us **day and night/ summer and winter**.

8 marks

2 a Why does the amount of the Moon we can see from Earth vary at different times in the month?

____

____

____

____

2 marks

b Explain why the Sun and the Moon both look the same size from Earth.

____

____

____

____

2 marks

levels 3-4

3 Complete this list showing the planets in our Solar System in order of their distance from the Sun, starting with the closest.

1 ____________

2 Venus

3 ____________

4 ____________

5 ____________

6 Saturn

7 ____________

8 ____________

9 ____________

7 marks

4 a Complete the **four** statements by drawing lines to join the boxes.

The average distance from Venus to the Sun is…	150 million km
The average distance from Pluto to the Sun is…	0.38 million km
The average distance from Earth to the Moon is…	5900 million km
The average distance from Earth to the Sun is…	108 million km

4 marks

b Which of these is a star?

The Moon ☐

The Earth ☐

The Sun ☐

Mars ☐

1 mark

Magnetic forces

levels 4-6

1

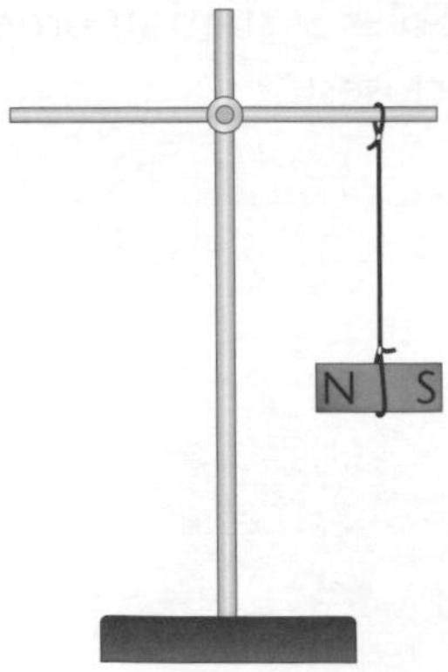

How could this apparatus be used to tell if a piece of iron was itself a magnet?

____

____

2 marks

2

2 marks

Draw the magnetic field you would expect to see around this magnet.

3 What is the difference between an ordinary magnet like this and an electromagnet?

____

____

1 mark

4 What element is used to make the core of an electromagnet?

1 mark

____

levels 4-6

5 Look carefully at this diagram.

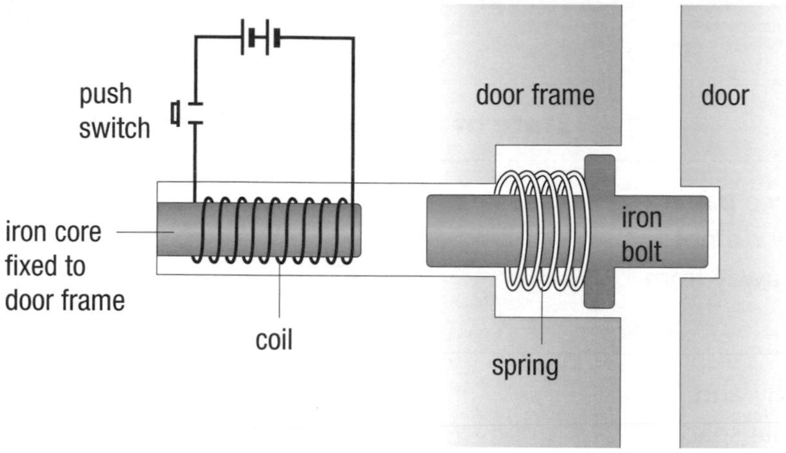

a When the switch is pushed, the iron bolt moves to the left and the door opens. Explain why this happens.

____

____

____

____

2 marks

b When the switch is released, what will the iron bolt do?

____

____

1 mark

c Would this door lock work if the bolt was made of aluminium?

____

1 mark

d Explain your answer.

____

____

____

2 marks

Solids, liquids and gases

levels 3-5

1 Complete the table below.

Description	State of matter	Particle diagram
The particles are in a fixed lattice pattern and although they vibrate they do not have enough energy to move away from each other.		
The particles have lots of energy and spread out to fill all the available space.		
The particles are in contact with each other but can move and slide over each other.		

6 marks

2 a Complete the table below to say which of the substances would be a gas, solid or a liquid at normal room temperature.

Substance	Melting point (°C)	Boiling point (°C)	Solid, liquid or gas
A	0	100	
B	–183	–162	
C	100	245	
D	–39	355	
E	1540	Above 2000	

5 marks

b Which of these do you know is water?

1 mark

____

c Which do you think might be iron?

1 mark

____

levels 3-5

3 **a** What happens to any substance when it gets hotter?

____

1 mark

b Explain your answer by describing what happens to the particles.

____

____

____

3 marks

4

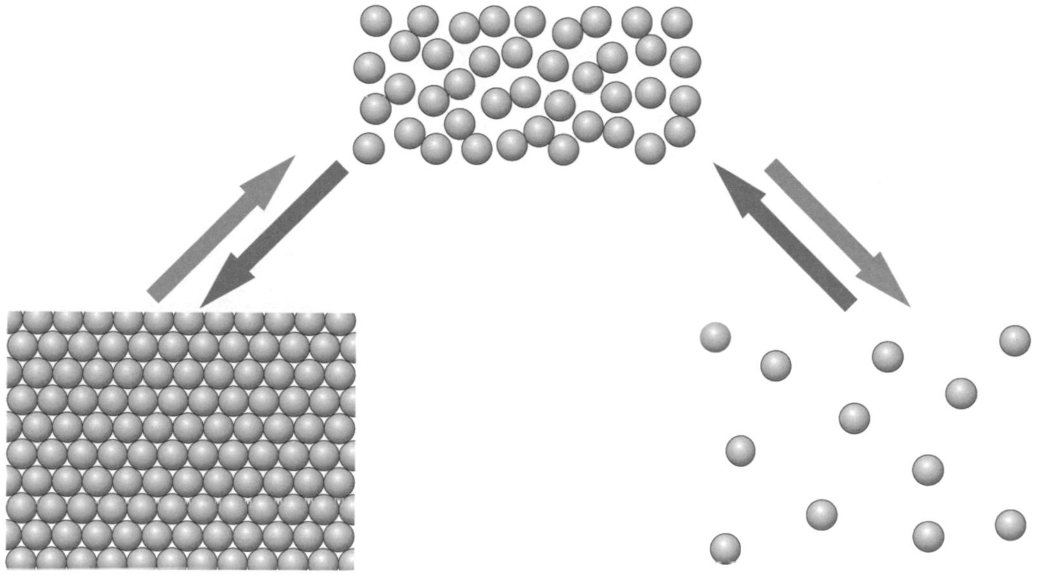

4 marks

Write the correct name of each change of state next to each arrow.

5 If you spray a small amount of perfume into a room, the people close to it will smell it straight away and, after a time, people at the other side of the room will be able to smell it too.

Explain why this happens by describing how the particles in a gas behave.

____

____

____

2 marks

Solubility and separation

levels 4-5

1 If you added 25 g of salt to 125 g of water, what mass of solution would you have?

______________________________ **2 marks**

2 Some students had a mixture of sand, salt and iron filings which they wanted to separate.

a Put these statements in order to show the sequence they followed to do this.

A Filter the mixture of sand, salt and water to separate the sand from the salt water solution.

B Add water to the sand and salt.

C Use a magnet to extract the iron filings.

D Heat the salt water solution so that the water evaporates leaving the salt behind.

______________________________ **4 marks**

b List the apparatus you would need to use for each stage.

____

____

____

______________________________ **4 marks**

3 Match words from the box below to the definitions.

solute	**solution**	**solvent**	**insoluble**

a Formed when a solid dissolves in a liquid. __________ **1 mark**

b The solid that dissolves in a liquid. __________ **1 mark**

c The liquid that a solid dissolves in. __________ **1 mark**

d When a solid will not dissolve in a particular liquid. __________ **1 mark**

levels 4-5

4 Look at the diagrams below of different methods of separating substances.

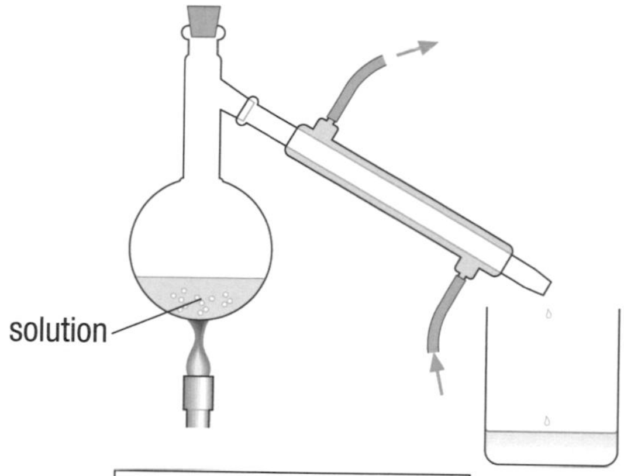

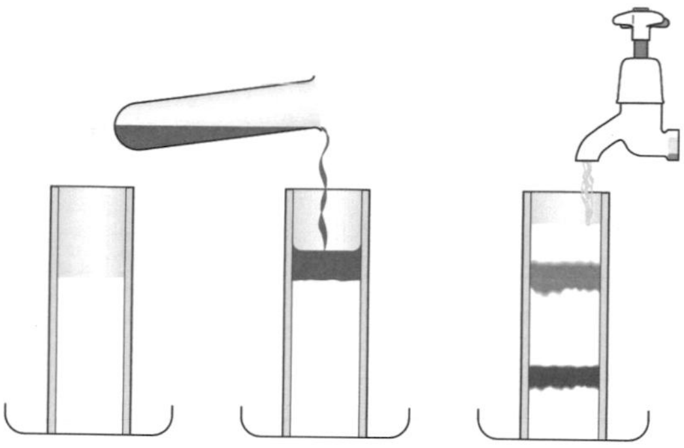

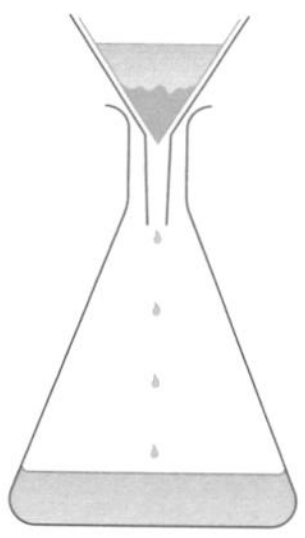

a Choose from the following words to label each separation technique with its correct name.

chromatography	**distillation**	**evaporation**	**filtration**

4 marks

b Match the correctly named separation technique to the mixture that it could be used for.

i Separating the different coloured food dyes that make up the colour of a purple Smartie. ____________ **1 mark**

ii The water from the dye in black ink. ____________ **1 mark**

iii To get a solution of dissolved coffee in water from large pieces of ground coffee beans. ____________ **1 mark**

iv To get blue copper sulphate crystals from a solution of copper sulphate in water. ____________ **1 mark**

Elements, compounds and mixtures

levels 5-6

1 a Complete the table to show which of these substances are elements, compounds and mixtures.

Substance	Element, compound or mixture
Oxygen	
Air	
Steel	
Iron	
Water	

5 marks

b Explain the difference between a compound and a mixture.

____

____

____

1 mark

2 Put the correct symbol next to the name of the element it represents.

P	**S**	**Na**	**K**	**H**	**O**	**C**	**Cu**	**Ni**	**N**

Element	Symbol	Element	Symbol
Hydrogen		Phosphorus	
Nitrogen		Sulphur	
Sodium		Potassium	
Oxygen		Carbon	
Copper		Nickel	

10 marks

levels 5-6

3 Look at the chemical formulae for these compounds and decide which elements have reacted together to produce them.

CO_2 ______________________ and ______________________

H_2O ______________________ and ______________________

NH_3 ______________________ and ______________________

NaCl ______________________ and ______________________

CuO ______________________ and ______________________

5 marks

4 Which of these statements about chemical and physical changes are true and which are false?

a In a chemical change new substances are formed. **TRUE/FALSE**

b In physical changes new substances are formed. **TRUE/FALSE**

c Chemical changes are easy to reverse. **TRUE/FALSE**

d Physical changes are easy to reverse. **TRUE/FALSE**

4 marks

5 a What is the common name for sodium chloride?

1 mark

____

b Describe the two elements that react to make sodium chloride.

i Sodium is ______________________________ **1 mark**

ii Chlorine is ______________________________ **1 mark**

Chemical reactions

levels 4-6

1 a Which is easier to reverse – a chemical change or a physical change?

____ 1 mark

b Give an example of a physical change of state.

____ 1 mark

c Give an example of a chemical reaction.

____ 1 mark

2 a What is the proper name for burning a substance in oxygen?

____ 1 mark

b What compound is formed when iron reacts with oxygen?

____ 1 mark

c What name do we usually give this compound?

____ 1 mark

3 Choose the correct words from the box to make up the word equations given below. You may need to use some words more than once.

water	**oxygen**	**magnesium oxide**	**carbon dioxide**	
sodium	**chlorine**	**magnesium**	**glucose**	**sodium chloride**

a The formation of common salt.

____________ + ____________ → ____________ 1 mark

b The oxidation of magnesium.

____________ + ____________ → ____________ 1 mark

c Photosynthesis.

____________ + ____________ → ____________ + ____________ 1 mark

levels 4-6

4 What is the proper name for a chemical reaction that takes in heat?

1 mark

5

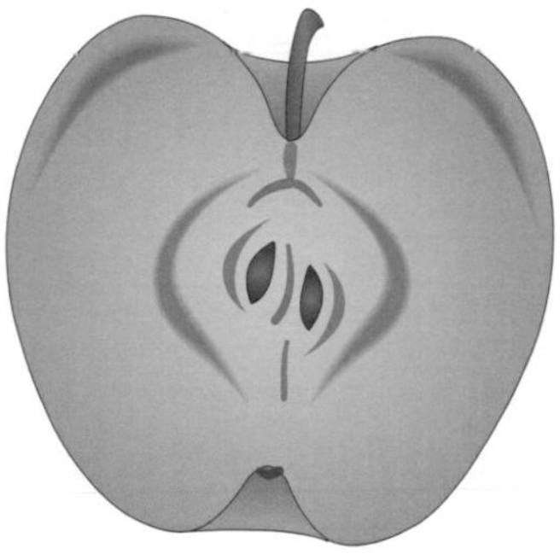

The same chemical reaction is happening in both these pictures.
What element is needed to make this reaction happen?

1 mark

6 Respiration is a chemical reaction.

a What are the reactants?

1 mark

b What are the products?

1 mark

Acids and alkalis

levels 4-6

1 What do we call a reaction where an acid is mixed with an alkali to form a substance with a pH of around 7?

____

1 mark

2 This is the pH scale.

1	2	3	4	5	6	7	8	9	10	11	12	13	14

Mark on this diagram where you would expect to find:

a lemon juice

b water

c hair shampoo

3 marks

3 a When an acid reacts with an alkali a certain type of compound is produced.

Complete the word equation for this type of reaction:

Acid + alkali → ________________ + ____________________

2 marks

b Complete the word equation for the reaction between hydrochloric acid and sodium hydroxide.

Hydrochloric acid + sodium hydroxide → __________ + __________

2 marks

c Complete the word equation for this reaction:

Acid + metal → ________________ + ____________________

2 marks

d Describe the test for the gas given off in this reaction.

____

____

1 mark

e What kind of salt is always formed in reactions with nitric acid?

____

1 mark

f Complete the word equation for this reaction:

Nitric acid + calcium hydroxide → ______________ + ______________

2 marks

levels 4-6

4 Sulphur dioxide is released into the air when fossil fuels are burned. What affect can this have on the environment?

____ **1 mark**

5 Circle the correct answer to show which of these would turn litmus paper blue and which would make it red.

Substance	**Colour of litmus**
Lemon juice	Red / blue
Toothpaste	Red / blue
Vinegar	Red / blue
Cola	Red / blue
Soap	Red / blue
Bleach	Red / blue

6 marks

6 Bee stings are acidic and wasp stings are alkaline. Suggest which of the substances in question 5 could be used to treat:

a A bee sting

____ **1 mark**

b A wasp sting

____ **1 mark**

c Explain how you made your choices.

____

____

____ **3 marks**

Metals and non-metals

levels 4-6

1 Decide which of these statements are properties of metals and which are properties of non-metals.

A Good conductors of heat

B Poor conductors of electricity

C Generally solids at room temperature

D Solids, liquids and gases at room temperature

E Shiny appearance

Add the letters in the correct column to complete the table below.

Properties of metals	**Properties of non-metals**

5 marks

2 a What needs to be present for the production of iron oxide?

1 ______________________

2 ______________________

3 ______________________

3 marks

b What name do we usually give to iron oxide?

____

1 mark

c Suggest **one** way in which iron surfaces can be protected from the formation of iron oxide.

____

1 mark

levels 4-6

3 Look at this table and decide which metal could be copper and which could be gold. Give your reasons.

Metal	Reacts with cold water	Reacts with dilute acid	Reacts with oxygen	Appearance
A	Yes	Yes	Yes	Silver grey
B	No	No	No	Yellow
C	No	Yes	Yes	Dark grey
D	No	Yes (slowly)	Yes	Yellow
E	Yes (slowly)	Yes	Yes	Grey

a Metal _____ is copper because ______________________________

____

2 marks

b Metal _____ is gold because ______________________________

____

2 marks

4 Place these metals in order of reactivity.

copper	**zinc**	**potassium**	**lead**	**mercury**

Most reactive ______________________________

____

____

____

Least reactive ______________________________

5 marks

PARTICLES

Rocks and the rock cycle

levels 3-5

1 Name the **three** main groups of rock.

1 ______________________________

2 ______________________________

3 ______________________________

3 marks

2 Complete the diagram by labelling the types of rock.

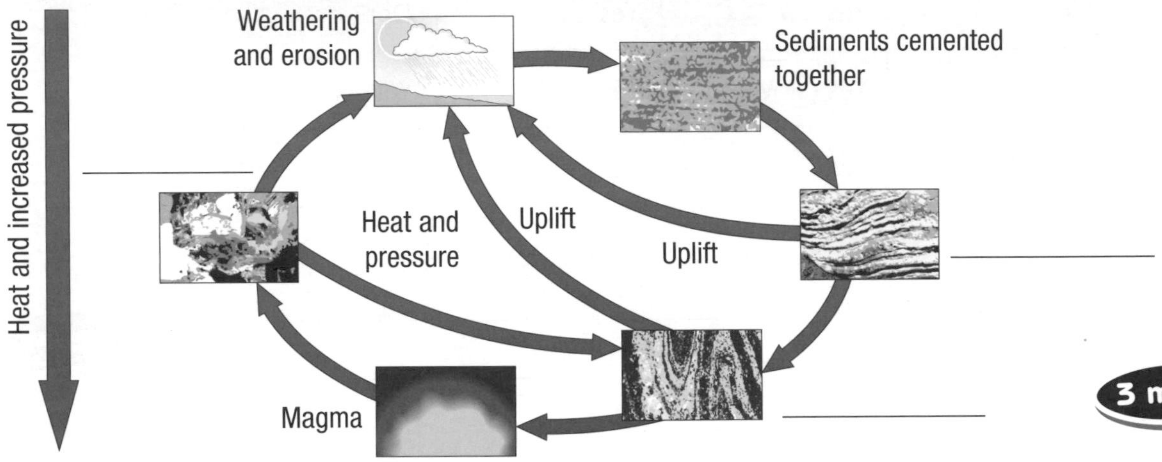

3 marks

3 Match the statement about rock structure to the explanation about how they are formed.

Sedimentary rocks contain fossils	Rocks that form when molten rock from volcanoes cool slowly have larger crystals than when the cooling process is very quick.
Granite is an igneous rock with large crystals	When sedimentary rocks are heated under pressure the resulting rock is much harder.
Limestone is a soft rock that crumbles easily	The remains of dead sea creatures fall to the sea bed with the sediment from rocks and get trapped between the layers.
Marble is a hard metamorphic rock	Rocks that form when layers of sediment build up on the sea bed are usually soft.

4 marks

levels 3-5

4 a What does the word 'metamorphic' mean?

1 mark

b What type of metamorphic rock is formed from sandstone?

1 mark

c How are metamorphic rocks such as marble different from sedimentary rocks such as limestone?

1 mark

5 Describe what is happening in each of these pictures.

a

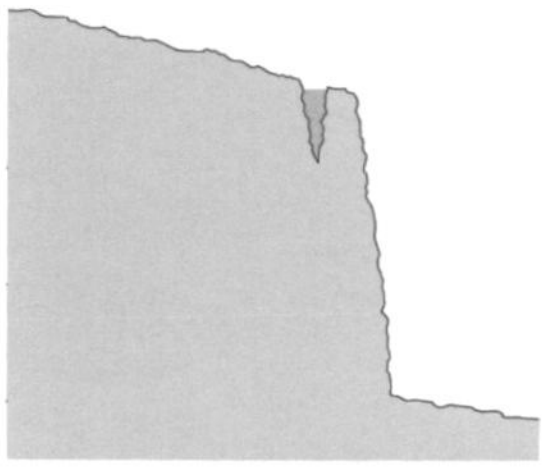

b

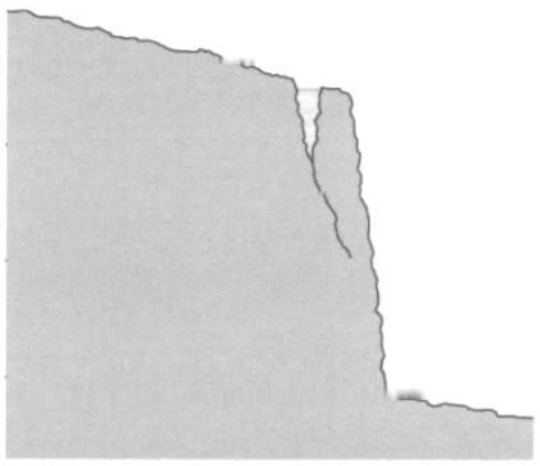

c

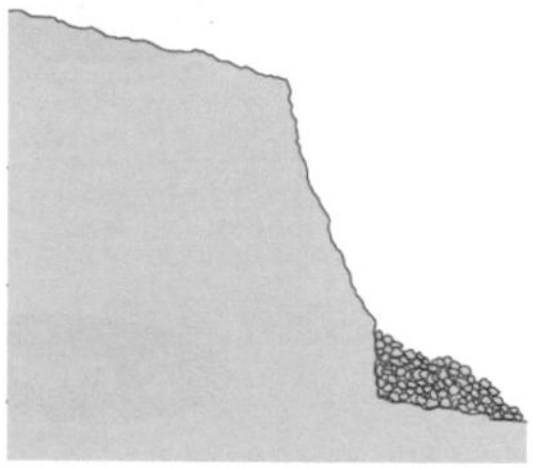

3 marks

Food chains and food webs

levels 3-5

1 Put these organisms into the right order for a food chain.

A Secondary consumer

B Producer

C Primary consumer

D Tertiary consumer

____

4 marks

2 Circle the correct word or phrase from the choices in bold to complete the passage.

Food chains and food webs always have a green plant at the beginning. This is because **all animals need to eat vegetables/green plants grow everywhere/only green plants can make their own food**. The first animal in a food chain is called **a producer/a primary consumer/a secondary consumer**. This animal is always **a herbivore/a carnivore/an omnivore**. The animals that eat the plants are then often eaten by other animals. The animal that is eaten is called **prey/a predator** and the animal that eats the other creature is called **prey/a predator**. In the food chain the predator is known as the **producer/primary consumer/secondary consumer**.

6 marks

3 What does the arrow in a food chain show?

____

1 mark

levels 3-5

4

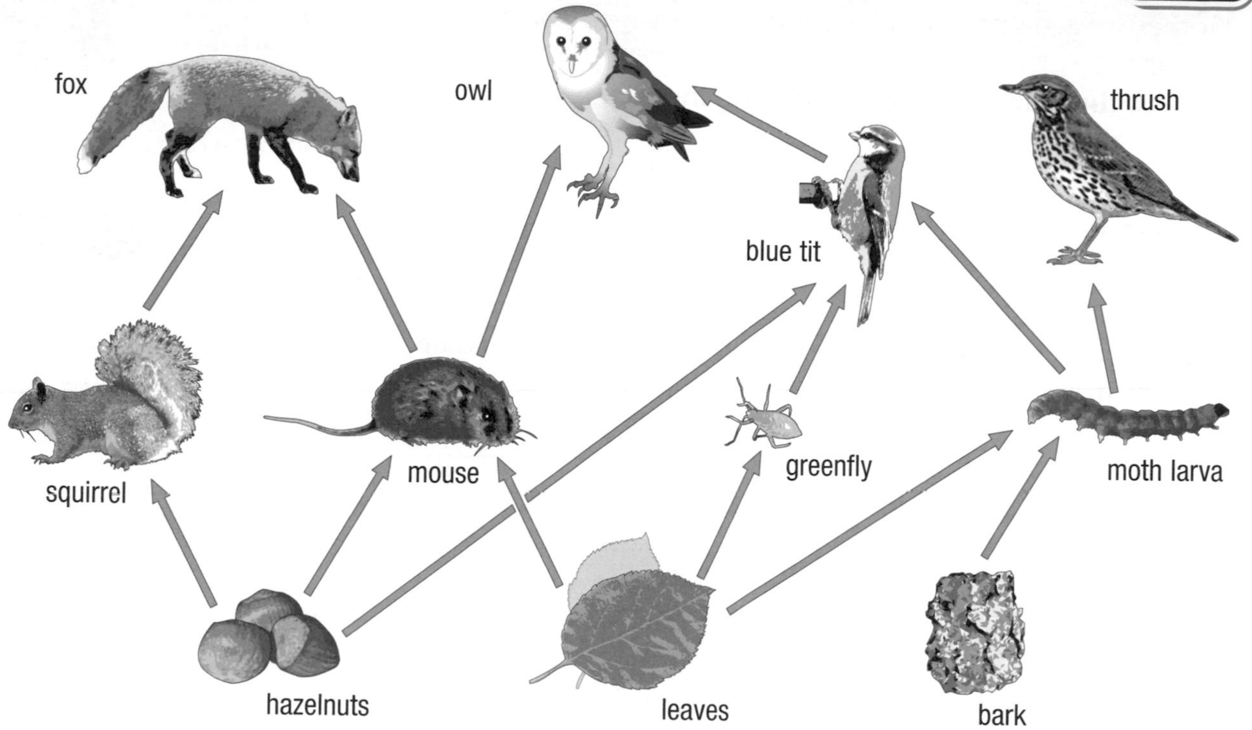

a Write **two** food chains that the owl is part of.

____

____

2 marks

b Draw a pyramid of numbers for **one** of the food chains you have chosen.

3 marks

Energy transfers in food chains and food webs

level 6

1 **a** What **three** main functions do living things use energy for?

____

____

____

3 marks

b Which of these represents the energy that can be passed up the food chain?

____

1 mark

2

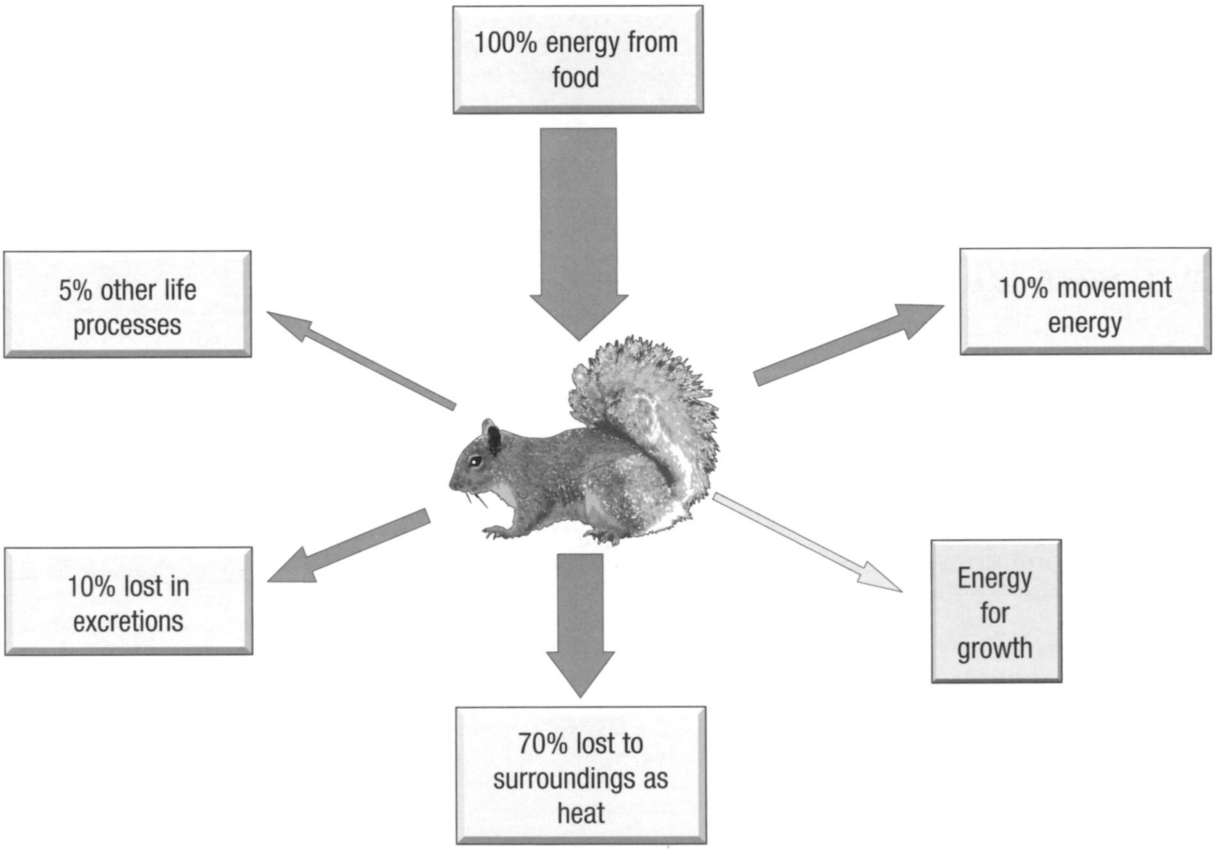

a Calculate the amount of energy the squirrel has left for growth.

____

____

2 marks

level 6

b Draw a pie chart to represent how the energy the squirrel takes in from its food is distributed.

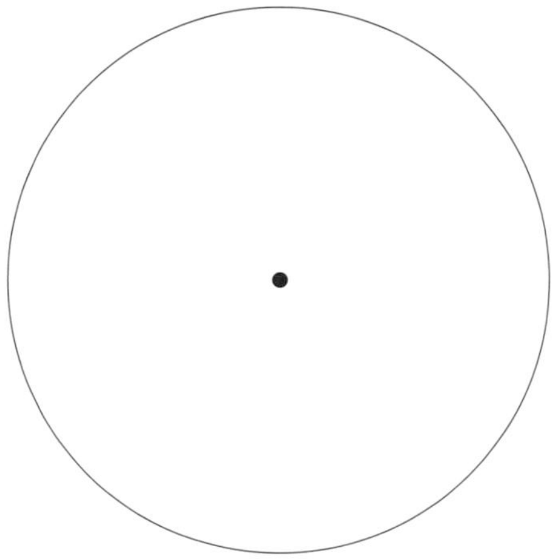

6 marks

3 Which of these statements are true and which are false?

a Most of the energy that an animal eats is lost to its surroundings as heat. **TRUE/FALSE**

b Food chains are never more than three or four organisms long because most creatures are very fussy about what they eat. **TRUE/FALSE**

c Food chains are only three or four organisms long because of the amount of energy lost at each stage. **TRUE/FALSE**

d About 10% of the energy an animal takes in as food is transferred to movement energy. **TRUE/FALSE**

e About 50% of the energy that an animal takes in as food is transferred to the next creature in the food chain. **TRUE/FALSE**

5 marks

Variation and inheritance

levels 4-6

1 Jane and Sarah are identical twins: they both have blue eyes; Sarah has blond hair but Jane has red hair.

a What do you think one of the twins has done to change her appearance?

____

1 mark

b Explain your answer.

____

____

____

2 marks

2 Robert and Matthew are brothers. Robert has red hair and Matthew has dark brown hair.

a Does this mean that one boy has changed his natural hair colour?

____

1 mark

b Explain your answer.

____

____

____

2 marks

3 The Jones family has five sons. They all have dark brown hair and three of them have blue eyes and two have brown eyes. Three of them can play the piano and two are very good swimmers.

Which of these characteristics are inherited from their parents and which are environmental characteristics?

Environmental	**Inherited**

4 marks

levels 4-6

4 A plant breeder is very keen to have plants with blue flowers as they sell the best. He takes 10 cuttings from each of six plants and this is what happens when the cuttings grow and flower.

Plant cuttings are taken from	Red flowering plants	Blue flowering plants
A	5	5
B	6	4
C	10	0
D	9	1
E	0	10
F	2	8

Blue flowers sell so well that he needs to take cuttings from at least three plants to make sure he has got enough.

a Which **three** should he choose?

____

____

____

3 marks

All his original plants are affected by a disease except plants A and B, which seem to be able to resist the disease.

b Which plant should he continue to take cuttings from?

____

1 mark

c Explain your answer.

____

____

____

3 marks

Adaptation

levels 3-4

1 Choose **two** characteristics that help polar bears to live in their habitat.

A A good sense of smell.

B Thick fur to trap heat and keep it warm.

C Sharp claws to help grip on icy surfaces.

D Small ears as it is quite quiet on the polar ice.

E Blue eyes to contrast with its white coat.

____

2 marks

2 a Look at the adaptations in the box below.

migration of birds	**hibernation**
deciduous trees	**nocturnal hunting**

Decide which are daily adaptations and which are seasonal adaptations to complete the table.

Daily adaptations	**Seasonal adaptations**

4 marks

b Explain why some animals hibernate.

____

____

____

2 marks

c What does nocturnal mean?

____

1 mark

d Some birds fly hundreds of miles to spend part of the year in one place and then rest in another. Suggest a reason why they do this.

____

____

2 marks

levels 3-4

3 From this list of plant adaptations, choose **three** factors that enable cacti to grow in hot dry desert conditions.

A Flowers that open in the day and close at night.

B Swollen stems to store water.

C Flowers that trap insects.

D Small spines for leaves.

E Long roots to find water below ground.

F Losing their leaves in winter.

____

3 marks

4 Imagine a habitat where:

it is very hot and wet in summer

it is very cold and wet in winter

there are a lot of trees that grow very lush in the summer but are all deciduous so have no leaves at all in winter

the ground is always wet and muddy

there are a lot of species of insect including those who feed on the blood of other creatures.

a Choose **one** adaptation that you think would be important for an ANIMAL living in this habitat and say why you have chosen it.

____

____

____

1 mark

b Choose **one** adaptation you think would be important for a PLANT living in this habitat and again say why this would be important.

____

____

____

1 mark

INTERDEPENDENCE Classification

levels 4-5

1 a What name is given to the group of animals that all have backbones?

____

1 mark

b This group of animals is further divided into **five** smaller groups – what are they?

1 ______________________________

2 ______________________________

3 ______________________________

4 ______________________________

5 ______________________________

5 marks

2 Which group of vertebrates does each of these characteristics apply to?

a Can live both on land and under water. ________________

b Have feathers. ________________

c Breathe through gills. ________________

d Feed their young on milk from the mother. ________________

e Have dry scaly skins. ________________

5 marks

3 Which group of **invertebrates** have three-sectioned bodies and three pairs of legs?

____

1 mark

4 A new species has recently been found in the rainforests of Borneo. It has a small body about the size of a saucer with two parts to it and four pairs of legs. It does not have a backbone.

Which group of invertebrates does it belong to?

____

1 mark

levels 4-5

5 The four main groups of Arthropods – the biggest group of invertebrates – are:

Insects

Arachnids

Crustaceans

Myriapods

Put the arthropods from the box into the right group in the table below.

grasshopper	**spider**	**lobster**	**millipede**
wasp	**scorpion**	**crab**	**dragonfly**

Insect	**Arachnid**	**Crustacean**	**Myriapod**

8 marks

INTERDEPENDENCE

Using keys to identify living things

levels 4-5

1 In a new supermarket the Manager is trying to decide where to put certain items. He draws up this key to help him.

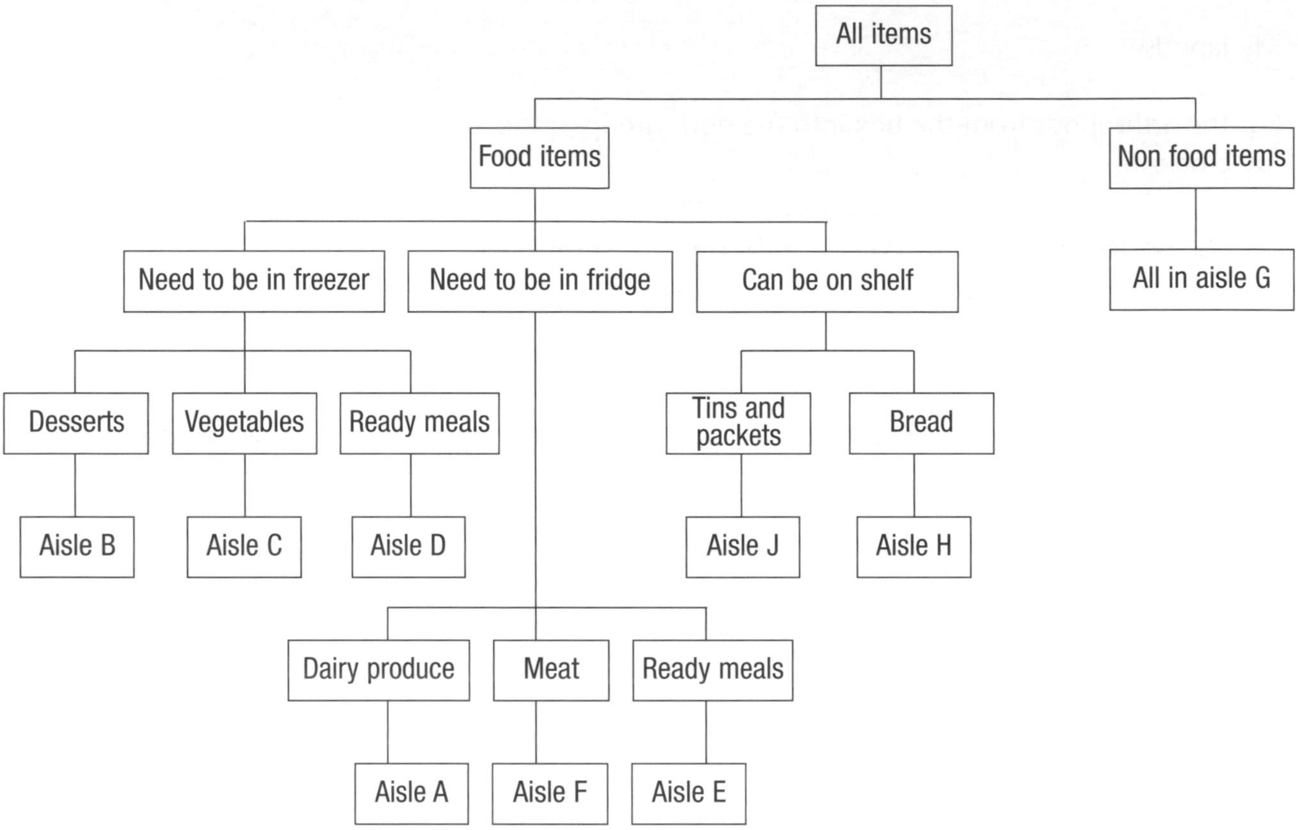

Using this key, decide which aisle these items should go in:

a Frozen peas ______________________

b Birthday cards ______________________

c A loaf of brown bread ______________________

d Chilled pizza ______________________

e Cheese ______________________

5 marks

levels 5-6

2

Horse

Walks on four legs, has hooves

Dog

Walks on four legs, gives birth to a number of young at once

Owl

Has feathers, lays eggs

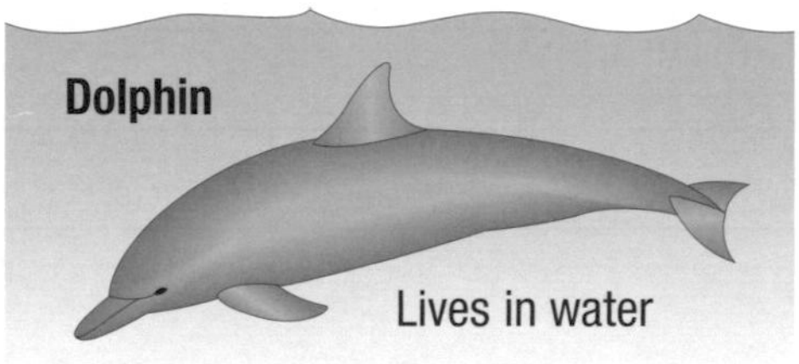

Dolphin

Lives in water

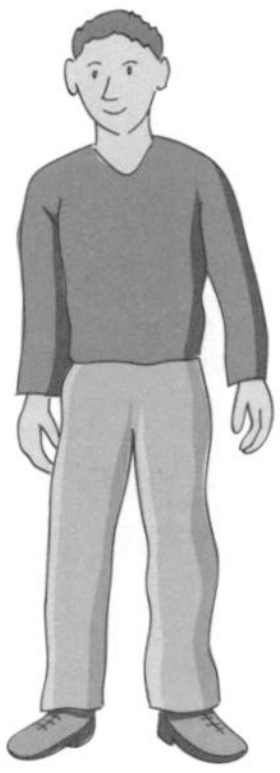

Human

Walks on two legs

Imagine you are an alien from outer space – you have just arrived on Earth and you want to know which species of animal is which.

Complete this key to help the alien identify these Earth creatures. The first question has been done for you. You should need to write **three** more questions.

Q1 Does the creature have feathers?
If YES, it is an owl.
If NO, go to question 2.

Q2 ____

If ________ , it is a ______________________________

If ______________________________ , go to question 3.

Q3 ____

If ________ , it is a ______________________________

If ______________________________ , go to question 4.

Q4 ____

If ________ , it is a ______________________________

If ________ , it is a ______________________________

3 marks

Competition among living things

levels **4-6**

1 What is meant when a species of plant or animal is said to be extinct?

1 mark

2 Explain why is there often a patch of bare earth under a large tree or shrub?

1 mark

3 Suggest why woodland plants often flower in early spring rather than later in the year when there is more sunlight.

2 marks

4 Foxes eat rabbits. If there is an outbreak of disease among rabbits and many die, explain what will happen to the fox population.

2 marks

levels 4-6

5 Many small flowering plants grow under the trees in woodlands. A number of trees are blown down.

To explain what will happen to the numbers of the small flowering plants and why, decide which of these statements are true and which are false.

a The numbers will stay the same because they are not affected by the trees. **TRUE/FALSE**

b The numbers will go up because there is more light so the plants will grow more. **TRUE/FALSE**

c The numbers will go down because they will no longer have the protection of the trees. **TRUE/FALSE**

d The numbers will go up because there will be more room so more seeds will germinate. **TRUE/FALSE**

4 marks

6 Look at the graph showing how the population of rabbits in a wood changed over time.

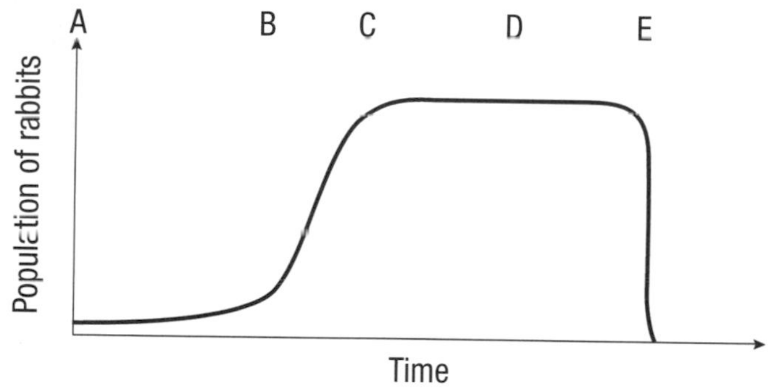

a What happened to the population of rabbits in the period from C to D?

____

b What time of year do you think might be represented by B?

____

c What happens to the population at D?

____

d Can you suggest what might have caused this?

____

4 marks

Human impact on the environment

levels 5-6

1 Tick the boxes to show which of these environmental problems can be caused by burning fossil fuels.

The damage to the ozone layer ☐

The greenhouse effect ☐

The cutting down of forests to create space to grow crops ☐

Global warming ☐

Acid rain ☐

2 marks

2 a What can be done to improve the habitat in a lake that has been affected by acid rain?

____

____

____

1 mark

b What kind of chemical reaction is involved?

____

1 mark

3 Describe the environmental damage done by the chemicals called CFCs.

____

____

____

2 marks

4 What illness in humans may be increasing because of damage to the ozone layer?

____

1 mark

levels 5-6

5 Circle the correct word or phrase from the choices in bold to complete the passage.

Chemicals that are used to kill pests are called **pesticides/herbicides**. An example is slug pellets which are used to kill slugs. Slugs in turn are eaten by **prey/predators** such as thrushes which are **prey/predators** of bigger birds such as sparrowhawks. The thrushes will eat a lot of slugs and so the pesticide will **spread out/build up** in their bodies. This might not be enough to kill the thrushes, but when a sparrowhawk eats a number of thrushes, the pesticide will **spread out/build up** in the body of the sparrowhawk and kill it.

5 marks

6 Describe how an increase in the human population of the Earth can affect other species of plants and animals.

____

____

____

____

____

____

2 marks

Asking questions and making predictions

level 5

1 For **each** of these investigations, write a clear question.

a To investigate candles burning in air.

Question ______________________________

____

____

b To investigate where woodlice like to live.

Question ______________________________

____

____

c To investigate the speed of different sized falling objects.

Question ______________________________

____

____

d To investigate the friction of different surfaces.

Question ______________________________

____

____

e To investigate energy in food.

Question ______________________________

____

____

5 marks

level 5

2 Make a prediction using your scientific knowledge for each of the questions on the previous page.

a I think that ______________________________

____

Because ______________________________

____

____

b I think that ______________________________

____

Because ______________________________

____

____

c I think that ______________________________

____

Because ______________________________

____

____

d I think that ______________________________

____

Because ______________________________

____

____

e I think that ______________________________

____

Because ______________________________

____

____

10 marks

Variables and fair tests

levels 4-6

1 For **three** of the investigations you thought about on the last page, decide what will be your independent variable, your dependent variable and what you will keep the same to make it a fair test.

a Question ______________________

Independent variable ______________________

Dependent variable ______________________

To make sure it is a fair test ______________________

____

3 marks

b Question ______________________

Independent variable ______________________

Dependent variable ______________________

To make sure it is a fair test ______________________

____

3 marks

c Question ______________________

Independent variable ______________________

Dependent variable ______________________

To make sure it is a fair test ______________________

____

3 marks

2 Which of the variables below are continuous and which are discontinuous?

a The thickness of the trunks of trees in a woodland.

CONTINUOUS/DISCONTINUOUS

1 mark

b The electric current flowing in a circuit.

CONTINUOUS/DISCONTINUOUS

1 mark

c The number of boys and the number of girls in each year group in a school.

CONTINUOUS/DISCONTINUOUS

1 mark

levels **4-6**

3 Circle the correct word or phrase from the choices in bold to complete this paragraph about some pupils carrying out an investigation.

When you want to carry out a scientific investigation you first need to decide on a question which enables you to see clearly what you are trying to find out. This will help you to choose the correct variables. The thing you are going to change is called the **dependent/independent/control** variable. The thing you measure is called the **dependent/independent/control** variable. To make your investigation a fair test you must **alter as many things as possible/only alter one variable**. The things you keep the same are called **dependent/independent/control** variables. You should **have as many of these as possible/only control one variable**. When you have taken your results, it is a good idea to display them in a chart or graph. This is because **it looks nice/it makes it easy to see trends in your results**. If your independent variable was discontinuous then you should draw a **bar chart/line graph**. If your independent variable was continuous you should draw a **bar chart/line of best fit**. Your independent variable should go along the ***x*-axis/*y*-axis** of your graph.

9 marks

4 In some experiments it can be very difficult to control all the factors other than the one you want to test. Suggest what kind of factors might be especially hard to control.

____

____

____

1 mark

Presenting results and drawing graphs

levels 4-6

1 Some pupils carried out an experiment to see if the temperature of water affected the amount of salt which would dissolve.

a What would be their independent variable?

______________________________ **1 mark**

b What would be their dependent variable?

______________________________ **1 mark**

c What factors should they keep the same?

1 ______________________________

2 ______________________________

3 ______________________________ **3 marks**

d In the box below, draw a results table for them to put their findings into.

2 marks

e What sort of graph or chart should they use to display these results?

______________________________ **1 mark**

levels 4-6

f Explain your answer.

2 marks

g Some pupils carried out this experiment and this is what they recorded.

We weighed out some salt and tried to dissolve it in water at different temperatures to see how much would dissolve. Different people tried different temperatures but we all used salt from the same packet and 150 ml beakers of water to keep it a fair test. We found that at 50 °C 3.9 g dissolved, at 80 °C it was 6 g, at 30 °C it was 1.7 g, at 70 °C it was 4.7 g, at 40 °C, 1.9 g and at 60 °C, 3.3 g.

Put their results into your table on page 176.

2 marks

h On the graph paper below display these results in the best possible way.

8 marks

Patterns and relationships

levels 4-5

1 Some pupils did an experiment to see if water evaporated more quickly in different conditions. They put some beakers of water in different places around the school and some outside.

Tom recorded the results for his group in his exercise book. They looked like this:

On the windowsill 145 ml after 3 days, on the teacher's desk 150 ml, on outside windowsill all water gone.

Peter's group recorded their results like this:

Location and temperature at start	Start volume (ml)	Volume after 1 day (ml)	Volume after 2 days (ml)	Volume after 3 days (ml)
Classroom windowsill (28 °C)	150	142	136	131
Teacher's desk (23 °C)	150	146	142	138
In corner of corridor (19 °C)	150	148	146	144
Outside windowsill (15 °C)	150	143	135	130

a Which set of results are better: Tom's or Peter's?

______________________________ **1 mark**

b Explain why.

____

____

______________________________ **2 marks**

c Can you see a pattern in Tom's results?

______________________________ **1 mark**

d Describe the relationship between temperature at the start and rate of evaporation in Peter's results.

____

______________________________ **2 marks**

levels 4-5

e Which line in Peter's results table spoils this pattern?

____

1 mark

f Can you suggest an explanation for this?

____

____

1 mark

g What can you see in Peter's results to show that they tried to make it a fair test?

____

1 mark

Before they collected their results, Tom's group wrote a prediction like this:

We think that the shape of the container will affect how quickly the water evaporates and the containers with a wide top will make the water evaporate faster than containers with a narrow top.

h Explain whether or not you think this is a good prediction.

____

____

____

1 mark

i Can they say from their results whether the prediction was right or wrong?

____

1 mark

j Describe an experiment they could do to test this prediction.

____

____

____

____

____

____

3 marks

k What pattern would they have been looking for in their results?

____

1 mark

Interpreting results and reading graphs

levels 4-5

1

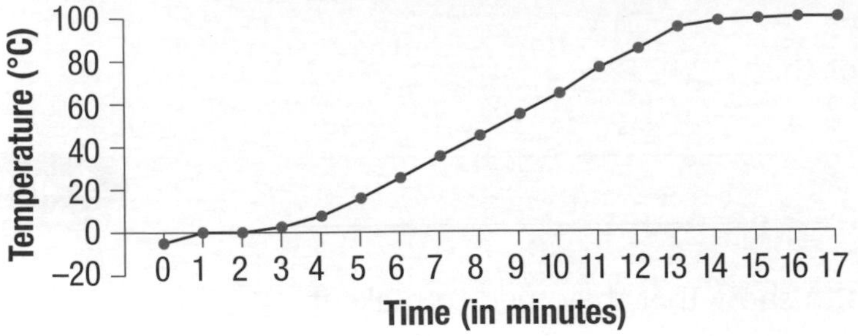

Look at the graph of temperature against time.

a After how long had all the ice melted?

____

1 mark

b How long did it take for the water to reach 40 °C?

____

1 mark

c At what time do you think someone observing this experiment would have started to notice bubbles in the water?

____

1 mark

The same water was then left to cool and the temperature again taken every minute.

d On the axes below sketch the shape that you think this graph would have.

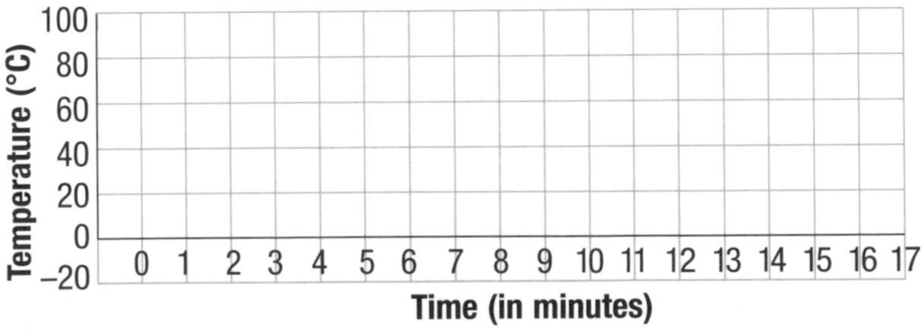

3 marks

e Explain your answer.

____

____

____

3 marks

levels 4-5

2 Look at the bar chart.

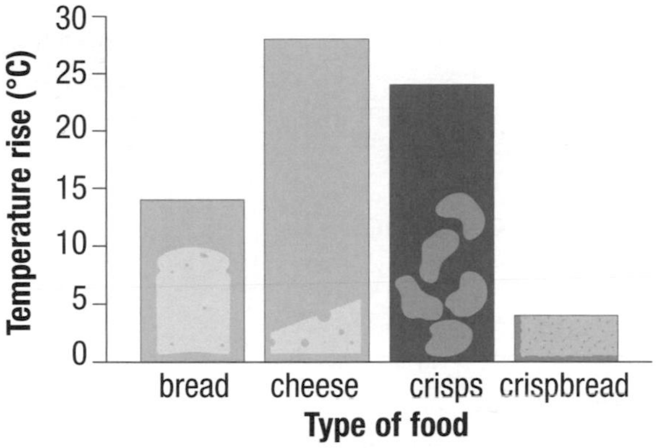

a From this chart put the foodstuffs in order from the one with the highest energy content to the one with the lowest.

Highest energy ____________________

____

____

Lowest energy ____________________

4 marks

b Explain how you made your choices.

____

____

____

1 mark

c Why have the results of this experiment been displayed in a bar chart and not a line graph?

____

____

1 mark

Evidence and conclusions

levels 5-6

1 Write down **three** sources of evidence you could make use of if you wanted to test an idea.

____

____

____

3 marks

2 In an experiment to see if bean shoots grew faster in warmer conditions, some pupils found these results after 10 days.

Temperature (°C)	**Height of bean shoot (cm)**
5	0
10	2
15	5
20	9
25	2
30	2
40	0

The pupils displayed their results in a graph.

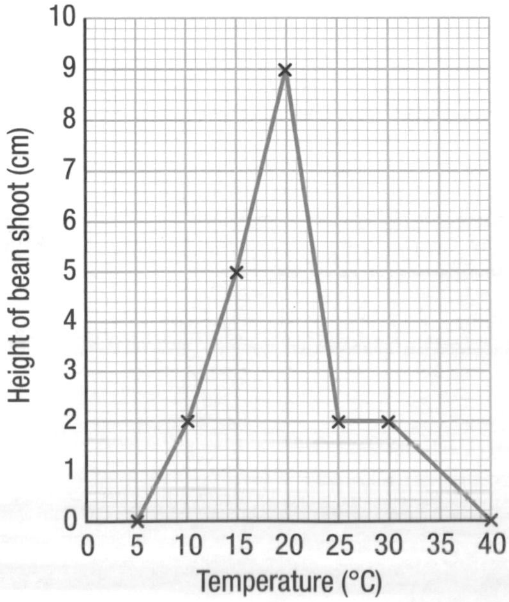

levels 5-6

a **i** Is this evidence to show that bean shoots grow faster in warmer conditions? **YES/NO** 1 mark

ii Explain your answer.

____

____

______________________________ 2 marks

b **i** Is this evidence to show that there is an ideal temperature at which to grow bean shoots? **YES/NO** 1 mark

ii Explain your answer.

____

____

______________________________ 2 marks

c **i** Is this evidence to show that bean shoots grow better if they get plenty of water? **YES/NO** 1 mark

ii Explain your answer.

____

____

______________________________ 2 marks

d **i** On the graph on page 182, is this a line of best fit? **YES/NO** 1 mark

ii Explain your answer.

____

____

______________________________ 1 mark

3 We now know that the Earth goes around the Sun, but in the past people thought it was the other way and that the Sun went round the Earth.

Suggest why you think scientific ideas change over time.

____

____

______________________________ 1 mark

Evaluating experiments

levels 5-6

1 If you were going to repeat the bean growing experiment on the last page, can you suggest **two** things that would make it better?

1 ______________________________

2 ______________________________

2 marks

2 Which of these experiments do you think were fair tests?

a A group of pupils increased the number of cells connected to an electrical circuit and read the current from an ammeter each time to see if the number of cells increased the current flowing in the circuit. **FAIR TEST/NOT FAIR TEST**

b Another group of pupils did the same experiment but this time they added more bulbs each time they increased the number of cells. Again they took readings from an ammeter to see if increasing the number of cells increased the current in the circuit. **FAIR TEST/NOT FAIR TEST**

c A class were testing a variety of shoes for friction by measuring the force needed to move them on different surfaces. Some of the surfaces were outside and the experiment was done over two lessons. On the day of the second lesson it rained. **FAIR TEST/NOT FAIR TEST**

3 marks

3 A group of pupils wanted to test the effect of fizzy drinks on pulse rate. They all drank some of their favourite fizzy drink and then measured their pulse rates.

a List **three** things that would have made this a better experiment.

1 ______________________________

2 ______________________________

3 ______________________________

3 marks

b Suggest why this might not have been a fair test even if they had done all of these things.

____

____

____

1 mark

levels 5-6

4 A farmer had had a problem for several years with a particular insect attacking his crop of maize. He decided to carry out an experiment. In one field he planted the same kind of maize but sprayed it regularly with a pesticide designed to kill this sort of insect. In another field he planted a new type of maize that is meant to be resistant to this insect.

What questions would he need to ask at the end of the year to see which, if either, of these had been successful?

____

____

____

3 marks

5 When new medicines are being tested, a group of people are given the new medicine and another group are not. Choose one of the following statements to explain why no-one ever knows which group they are in.

A New medicines are always very expensive.

B The people who are not given the new medicine are a control group to see if what happens to the others is really because of the new medicine.

C If the new medicine doesn't work properly then you have only harmed half as many people.

____

1 mark

1 a Which of these sources of energy are renewable and which are non-renewable?

Draw a line from each energy source to the correct box.

Energy source

Energy source	
wind power	
coal	**RENEWABLE**
solar power	
biomass	
natural gas	**NON-RENEWABLE**
oil	

3 marks

b Where did the energy that is stored in all of these sources come from?

____

1 mark

2

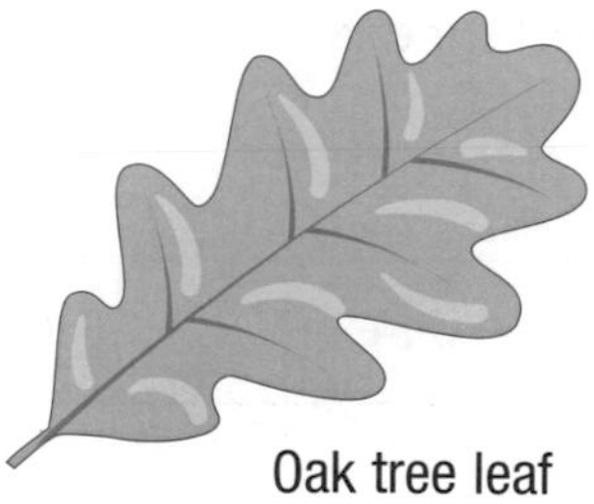

Oak tree leaf

Blue tit

Sparrowhawk

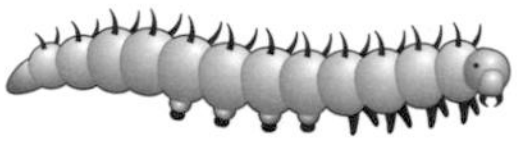

Caterpillar

a Arrange these living things into a food chain below.

2 marks

b Explain how you chose the first thing in your food chain.

1 mark

c Which **three** structures do plant cells have that animal cells do not?

1 ___

2 ___

3 ___

3 marks

d Which **one** of these do plants need to make their own food?

1 mark

Total

maximum 11 marks

3 The pH scale is used to measure how acidic or alkaline a substance is.

1	2	3	4	5	6	7	8	9	10	11	12	13	14

☐ 1 mark

a Mark on the scale where you would expect to find an acid.

b In the box below, put the pH number you would expect for each of these substances.

Substance	**pH**
Lemon juice	
Water	
Sodium hydroxide	

☐ 3 marks

4

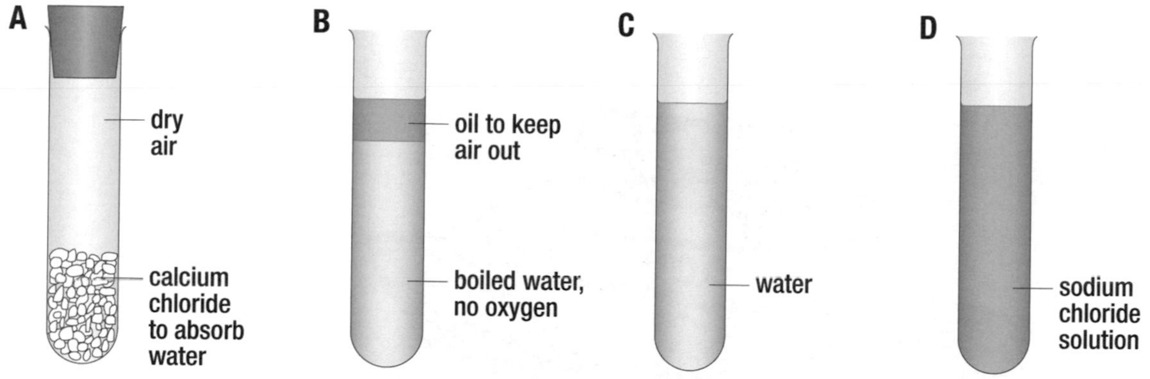

Some students set up an experiment to see what made iron nails go rusty. They put a nail into each of the test tubes and left them for a week. At the end of the week they examined the nails.

a Give the letter of the test tube that you would expect to contain the nail with the most rust?

____

1 mark

b Two nails will not rust at all. Give the letters of the test tubes containing these nails.

______________________ and ______________________

1 mark

c If instead of iron nails, the students had put gold rings into the test tubes and left them for a week – what would they have seen?

____

____

____

1 mark

Total

maximum 8 marks

5

The boat is floating on the water.

2 marks

a Draw **two** arrows on the diagram to show the forces and label them.

b What can you say about the forces acting on the boat?

____

____

____

1 mark

6 A breeder of pedigree dogs wants as many puppies as possible who are single colour rather than black and white. He looked at the puppies from his most recent litters.

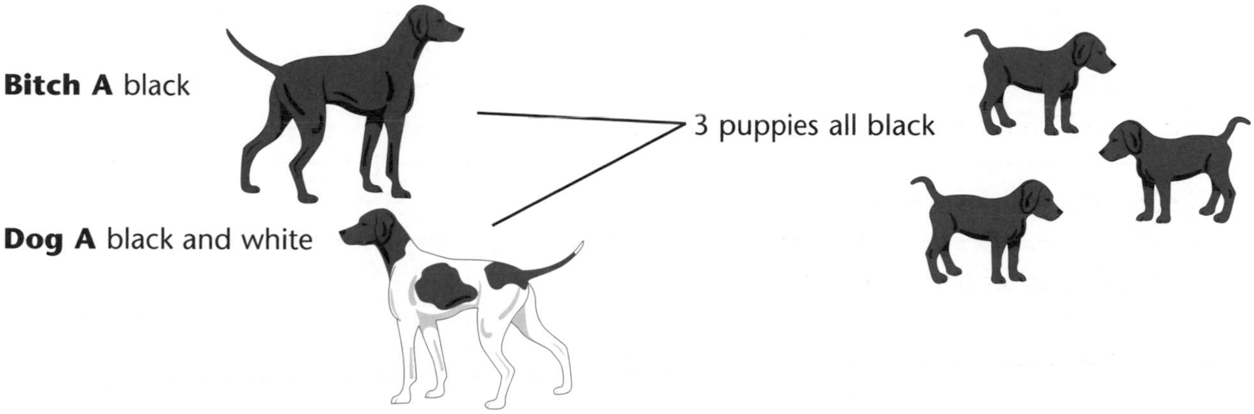

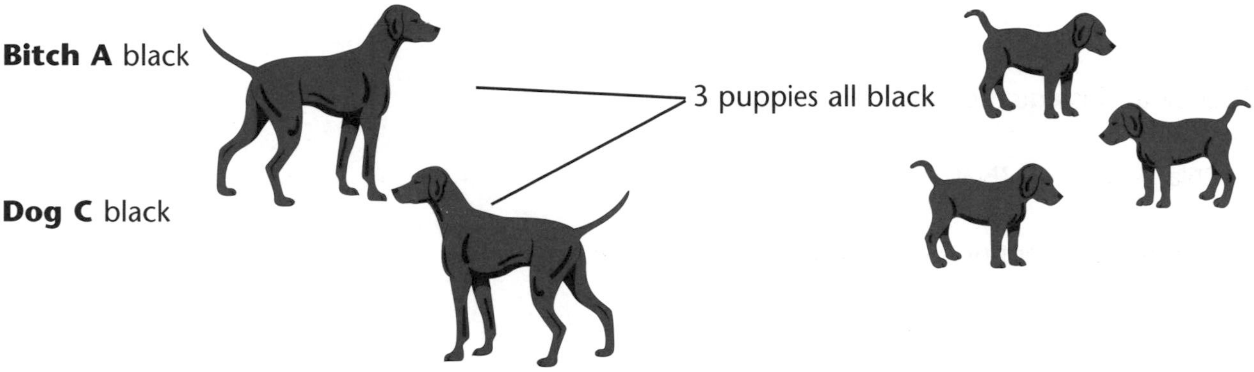

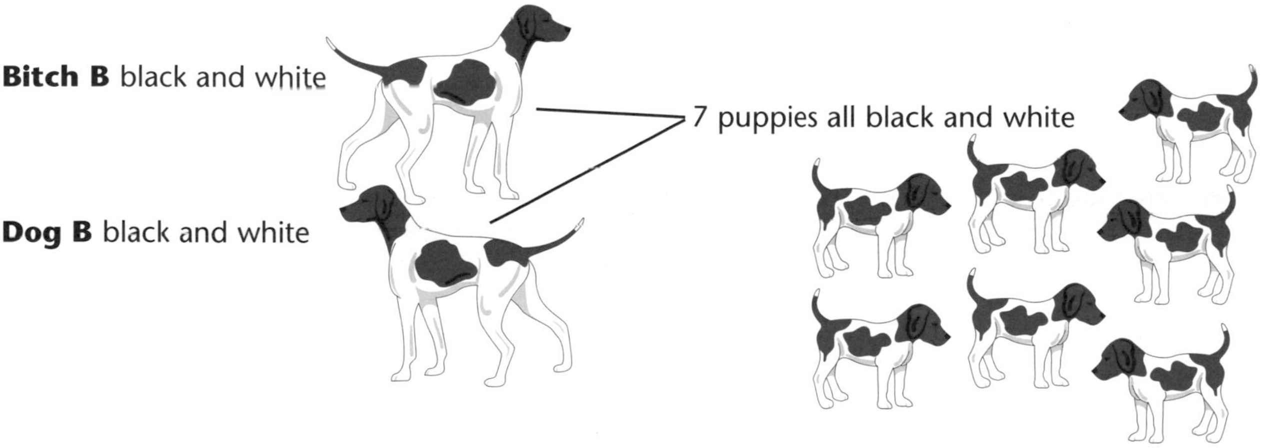

a Which parents should he choose to give the best chance of a large litter of all black puppies?

Bitch ______________________ Dog ______________________

1 mark

b Explain your choice.

____

____

____

2 marks

Total

maximum 6 marks

7 Choose a separating technique from the box for each mixture in the table.

chromatography	**distillation**	**evaporation**	**filtration**

To get sand from a mixture of sand and water	
To get water from black ink	
To get salt crystals from sea water	
To find how many food dyes are in a blue Smartie	

☐ 4 marks

8 Look at this equation for a chemical reaction:

$2Na + Cl_2 \rightarrow 2NaCl$

a Can you identify the compound that is made here:

i by its proper name?

____

☐ 1 mark

ii by its everyday name?

____

☐ 1 mark

b What are the names of the **two** elements that go into this reaction?

____________________ and ____________________

☐ 2 marks

c How do we know that a chemical reaction has taken place?

____

☐ 1 mark

9 Scientists need to collect evidence to help them develop their ideas. Evidence can come from a lot of different sources.

a In the list below, tick the boxes that you think would be sources of evidence.

Source of information	**Evidence**
An experiment you carried out at school.	☐
What your Granny thinks.	☐
What your teacher thinks.	☐
The results of a survey published in a scientific journal.	☐
A TV interview with a famous scientist about an experiment she has been doing.	☐
Something written in your science textbook.	☐

☐ 3 marks

To gather evidence it is sometimes necessary to carry out an experiment. All experiments need a factor to change (the independent variable) and a factor to observe or measure (the dependent variable).

b For each of the enquiries below, decide what would be a suitable independent and dependent variable.

i Do plants grow better in bright light?

Independent variable ______________________

Dependent variable ______________________

☐ 2 marks

ii What material is best for insulating cups of hot drinks?

Independent variable ______________________

Dependent variable ______________________

☐ 2 marks

iii Does the amount of water affect the growth of bean plants?

Independent variable ______________________

Dependent variable ______________________

☐ 2 marks

Total

maximum 18 marks ☐

10 This information was given on the labels of some foods bought in a supermarket.

Per 100 g	**Food A**	**Food B**	**Food C**
Energy	477 kcal	141 kcal	340 kcal
Protein	4.5 g	3.5 g	10.1 g
Fat	18.3 g	7.0 g	22.6 g
Carbohydrate	73.6 g	16.1 g	25.2 g

a Why is the information given 'Per 100 g'?

____

____

2 marks

b Which food has the highest energy content?

____

1 mark

c If you were given samples of foods A, B and C, how could you test them to find out which was which? Describe below an experiment you could carry out.

____

____

____

____

____

____

____

____

____

____

____

____

____

____

3 marks

11 When fossil fuels are burned some gases are released into the atmosphere. One of the gases causes acid rain.

a What is the name of this gas?

______________________________ 1 mark

b Explain how this gas produces acid rain.

____

____

______________________________ 2 marks

c What can happen when this rain falls onto lakes and rivers?

____

____

______________________________ 2 marks

d What can be done to correct this?

____

____

______________________________ 1 mark

e What is the name of the chemical reaction that takes place?

______________________________ 1 mark

Total

maximum 13 marks

12

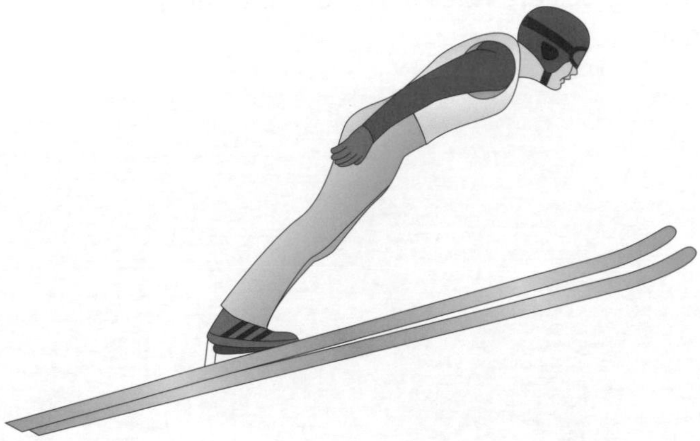

Look at the picture of the ski jumper.

a Describe **two** factors she has used to increase her maximum possible speed through the air.

1 ______________________________

2 ______________________________

2 marks

b What is the correct name for the maximum speed she can achieve?

____

1 mark

c The car in the picture below is not travelling at its maximum speed, its speed is still increasing.

Draw arrows on the diagram to show the forces acting on the car.

2 marks

d **i** In the course of a journey the car travels 100 miles in 4 hours. What is its average speed?

____

____

____

____

____

2 marks

ii Does this mean that the car has travelled at the same speed for the whole 100 miles?

____

1 mark

iii Explain your answer.

____

____

____

____

2 marks

Total

maximum 10 marks

13 Some pupils did an experiment to see if jelly dissolved more quickly in hotter water. This table shows their results.

Temperature (°C)	Time for jelly to dissolve (minutes)
30	12.6
40	10.9
50	9.2
60	9.1
70	5.8
80	4.1

a Name **two** factors or variables that they should have kept the same in order to make sure their experiment was a fair test.

____

____

2 marks

b **i** Use the results to plot a graph.
Label the axes and draw a line of best fit through the points.

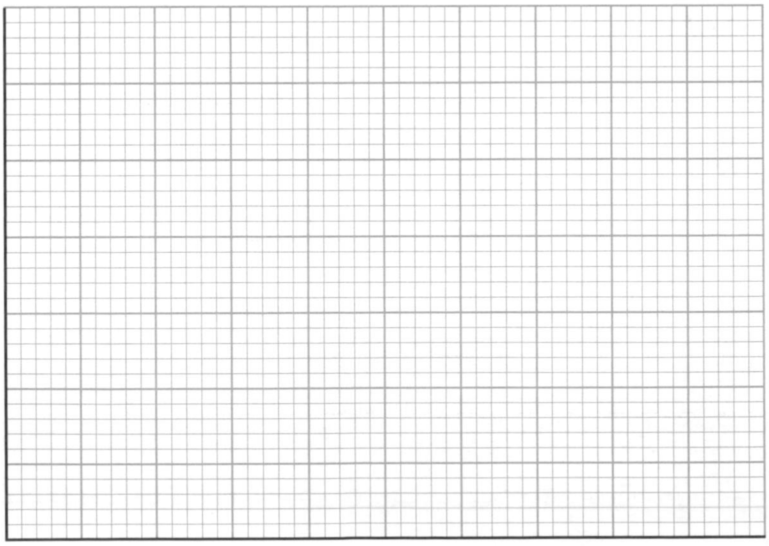

5 marks

ii There is one result which seems to be anomalous (wrong).
Draw a circle around this point on your graph.

1 mark

c One of the pupils wrote this in their exercise book as a conclusion:

> The temperature of the water did affect how quickly the jelly dissolved.

Another pupil said this was not a very scientific conclusion.

i Why do you think this conclusion is not very scientific?

____

____

____

1 mark

ii Write a better conclusion for this experiment.

____

____

____

1 mark

Total

maximum 10 marks

14

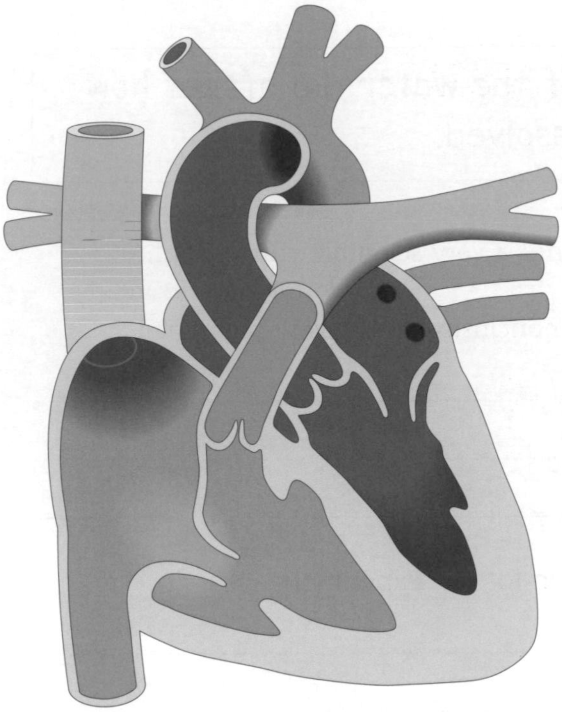

a **i** In which of the systems of the human body is this the major organ?

____

1 mark

ii The blood in the left-hand side of the heart has come from the lungs. Which gas is dissolved in this blood?

____

1 mark

iii What is the correct name for blood with this gas dissolved in it?

____

1 mark

b These cells enable the blood to carry this gas.
Give **two** ways they are adapted to carry out that function.

1 ______________________________

2 ______________________________

2 marks

c **i** What is the name of the chemical reaction that every cell in the body needs this gas for?

____

1 mark

ii Write the word equation for this chemical reaction.

____

____

2 marks

d Which organ is responsible for removing the waste gas from this reaction out of the body?

____

1 mark

Total

maximum 9 marks

15 Some students wanted to know if drinking cola increased their pulse rate. They all drank a glassful of cola taking care to drink the same amount each to make sure it was a fair test. This was the question they asked:

> Does drinking a glass of cola make your pulse rate higher?

This was their prediction:

> We predict that we will all have a higher pulse rate after drinking a glass of cola than before.

These were their results:

Name	**Pulse rate after drinking 200 ml of cola drink**
John	65
Sarah	72
Peter	68
James	67
Gemma	69

a **i** Do you think they have the right results to answer their question and test their prediction?

____ 1 mark

ii Explain your answer.

____

____

____ 1 mark

This was their conclusion:

From our results we conclude that girls have a higher pulse rate than boys.

b **i** Is this a reasonable conclusion from their results?

____ 1 mark

ii Explain your answer.

____

____

____ 1 mark

c Why is it always hard to obtain reliable evidence from experiments on living things even if you are very careful to do everything right?

____

____

____ 1 mark

Total

maximum 5 marks

Revision checklist

CELLS

I am able to …

- Describe the structure of plant and animal cells, the things that are the same and the things that are different ☐
- Describe the ways in which some cells are adapted to carry out their special function ☐
- Explain how cells divide to make new cells ☐
- Describe how similar cells group together to make tissues ☐
- Describe how tissues group together to make organs ☐
- Describe how organs work together in the systems of the body, i.e. the digestive system, the reproductive system, the circulatory system ☐
- Recognise the characteristics of living things and explain how the tissues, organs and organ systems enable these characteristics to happen ☐
- Describe how plants make their own food by photosynthesis ☐
- Explain that all living things use food for energy to allow them to move, to grow and to maintain their correct temperature ☐
- Explain how living things release energy from food by respiration ☐

ENERGY

I am able to …

- Recognise the difference between renewable and non-renewable sources of energy ☐
- Describe the advantages and disadvantages of using both kinds of energy source ☐
- Explain how electricity is generated in power stations, and the advantages of using different kinds of energy resource in the generation of electricity ☐
- Describe how electrical current is carried around a circuit ☐
- Recognise the difference between a series and a parallel circuit ☐
- Describe the ways in which energy can change its form, although it can neither be created nor destroyed ☐
- Describe the ways in which energy, including thermal energy, can be transferred ☐
- Explain that energy transfers are never 100% efficient as some energy is transferred at each stage in a form where it cannot readily be used ☐
- Describe how humans and other animals use food as a source of energy ☐
- Explain how the energy content of different foods varies ☐
- Explain how a range of different foods are needed to make up a balanced diet, and why different people need different diets ☐
- Explain how energy can be transferred as sound and as light ☐
- Explain how the frequency and amplitude of a sound wave are related to the pitch and loudness of the sound ☐
- Explain how light is reflected and refracted ☐
- Describe how white light is made up of a range of different colours ☐

FORCES

I am able to …

- Explain how balanced and unbalanced forces affect the movement of objects ☐
- Calculate speed ☐
- Describe how friction acts to oppose motion ☐
- Recognise how air resistance is a form of friction ☐
- Explain how a streamlined shape can reduce air resistance ☐
- Describe the relationship between shape, air resistance and terminal velocity ☐
- Explain how pressure is related to force and surface area ☐
- Explain how gravity affects the movement of objects ☐
- Describe the movement of the Earth around the Sun and the Moon around the Earth ☐
- Explain why we have day and night, summer and winter, and why the Moon looks different at different times ☐
- Describe the existence of a magnetic field around the Earth ☐
- Recognise the ways in which electromagnets can be made stronger ☐
- Recognise the similarities and differences between magnets and electromagnets ☐

PARTICLES

I am able to …

- Describe the behaviour of particles in solids, liquids and gases ☐
- Understand how this behaviour explains physical changes of state such as melting and evaporating ☐
- Describe how to separate one substance from another by a variety of means and to be able to choose the best separating technique in any situation ☐
- Explain what happens when a solid dissolves in a liquid ☐
- Explain the difference between an element, a compound and a mixture ☐
- Recognise the chemical symbols for the first 20 elements in the Periodic Table ☐
- Use those symbols to identify which atoms are present in a molecule of a compound ☐
- Explain the difference between chemical reactions and physical changes of state ☐
- Describe, and give examples of, how the products of chemical reactions can be very different from the reactants with which the reaction started ☐
- Describe chemical reactions in word equations ☐
- Recognise the characteristics of metals and non-metals ☐
- Explain how different metals react with water, steam and acid and use this to describe the reactivity series of metals ☐
- Describe the reactions of metals with water, steam and acid in word equations ☐
- Recognise that rusting and combustion are examples of chemical reactions involving oxygen ☐
- Explain how the pH scale is used to measure acids and alkalis ☐
- Identify the pH of some common substances ☐
- Explain how indicators can be used ☐
- Recognise that acids and alkalis react together to form a neutral compound and how this can be used ☐

- Recognise the three kinds of rock
- Explain how the structure and properties of rocks are related to the process by which they are formed
- Describe the rock cycle
- Explain the effects of physical and chemical weathering on rocks

INTERDEPENDENCE

I am able to ...

- Describe the relationships between different organisms that make up a food chain
- Explain how energy is passed through a food chain
- Understand why food webs are more useful in explaining the relationships between organisms than food chains
- Explain why there is always a green plant at the start of every food chain
- Describe the variations within and between species
- Explain the difference between inherited and environmental characteristics
- Describe how plants and animals have adapted in ways that enable them to survive better in their habitats
- Describe the main classification groups of living things and classify organisms according to their features
- Use keys to classify unknown organisms
- Describe how living things compete for resources such as water, light, food and space
- Understand the impact that humans have on the planet and on other species

SCIENTIFIC ENQUIRY

I am able to ...

- Identify the variables or factors in an enquiry to be changed, to be measured and to be controlled
- Recognise which is the independent variable and which is the dependent variable
- Explain that all factors other than the independent variable must be kept the same to ensure a fair test
- See trends and patterns in results
- Present results clearly and draw conclusions from results
- Make accurate measurements using the correct instrument and explain why repeating results can make them more reliable
- Obtain information from charts and graphs
- Present information clearly in charts and graphs
- Draw conclusions from data presented in a variety of ways
- Evaluate an experimental procedure and suggest improvements
- Evaluate the reliability of conclusions drawn from experiments and data
- Identify sources of evidence and evaluate that evidence
- Describe the ways in which scientific ideas have changed over time as the available evidence has changed

Notes

Notes

Workbook answers

Pages 98–99 Cell structure

1

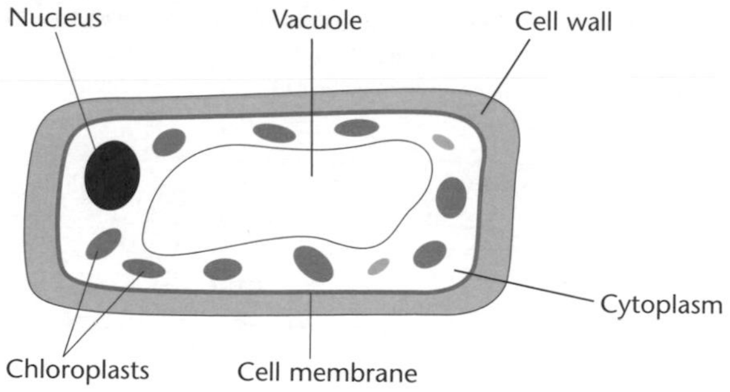

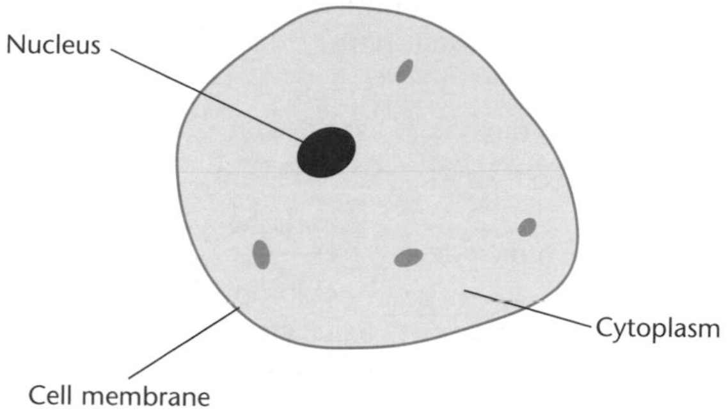

(1 mark for each label)

2 a Nucleus **b** Cytoplasm **c** Cell membrane
(1 mark each any order)

3 a Cell wall **b** Vacuole **c** Chloroplasts
(1 mark each any order)

4

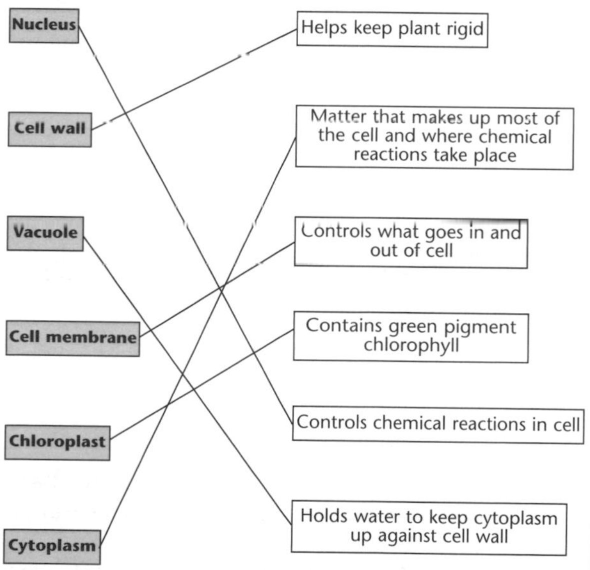

(1 mark for each correct link)

5 Chloroplasts contain the green pigment chlorophyll which plants use for photosynthesis

6 The cell membrane controls what goes in and out of the cell – this is important for all types of cell

Pages 100–101 Specialist cells

1 a Chloroplasts

b Root hair cells are underground *(1)* and so cannot carry out photosynthesis so do not need chloroplasts *(1)*

c They are long and narrow

2 a Both sperm and egg cells are adapted by having only half the genetic material of other cells

b Egg cells have a supply of food to provide energy for the embryo

3 a **Cell A** Nerve cell *(1)* **Cell B** Red blood cell *(1)*

b **i** Cell A is very long and thin

ii This enables it to carry messages to all parts of the body

c **i** Cell B is biconcave

ii This gives it the biggest possible surface area for trapping oxygen

Pages 102–103 Tissues and organs

1 a D C B A
(1 mark for each diagram in correct order)

b Tissues

2 a Movement *(1)* Respiration *(1)* Sensitivity *(1)* Growth *(1)* Reproduction *(1)* Excretion *(1)* Nutrition *(1)*

b Growth *or* Respiration (as the chemical reaction takes place in every cell in the body)

c **Excretion** Any 1 of kidneys, lungs or skin
Nutrition Any organ of the digestive system

d **i** Leaf

ii Nutrition

3 a Respiration

b Muscle tissue *(1)* Nerve tissue *(1)*

c A system

Pages 104–105 The digestive system

1 a A stomach *(1)* B large intestine *(1)* C small intestine *(1)*

b **i** C small intestine

ii A stomach

iii B large intestine

2 a Enzymes

b Saliva

3 a Growth *(1)* Movement *(1)* Warmth *(1)*

b Growth

Pages 106–107 The reproductive system

1 **a** Label drawn to uterus

b Label drawn to placenta

c Because the harmful substances will pass to the baby *(1)* It will mean the baby gets less nutrients/oxygen, which can lead to low birth weight *(1)*

2 **a** Every 28 days

b Ovulation

c The uterus wall becomes thicker so that a fertilised egg can be implanted

d The uterus wall breaks down *(1)* and is passed out of the body with the unfertilised egg *(1)*

e The menstrual cycle

f It has only half the genetic material OR Has a supply of food

g 40 weeks

Pages 108–109 The circulation system

1 a & b

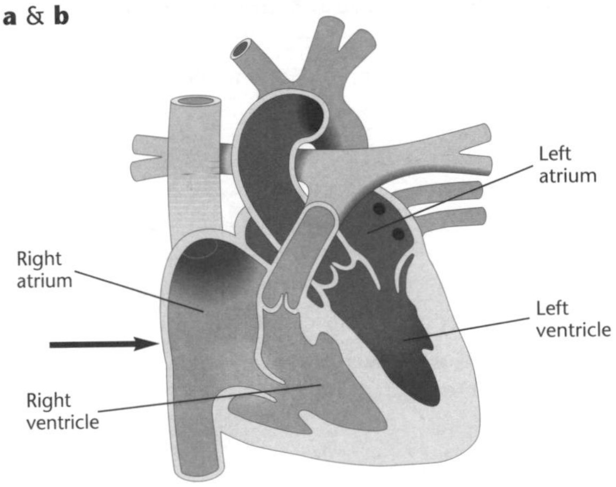

(1 mark for each label and 1 mark for arrow)

c Left-hand side

d Blood is sent by the heart to the lungs to collect a supply of oxygen *(1)*
The blood with oxygen – called oxygenated blood – then comes back into the left-hand side *(1)* of the heart and is then sent off around the body *(1)*

(Maximum of 2 marks for any of above)

2 **a** Artery

b Thick muscular walls *(1)* to stand the pressure of the blood being pumped away from the heart *(1)*

3 Cell → tissue → organ → system → organism
(1 mark for each one in correct place)

4 **a** Breathing is the mechanism by which we take in oxygen and get rid of carbon dioxide *(1)* through the lungs *(1)* Respiration is the chemical reaction that takes place in every cell in the body *(1)* to release energy from food *(1)*

b To speed up the flow of blood to your muscles *(1)* to deliver the oxygen and glucose you need *(1)* and take away the carbon dioxide *(1)*

Pages 110–111 Photosynthesis

1 Because only plants can make their own food *(1)* by trapping the energy in sunlight/by photosynthesis *(1)*

2 **a**

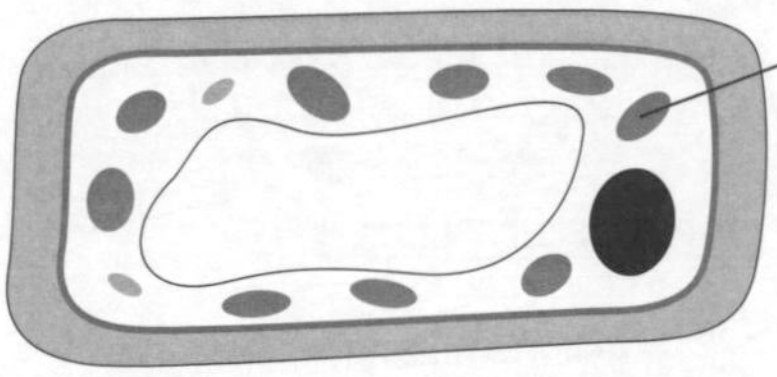

b Root (hair) cells

c Because they are underground and cannot be used in photosynthesis

3 **a** Carbon dioxide *(1)* Water *(1)*

b Oxygen

c Carbon dioxide + water $\xrightarrow[\text{chlorophyll}]{\text{light}}$ glucose + oxygen

(1 mark for reactants, 1 for products, 1 for conditions; each given only if written in correct format)

4 As the shrub grew and became more dense, it blocked the light from the area underneath *(1)* This meant that the grass could not carry out photosynthesis and so could not grow *(1)*

5 In the light, plants are carrying out both photosynthesis and respiration *(1)* They take in more carbon dioxide for photosynthesis then they give out by respiration, and photosynthesis gives out oxygen *(1)* In the dark there is no photosynthesis only respiration so carbon dioxide is given out, but no carbon dioxide is taken in or oxygen given out *(1)*

Pages 112–113 Energy resources

1 **a** Coal *(1)* Oil *(1)* Natural gas *(1)*
(If more than 3 boxes ticked, deduct 1 from total score)

b Non-renewable

c Because they took millions of years to make *(1)* and so it is not possible to make any more *(1)*

2 **a** Carbon dioxide *(1)* Sulphur dioxide *(1)*

b Carbon dioxide causes the green house effect / global warming *(1)* Sulphur dioxide causes acid rain *(1)*
(Must be specific answers not just pollution)

c Carbon dioxide

4 a

Energy source	Advantage	Disadvantage
Coal	**C** Can be used anywhere and when burned gives off a large amount of heat.	**A** Will one day run out and it is not possible to make more.
Wind power	**F** Is clean to use and renewable.	**E** Can only be used where the conditions are right.
Biomass	**B** Supplies can be fairly easily replaced.	**D** Although not a fossil fuel, still gives off greenhouse gases.

(1 mark for each correct box)

5 a The Sun

b Solar panels

c It can only be used in daylight/when the Sun is shining

Pages 114–115 Generating and using electricity

1 a

B Fuel is burned in a furnace to release energy in the form of heat.

↓

D The heat from the furnace heats the water in the boiler which creates steam.

↓

A The steam turns a turbine.

↓

C The turbine turns a magnet inside a generator which produces the electricity.

(1 mark for each one correct)

b Burning the fuel to give off heat to make steam

2 a **Heat loss from a house**

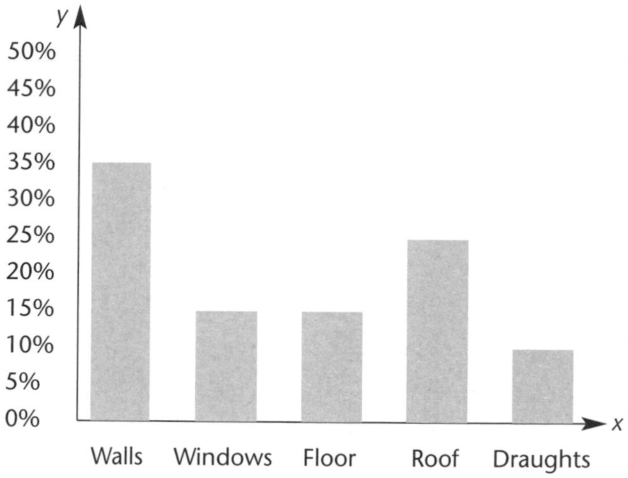

(maximum 3 with 1 deducted for each incorrect bar to minimum of zero)

b
i FALSE
ii TRUE
iii TRUE
iv FALSE
v FALSE
vi TRUE

c B

Pages 116–117 Electrical circuits

1

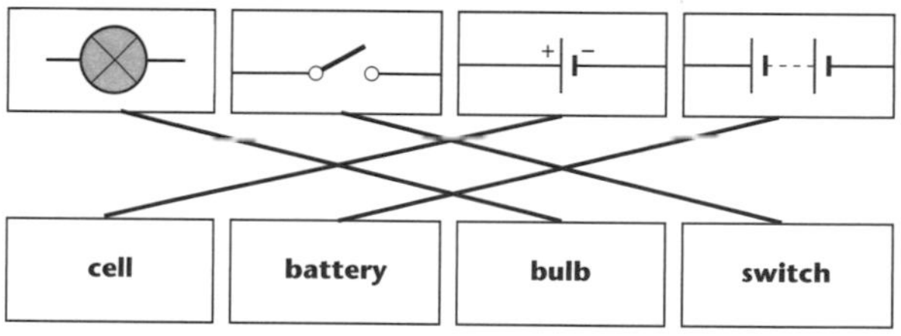

(1 mark for each correct match of symbol to component)

2 a In series circuit, current is always the same

b If one bulb breaks, the other will as well

3 a A2 and A3

b A1 will be the sum of A2 and A3

c If bulb X went out, bulb Y would stay lit OR nothing would happen

4 a A – there is only one lead from the cell (battery) to the bulb

B – both leads are going into the same terminal of the cell

C – the bulb is broken

(In each case the circuit is not complete, but for the mark it is necessary to say why)

b

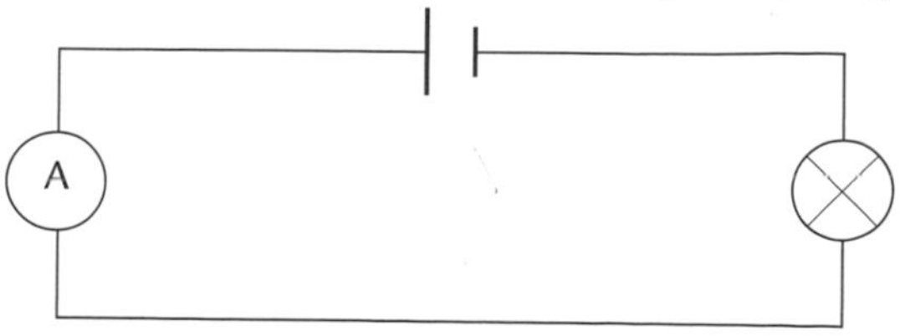

Pages 118–119 Energy transformation

1 Heat or thermal energy

2 Sound travels by vibrations of particles, in a vacuum there are no particles so the energy cannot be transferred

3 a

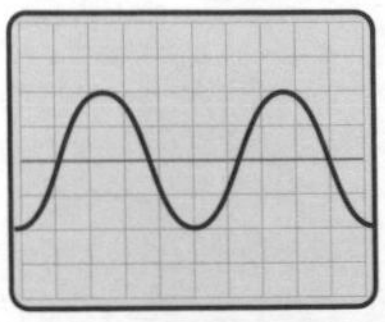

b

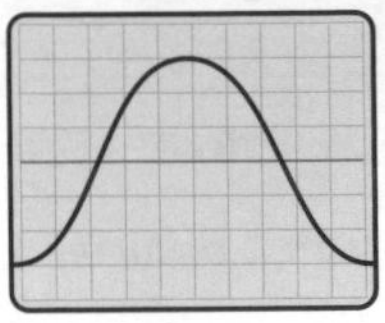

4 a Gravitational potential

b Kinetic

c Sound and heat *(1 mark for both correct)*

5 a C

b Chemical potential energy

Pages 120–121 Energy transfer

1 a Heat *(1)* Light *(1)* Sound *(1)*

b Heat

2 a Aluminium *(1)* Copper *(1)*

b Because they are metals *(1)* and metals conduct heat *(1)*

c Because wood does not conduct heat/is an insulator *(1)* and so a wooden spoon will not get hot in the way a metal one would *(1)*

3 a Because when the water nearest to the element is heated, it rises by convection *(1)* and the cold water from the top falls and is heated in its turn *(1)*

b Radiation

c The air above the hot liquid is heated by convection *(1)*, the heat is conducted through the side of the cup *(1)* and is then radiated out into the surroundings *(1)*

4 a TRUE

b FALSE

c TRUE

d FALSE

e TRUE

Pages 122–123 Energy from food

1 A green plant

2 a Respiration

b Glucose + oxygen → carbon dioxide + water + energy

(1 mark for reactants, 1 for products, 1 for energy – all only given if in correct format)

c Movement *(1)* Growth *(1)* Warmth *(1)*

3 a A

b A

c A

d B

e B

f Meal B contains protein, some carbohydrate, some fat and plenty of vitamins and minerals, so all the food groups are there *(1)* Meal A does contain some protein but too much carbohydrate, sugar and fat and hardly any vitamins and minerals *(1)*

4 a 2000 kcal

b 4000 kcal

c 3000 kcal

d 1500 kcal

5 So it is possible to directly compare the energy values of different foods

Pages 124–125 Sound and light

1 It is possible to tell what a sound will be like by looking at the wave. If the wave has a high **frequency** *(1)* then the sound will have a **high** *(1)* pitch. The **amplitude** *(1)* of the wave tells us whether it will be loud or quiet.

2 a Sound B

b Sound B

3 a Luminous

b

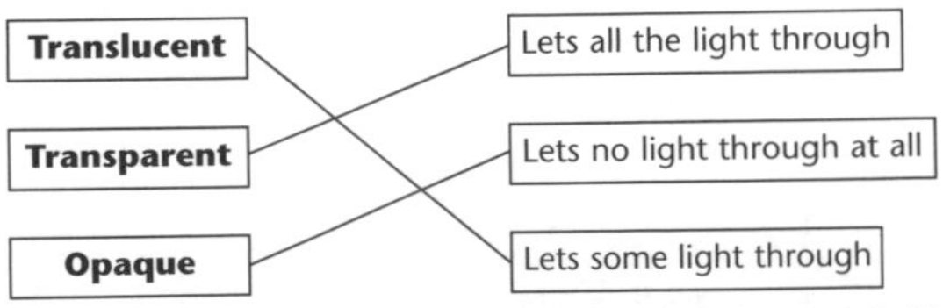

(1 mark each for each correct link)

4

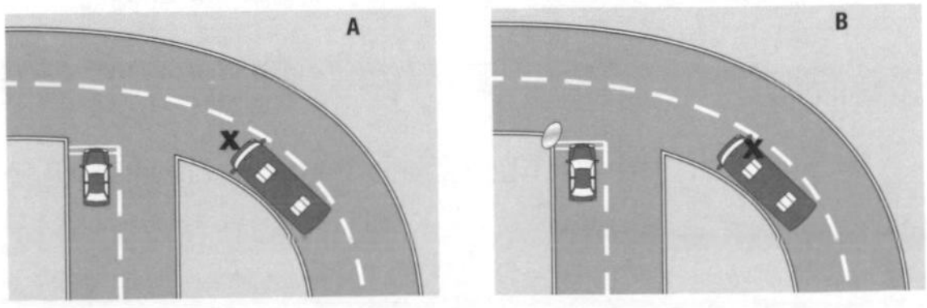

5 **a** FALSE
b TRUE
c TRUE
d FALSE
e FALSE
f TRUE

6 As there is no atmosphere, there are no particles, so sound waves cannot travel *(1)* Radio waves, like light, can travel through a vacuum *(1)*

Pages 126–127 Reflection, refraction and seeing colour

1 We are able to see objects because light is **reflected** into our eyes. The angle at which light strikes a surface is called the **angle of incidence**. The angle at which light is reflected from a surface is called the **angle of reflection**. The angle of reflection is always **the same** as the angle of incidence.

White light is a mixture of **seven** colours and objects that look white reflect **all** of these colours. Objects that look black reflect **none** of the colours of the spectrum and objects that look coloured reflect **some** of the colours. Although light always travels in straight lines, it will change direction at the boundary between two substances. This is called **refraction**. This can make water look **shallower** than it really is.

(1 mark for each correct choice)

2 (1 RED)
2 ORANGE
3 YELLOW
4 GREEN
5 BLUE
6 INDIGO
7 VIOLET *(Total 3 marks, deduct 1 mark for each incorrect answer to minimum of zero)*

3 Because there is a red filter in front of the white light bulb *(1)* The red filter absorbs all the other colours and only allows red light to pass through *(1)*

4

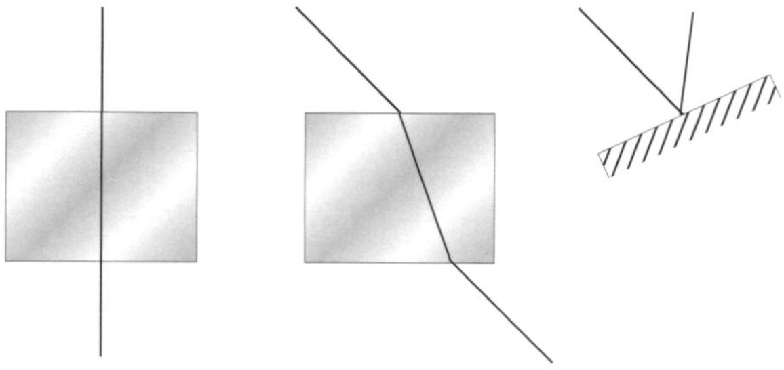

(1 mark per diagram)

5 **a** All the colours in the spectrum
b Not reflecting any colours but absorbing all of them
c Red light

Pages 128–129 Balanced and unbalanced forces

1 **a** FALSE
b TRUE
c TRUE
d FALSE
e TRUE

2 The chair is pushing up on the person sitting in it with an equal force acting in the opposite direction

3 **a** A
b B

4 **a** B
b Because it has the greatest surface area *(1)* so that the force of the person's weight will be spread over the greatest possible area so will reduce the pressure *(1)* and reduce the risk of sinking into the ground

Pages 130–131 Speed and motion

1 **a** B and C
b

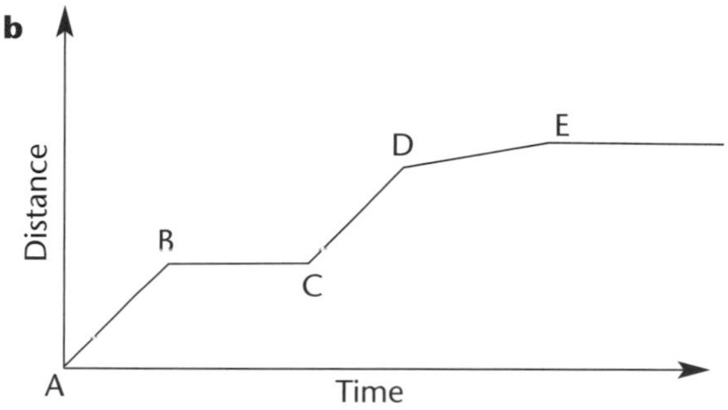

2

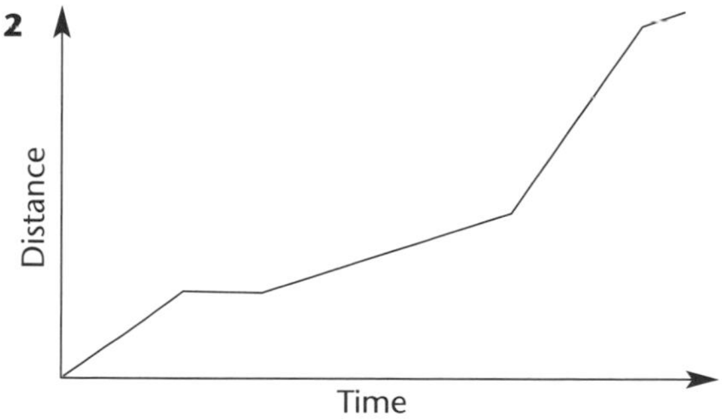

(5 marks in total, 1 for each section of the graph)

3

Speed	Distance	Time
50 km/h	250 km	5 h
15 m/s	1500 m	**100 s**
30 m/s	**9000 m**	300 s

(1 mark for each correct entry)

4 **a** 20 ÷ 40 = average speed = 0.5 miles per minute or 30 miles per hour
b 30 miles

Pages 132–133 Friction

1 **a** Box A *(1)* Box C *(1)*

b Box A would move to the left *(1)* Box C would move to the right *(1)*

c For the box to move the push force needs to be greater than the friction force

2 **a** Suitable friction from picture such as brakes, wheels on ground, etc.

b Suitable friction from picture such a where wheels meet axle, etc.

3 To reduce the friction between the moving parts *(1)* To prevent wear and tear *(1)* To reduce heating *(1)*

(Any 2, 1 mark each)

4 Wear suitable clothing *(1)* Maintain streamlined position *(1)* Design of sleigh *(1)* *or* Any sensible suggestions *(1)* *(Any 3, 1 mark each)*

Pages 134–135 Streamlining and air resistance

1 Air resistance gets greater as you go faster

2 **a** To move quickly and easily through water as it is harder to move through water than through air

b Increases the top speed *(1)* which means that at any speed the force needed from the engine is less, so less fuel is used *(1)*

3 **a** Air resistance gets greater

b In all 4 diagrams, the downward arrow representing acceleration due to gravity should be the same

A The upward arrow is quite small as there is little air resistance

B Upward arrow is greater, almost as large as the downward force arrow as she nears terminal velocity

C Upward arrow increases a lot when the parachute is opened

D Upward arrow is greater still and equals the downward arrow as terminal velocity has been reached

(1 mark for each correct set of arrows)

4 Terminal velocity

Pages 136–137 Gravity

1 10 newtons (10 N)

2 Towards the centre of the Earth (NOT downwards)

3

	On Earth	**In deep space**	**On the Moon**
Mass	**90 kg**	**90 kg**	90 kg
Weight	**900 N**	**0 N**	**150 N**

(1 mark for each correct entry)

4 **a** It would increase

b A larger planet has a larger gravitational force and as weight depends on mass and gravitational force *(1)* although his mass would stay the same, his weight would increase *(1)*

5 C

6 **a** Air resistance

b On the moon, there is no atmosphere so there is no air resistance

Pages 138–139 The Earth and beyond

1 The Moon orbits the Earth approximately once every **28 days**. The moon is a **non-luminous** object which we can see because it reflects the light from the Sun which is a **luminous** object.

The Earth orbits the Sun approximately once every **365 days**. This length of time gives us our **year**. The Earth is tilted on its axis so different parts of the Earth's surface face towards it at different times in its orbit around the Sun. This is what gives us **summer and winter**. The Earth also rotates on its own axis once every **24 hours** and this is what gives us **day and night**.

(1 mark for each correct choice)

2 **a** We can only see the part of the Moon that is facing towards the Sun *(1)* This changes as it orbits around the Earth *(1)*

b The Sun is much bigger than the Moon *(1)* but it is much much further away *(1)*

3 [Numbered list below is correct]

1 Mercury

3 Earth

4 Mars

5 Jupiter

7 Uranus

8 Neptune

9 Pluto *(1 mark for each correct answer)*

4 **a** The average distance from Venus to the Sun is... **108 million km**

The average distance from Pluto to the Sun is... **5900 million km**

The average distance from Earth to the Moon is... **0.38 million km**

The average distance from Earth to the Sun is... **150 million km**

(1 mark for each correct line)

b The Sun

Pages 140–141 Magnetic forces

1 The suspended magnet will move away from one end of the piece of iron when it is brought close to it *(1)* because a magnet can attract an ordinary iron bar but it can only repel another magnet *(1)*

2

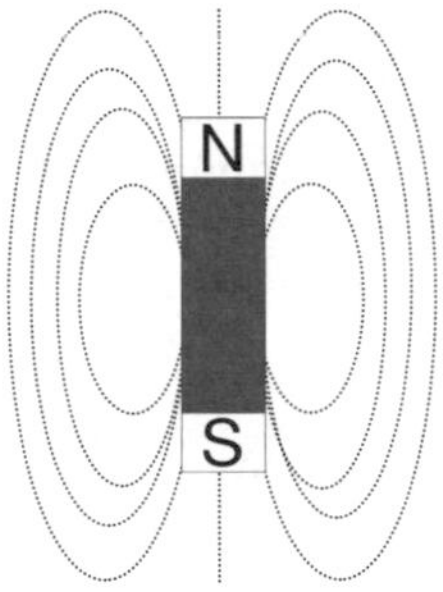

3 In an electromagnet, the magnetic field can be switched on and off, in a bar magnet it cannot be controlled in this way

4 Iron

5 **a** When the switch is pushed it completes the circuit and magnetises the iron core *(1)* This magnet attracts the iron bar in the door lock towards it so it moves to the left *(1)*

b When the switch is released, the core is no longer a magnet so the iron bar moves back to the right

c No

d The door lock only works because the electromagnet can attract the iron bar when the circuit is switched on *(1)* If the bolt was made of aluminium, which is not magnetic, this would not happen *(1)*

Pages 142–143 Solids, liquids and gases

1

Description	State of matter	Particle diagram
The particles are in a fixed lattice pattern and although they vibrate they do not have enough energy to move away from each other.	**Solid**	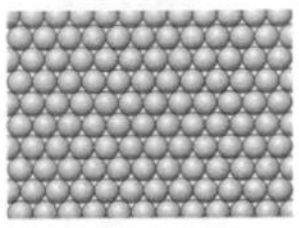
The particles have lots of energy and spread out to fill all the available space.	**Gas**	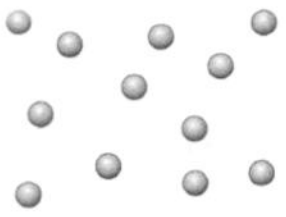
The particles are in contact with each other but can move and slide over each other.	**Liquid**	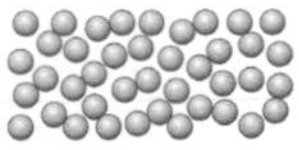

(1 mark for each correct entry)

2 **a**

Substance	Melting point (°C)	Boiling point (°C)	Solid, liquid or gas
A	0	100	**Liquid**
B	–183	–162	**Gas**
C	100	245	**Solid**
D	–39	355	**Liquid**
E	1540	Above 2000	**Solid**

b A

c E

3 **a** It expands

b When a substance gets hotter it means that the particles have more thermal energy *(1)* When particles have more thermal energy they vibrate more or move more *(1)* which means that the space between them gets greater *(1)* The space between the particles getting greater means the substance expands *(1)*

(Any 3 of above, 1 mark each)

4

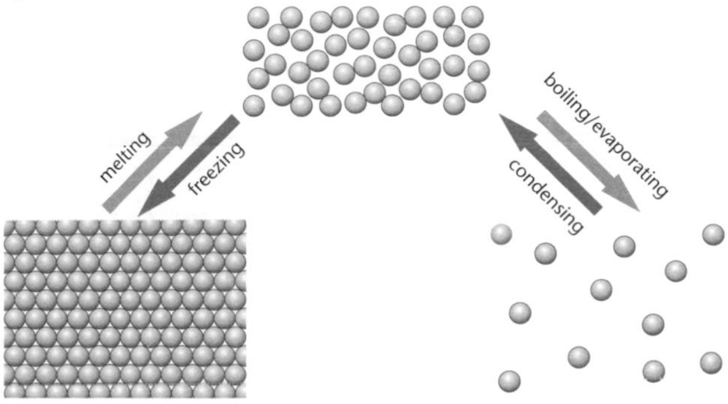

(1 mark for each correct label)

5 The particles in a gas are free to move around and fill up all the available space *(1)* This means that the particles of the perfume will move around with the gas particles in the air in the room and will gradually reach all parts of the room *(1)*

Pages 144–145 Solubility and separation

1 150 g *(1 mark for correct numerical answer and 1 for unit)*

2 a C B A D

b C Bar magnet

B Beaker or possibly conical flask

A Filter funnel, filter paper and conical flask

D Bunsen burner, tripod and gauze and evaporating basin

(1 mark for each correct stage)

3 a Solution

b Solute

c Solvent

d Insoluble

4 a

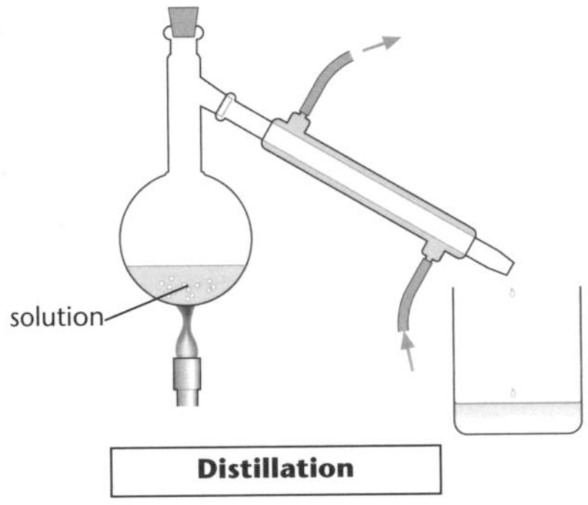

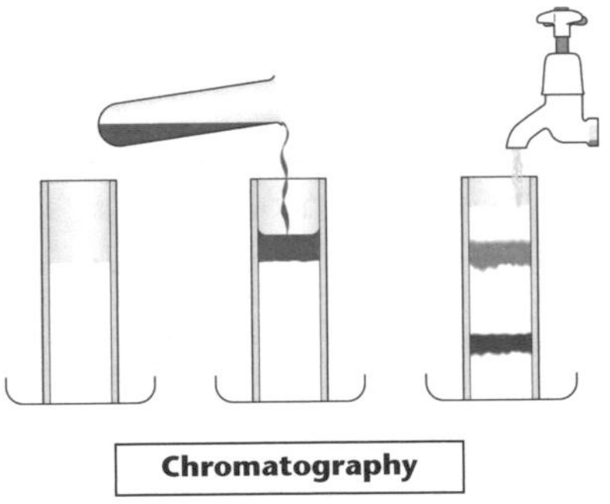

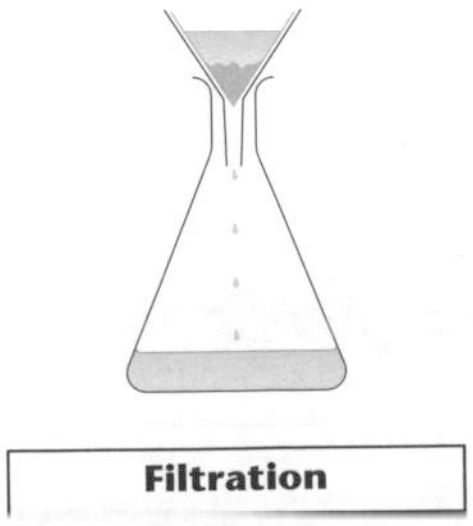

(1 mark for each correctly labelled diagram)

b i Chromatography

ii Distillation

iii Filtration

iv Evaporation

Pages 146–147 Elements, compounds and mixtures

1 a

Substance	Element, compound or mixture
Oxygen	**Element**
Air	**Mixture**
Steel	**Compound**
Iron	**Element**
Water	**Compound**

(1 mark for each correct entry)

b In a compound a chemical reaction has taken place, but in a mixture the different substances have not reacted with each other

2

Element	Symbol	Element	Symbol
Hydrogen	**H**	Phosphorus	**P**
Nitrogen	**N**	Sulphur	**S**
Sodium	**Na**	Potassium	**K**
Oxygen	**O**	Carbon	**C**
Copper	**Cu**	Nickel	**Ni**

3 CO_2 **Carbon** and **oxygen**

H_2O **Hydrogen** and **oxygen**

NH_3 **Nitrogen** and **hydrogen**

NaCl **Sodium** and **chlorine**

CuO **Copper** and **oxygen**

(1 mark for each correct pair of elements)

4 a TRUE

b FALSE

c FALSE

d TRUE *(1 mark each)*

5 Salt

b i Sodium is a soft grey metal

ii Chlorine is a green poisonous gas used as a disinfectant

Pages 148–149 Chemical reactions

1 a Physical change

b Ice melting, water boiling, etc.

c Neutralisation, oxidation, combustion, corrosion, etc.

2 a Combustion

b Iron oxide

c Rust

3 **a** Sodium + chlorine → Sodium chloride

b Magnesium + oxygen → magnesium oxide

c Carbon dioxide + water $\xrightarrow[\text{chlorophyll}]{\text{light}}$ oxygen + glucose

4 Endothermic

5 Oxygen

6 **a** Oxygen and glucose

b Carbon dioxide and water

Pages 150–151 Acids and alkalis

1 Neutralisation

2 **a** Around pH 3

b pH 7

c Slightly alkaline, about pH 8

3 **a** Acid + alkali → **salt** + **water**

(1 mark for each correct product)

b Hydrochloric acid + sodium hydroxide → **sodium chloride** + **water**

(1 mark for each correct product)

c Acid + metal → **salt** + **hydrogen**

(1 mark for each correct product)

d A lighted splint placed at the mouth of a test tube of hydrogen will 'pop'

e A nitrate

f Nitric acid + calcium hydroxide → **calcium nitrate** + **water**

(1 mark for each correct product)

4 Can cause acid rain *or* Can mix with water and make the rain acidic, etc.

(1 mark for a specific answer – just pollution is not enough)

5

Substance	Colour of litmus
Lemon juice	**red**
Toothpaste	**blue**
Vinegar	**red**
Cola	**red**
Soap	**blue**
Bleach	**blue**

6 **a** Toothpaste or soap NOT bleach

b Lemon juice *or* vinegar *or* cola

c Bee stings need something alkaline to neutralise the acid. Wasp stings need something acidic

(1 mark for suitable explanation, 1 for getting the neutralising bit, and 1 for realising that it is not good to put bleach on the skin)

Pages 152–153 Metals and non-metals

1

Properties of metals	Properties of non-metals
A Good conductors of heat	**B** Poor conductors of electricity
C Generally solids at room temperature	**D** Solids, liquids and gases at room temperature
E Shiny appearance	

(1 mark for each correct entry)

2 **a** **1** Iron **2** Oxygen **3** Water

(1 mark each – any order)

b Rust

c Any 1 from: paint oil galvanising *or* any reasonable protective suggestion

3 **a** Metal **D** *(1)* is copper. Because it is yellow *or* It doesn't react with water *or* It reacts with dilute acid and with oxygen *(1 mark for any of these)*

b Metal **B** *(1)* is gold. Because it is yellow *or* It does not react with anything *(1 mark for either of these)*

4 Potassium

Zinc

Lead

Copper

Mercury *(1 mark for each correctly placed metal)*

Pages 154–155 Rocks and the rock cycle

1 Igneous *(1)* Metamorphic *(1)* Sedimentary *(1)*

2

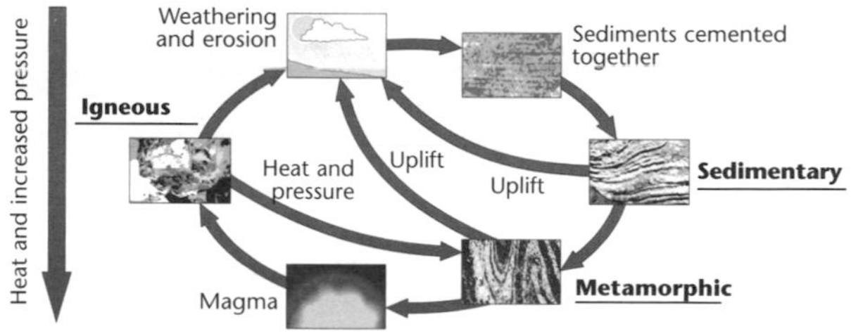

(1 mark for each correct label)

3

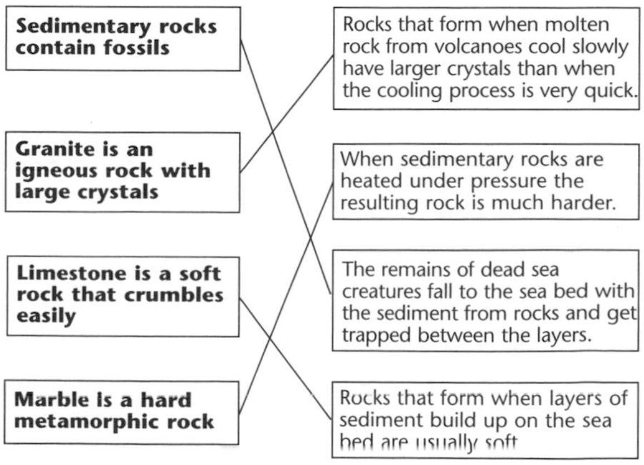

(1 mark for each correct link)

4 **a** Changed
b Quartzite
c Metamorphic rocks are much harder/denser than sedimentary ones

5 **a** Rainwater collects in cracks
b When the temperature falls below 0 °C, the water freezes and expands making the crack bigger
c After repeated freezing and thawing the rock fragment breaks off

Pages 156–157 Food chains and food webs

1 B C A D *(1 mark for each if in correct order)*

2 Food chains and food webs always have a green plant at the beginning. This is because **only green plants can make their own food**. The first animal in a food chain is called **a primary consumer**. This animal is always a **herbivore**. The animals that eat the plants are then often eaten by other animals. The animal that is eaten is called **prey** and the animal that eats the other creature is called **a predator**. In the food chain the predator is known as the **secondary consumer**.
(1 mark for each correct choice)

3 The direction in which the energy travels

4 **a** Any food chain with an owl at the end:
hazelnuts → mouse → owl
hazelnuts → blue tit → owl
leaves → greenfly → blue tit → owl
leaves → mouse → owl
bark → moth larva → blue tit → owl
leaves → moth larva → blue tit → owl
(1 mark each for any 2 correct ones provided the arrows are going in the right direction)

b The pyramid of numbers needs to be correct for the food chain chosen to gain the marks

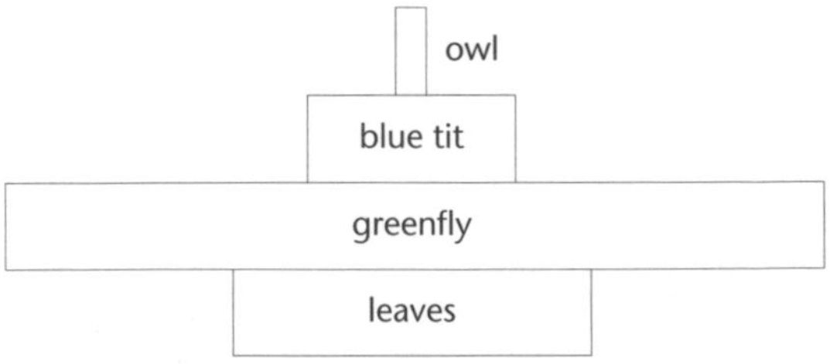

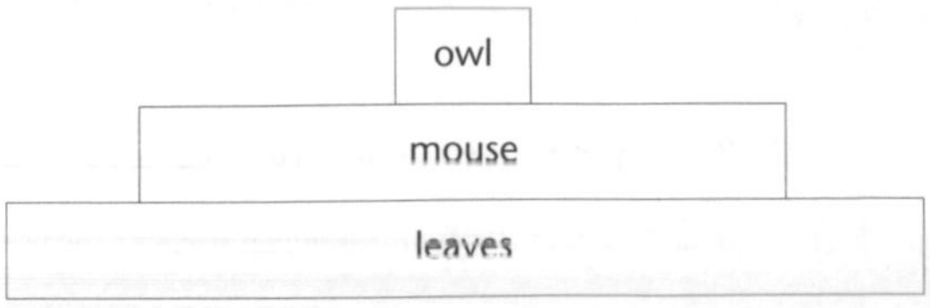

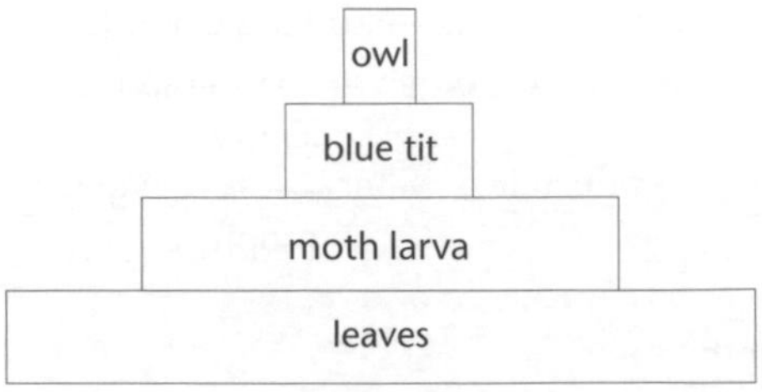

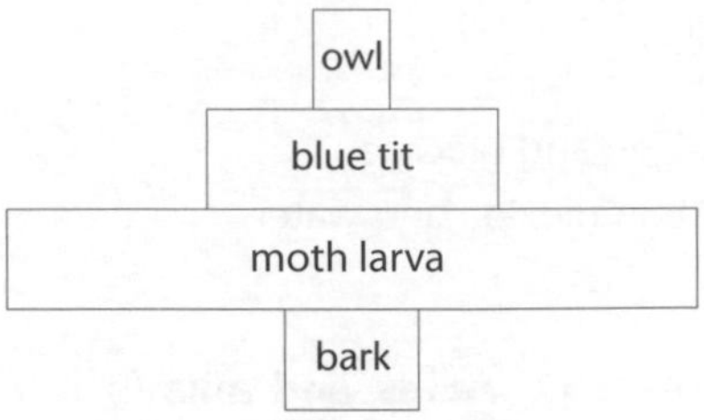

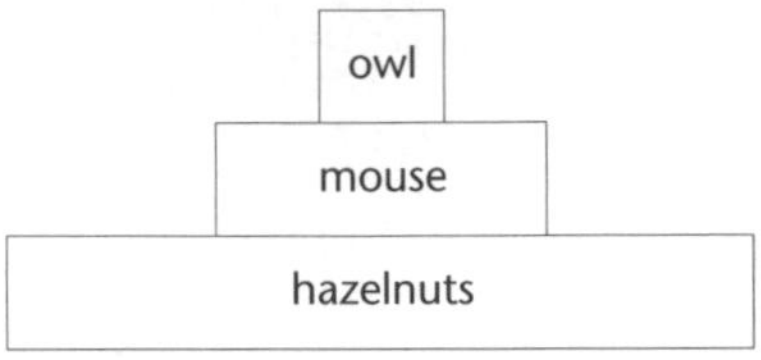

(1 mark for correct order, 1 mark for producer at bottom, 1 mark for correct sizing of boxes)

Page 158–159 Energy transfers in food chains and food webs

1 **a** Growth *(1)* Movement *(1)* Warmth *(1)*
b Only the energy used for growth can be passed up the food chain

2 **a** Total of energy used for other purposes 95% (5 + 10 + 10 + 70)
Energy left for growth 5% (100 – 95)
(1 mark for correct calculation and 1 for %)

b

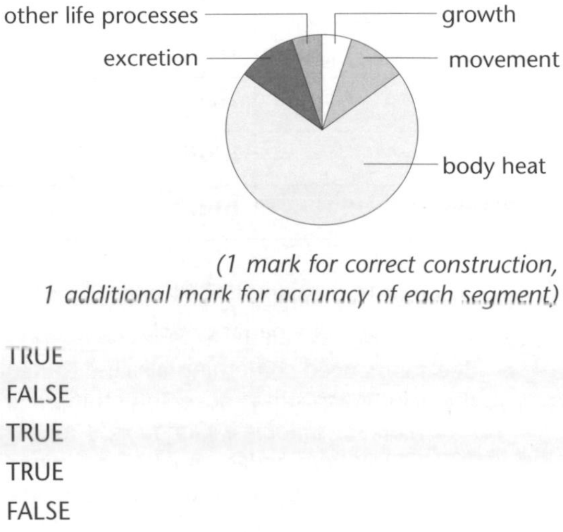

(1 mark for correct construction, 1 additional mark for accuracy of each segment)

3 **a** TRUE
b FALSE
c TRUE
d TRUE
e FALSE

Pages 160–161 Variation and inheritance

1 a One of the twins must have dyed her hair

b If they are identical twins then all the characteristics that they inherit will be the same. Hair colour is an inherited characteristic *(1)*, they have different coloured hair so one of them must have altered this *(1)*

2 a No

b Brothers do not have exactly the same inherited characteristics in the way that identical twins do *(1)* It is possible for many combinations of inherited characteristics to be present in any one family *(1)*

3

Environmental	Inherited
Playing the piano	Hair colour
Swimming	Eye colour

(1 mark for each correct entry)

4 a E *(1)* F *(1)* A *(1)*

b A

c Because Plant A gives more blue flowers than Plant B. If these two are the only ones resistant to disease, then using Plant A is the best way of getting blue disease-resistant flowers

Pages 162–163 Adaptation

1 B *(1)* C *(1)*

2 a

Daily adaptations	Seasonal adaptations
Nocturnal hunting	**Migration of birds**
	Hibernation
	Deciduous trees

(1 mark for each correct entry)

b So that they are asleep and using less energy *(1)* in the winter months when food is scarce *(1)*

c Creatures that sleep in the day and hunt for their prey at night *(1)*

d To find new sources of food *(1)* they spend half the year in each hemisphere so that they are always in summer when food is plentiful but do not stay in one place for the winter when there would be very little to feed on *(1)*

3 B *(1)* D *(1)* E *(1)*

4 a & b There are almost an infinite number of answers to this question so award 1 mark each for any sensible suggestion that relates to any of the features of the habitat for an animal and for a plant.

Pages 164–165 Classification

1 a Vertebrates

b Amphibians *(1)*
Birds *(1)*
Mammals *(1)*
Fish *(1)*
Reptiles *(1)*

2 a Amphibians
b Birds
c Fish
d Mammals
e Reptiles

3 Insects

4 Arachnids

5

Insect	Arachnid	Crustacean	Myriapod
Grasshopper	**Spider**	**Crab**	**Millipede**
Dragonfly	**Scorpion**	**Lobster**	
Wasp			

(1 mark for each correct entry)

Pages 166–167 Using keys to identify living things

1 a Aisle C
b Aisle G
c Aisle H
d Aisle E
e Aisle A

2 Any 3 questions that enable identification to be made, for example:

Q2 Does it live in water? If YES, it is a dolphin If NO, go to question 3.

Q3 Are its young usually born in large numbers? If YES, it is a dog If NO, go to question 4.

Q4 Does it walk on two legs or four? If two legs, it is a human. If four legs, it is a horse.

(1 mark for each question that allows a mammal to be identified)

Pages 168–169 Competition among living things

1 No individuals of that species are still alive

2 Because the large tree will block the light from the ground below and no other plants can grow without light *or* Competition for light/water

3 In spring although there is less light, there is more under the trees than there will be in the height of summer *(1)* when all the trees are in leaf *(1)*

4 The fox population will go down *(1)* because they will have less food *(1)* (*NOT all the foxes will die*)

5 **a** FALSE **b** TRUE **c** FALSE **d** TRUE

6 **a** The population of rabbits is stable/it does not change
b Spring or early summer
c The population drops suddenly
d Sensible suggestions such as increase in a predator *or* reduction in food supply *or* disease

Pages 170–171 Human impact on the environment

1 The greenhouse effect *(1)* Global warming *(1)*

2 **a** It can be sprayed with an alkali
b Neutralisation

3 Cause damage to the ozone layer *(1)* in the upper atmosphere. This layer protects the Earth by filtering out some of the harmful UV rays from the Sun *(1)*

4 Skin cancers

5 Chemicals that are used to kill pests are called **pesticides**. An example is slug pellets which are used to kill slugs. Slugs in turn are eaten by **predators** such as thrushes which are **prey** of bigger birds such as sparrowhawks. The thrushes will eat a lot of slugs and so the pesticide will **build up** in their bodies. This might not be enough to kill the thrushes but when a sparrowhawk eats a number of thrushes, the pesticide will **build up** in the body of the sparrowhawk and kill it.
(1 mark for each correct choice)

6 More people need more space, so trees and forests are cut down to make space – animals bred for food need grazing which again can mean forests are cut down. Either of these can mean that not only the trees but also other animals and plants that live in the forests no longer have a habitat.
(2 marks for a sensible answer)

Pages 172–173 Asking questions and making predictions

1 Key here is a sensible measurable question. The following are examples but are not the only correct answers.
a Does the amount of oxygen affect the length of time for which a candle will burn?
b In what conditions are the most woodlice found?
c Does the size of an object affect the speed at which it falls if dropped?
d Is more force needed to move an object on different surfaces?
e Do different foodstuffs contain different amounts of energy?

2 Again sensible answers which need to follow on from the questions above. It is OK if they are wrong as shown in the falling objects one here as the judgement is on the sense of the prediction and reason – it is of course better it they are right!
a I think that a candle will burn for longer in a bigger volume of air *(1)*
Because air contains oxygen which is needed for combustion *(1)*
b I think that most woodlice will be found in the darkest coolest place possible *(1)*
Because in the wild woodlice are usually found under stones and in other damp dark places *(1)*
c I think that bigger objects will fall faster *(1)*
Because gravity will have more effect on a bigger object *(1)*
d I think that more force will be needed to move an object on a rough surface *(1)*
Because rough surfaces have more friction *(1)*
e I think that different foodstuffs have different amounts of energy *(1)*
Because I know that eating some foods makes you fat more than eating others *(1)*

Pages 174–175 Variables and fair tests

1 **a–c** Answers will follow on from what went before but suitable examples are given here.

– Does the amount of oxygen affect the length of time for which a candle will burn?
Independent variable – the volume of air/ oxygen *(1)*
Dependent variable – the length of time for which the candle burns *(1)*
To make sure it is a fair test – same size of candle/ length of wick/ same shape of container *(1)*

– In what conditions are the most woodlice found?
Independent variable – conditions *(1)*
Dependent variable – number of woodlice *(1)*
To make sure it is a fair test – woodlice must have time to make choice/ do not interfere with choice/ same size compartment for each set of conditions *(1)*

– Does the size of an object affect the speed at which it falls if dropped?
Independent variable – size of object *(1)*
Dependent variable – time taken to fall to the ground *(1)*
To make sure it is a fair test – drop objects from same height/keep shape of object the same *(1)*

– Is more force needed to move an object on different surfaces?
Independent variable – surface *(1)*
Dependent variable – force needed to make object move *(1)*
To make sure it is a fair test – same object used on all surfaces/ Newton meter held at same angle *(1)*

– Do different foodstuffs contain different amounts of energy?
Independent variable – type of food *(1)*
Dependent variable – energy released measure by increase in temperature of water when food is burned *(1)*
To make sure it is a fair test – same volume of water, same mass of food, same experimental procedure e g food held at same distance from test tube of water *(1)*
(Total 9 marks for parts a, b and c)

2 **a** Continuous
b Continuous
c Discontinuous

3 When you want to carry out a scientific investigation you first need to decide on a question which enables you to see clearly what you are trying to find out. This will help you to choose the correct variables. The thing you are going to change is called the **independent** variable. The thing you measure is called the **dependent** variable. To make your investigation a fair test you must **only alter one variable**. The things you keep the same are called **control** variables. You should **have as many of these as possible**. When you have taken your results, it is a good idea to display them in a chart or graph. This is because **it makes it easy to see trends in your results**. If your independent variable was discontinuous then you should draw a **bar chart**. If your independent variable was continuous you should draw a **line of best fit**. Your independent variable should go along the **x-axis** of your graph. *(1 mark for each correct choice)*

4 Any sensible suggestion with the idea of factors involving living things

Pages 176–177 Presenting results and drawing graphs

1 **a** The temperature of the water
b The mass of salt
c Volume of water *(1)* Size of salt grain *(1)* Whether or not solution is stirred *(1)*

d

Temperature of water (°C)	Mass of salt dissolved (g)

(1 mark for correct headings and 1 for units)

e A line of best fit
f Because the independent variable *(1)* is continuous *(1)*

g

Temperature of water (°C)	Mass of salt dissolved (g)
30	1.7
40	1.9
50	3.9
60	3.3
70	4.7
80	6.0

(2 marks if all in correct order, deduct 1 mark for any out of order to minimum of zero)

h Graph to show the mass of salt that will dissolve in 150 ml of water at different temperatures

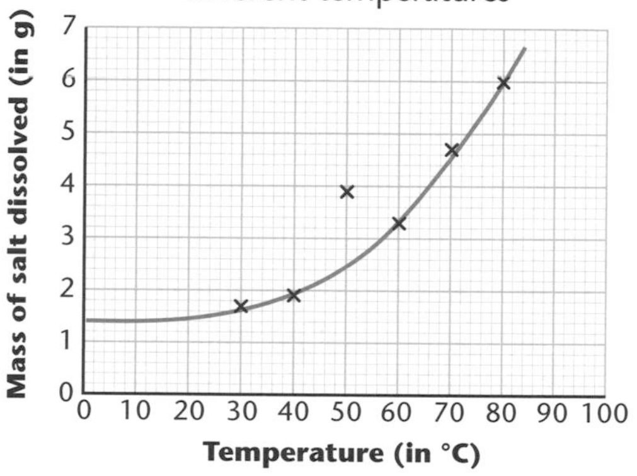

Suitable title *(1)* Axes labelled and suitable scales *(2)* Points plotted accurately *(3)* Smooth curve drawn *(1)* ignoring anomalous result *(1)* Bar chart – no marks!

Pages 178–179 Patterns and relationships

1 **a** Peter's
b They have taken more measurements *or* They have recorded their results more carefully/in more detail *or* They have put their results in a clear table *(Any 2 sensible comments, 1 mark each)*
c No
d Most of Peter's results show the relationship of the higher the temperature *(1)* the faster the water evaporates *(1)*
e The last one *or* The one on the outside windowsill
f Outside there may have been wind as well *or* It may have been a very sunny place, etc.
g The volume of water at the start is always the same
h It is a good prediction because they have given a scientific reason
i No
j The same volume of water/in different shaped containers/left in same place/for same length of time and the volume of water measured at the end *(Any 3, 1 mark each)*
k As the diameter of the container increases, the amount of water that evaporates increases

Pages 180–181 Interpreting results and reading graphs

1 **a** 3 minutes

b 8 minutes

c Around 11 or 12 minutes

d

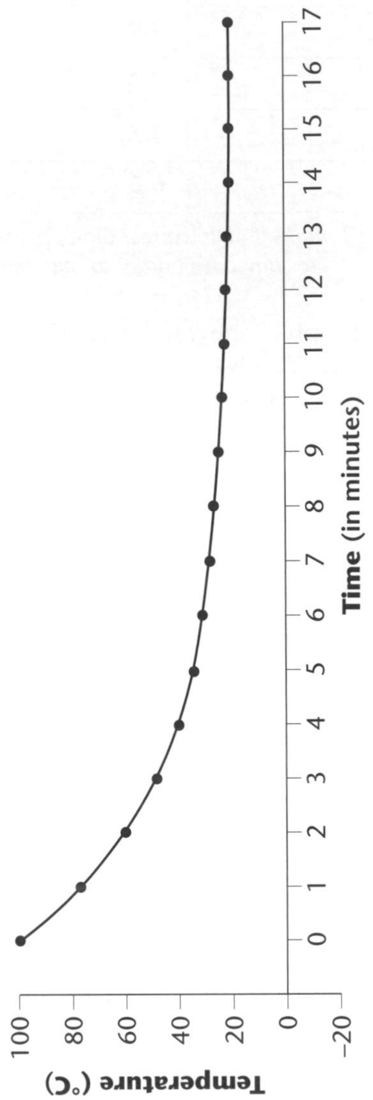

Smooth curve falling quickly at first *(1)* then rate slowing *(1)* until levelling off at room temperature *(1)*

e Matching each of the points above, i.e. water will cool more quickly at first *(1)* then slow down *(1)* before levelling off at room temperature *(1)*

2 **a** Cheese Crisps Bread Crispbread

(1 mark for each in correct order)

b The food with the highest energy will cause the greatest rise in temperature of the water

c Because the independent variable is discontinuous

Pages 182–183 Evidence and conclusions

1 Anything sensible such as – an experiment done yourself *or* Results from an experiment someone else has done *or* Data collected by a reliable source and reported in a journal or book, etc.

2 **a** **i** No

ii The beans seem to grow fastest in mid temperature conditions *(1)* but just as slowly in very warm conditions as in the cold *(1)*

b **i** Yes

ii The beans kept at 20 °C grow much better *(1)* than at any other temperature *(1)*

c **i** No

ii There is no information given about the amount of water the beans received *(1)* To make it a fair test they should all have been given the same amount of water *(1)*

d **i** No

ii Because a line of best fit would give a smooth curve as near as possible to the majority of points NOT because a line of best fit is always a straight line!

3 Better equipment allows us to make better measurements and gain better evidence *(1)*

Pages 184–185 Evaluating experiments

1 Grow more than one bean shoot at each temperature *(1)* Ensure that apart from temperature the conditions for the bean shoots were exactly the same *(1)* *or* any sensible suggestion

2 **a** FAIR TEST

b NOT FAIR TEST

c NOT FAIR TEST

3 **a** Same type of drink/Same amount of drink/Test rest pulse rate and measure difference/Measure pulse rate at same time interval after drinking

(Any 3, 1 mark each)

b Sensible suggestion about difficulties of using humans as experimental subjects

4 How much maize did he get from the field with the new type of maize in compared with that field in previous years?

How much maize did he get from the sprayed field compared with previous years?

Was it generally a good or bad year in terms of weather and other conditions?

What was the relative cost of the new maize and the spraying? *(Any 3, 1 mark each)*

5 B

Practice paper answers

Pages 186–187

1 a

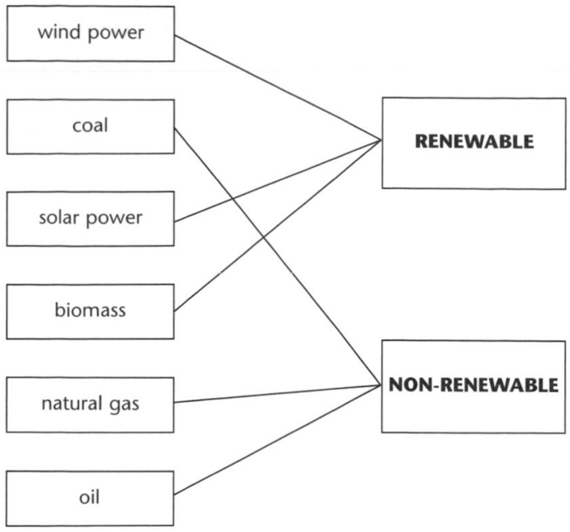

(Total 3 marks, deduct 1 mark for each incorrect line to a minimum of zero)

b The Sun *(1)*

Max 4 marks

2 a Oak tree leaf → caterpillar → blue tit → sparrowhawk

Organisms in correct order *(1)* Arrows in correct direction *(1)*

b The first thing in a food chain is always a green plant *(1)*

c Cell wall *(1)* Vacuole *(1)* Chloroplasts *(1)* (any order)

d Chloroplasts *(1)*

Max 7 marks **Maximum 11 marks**

Pages 188–189

3 a Arrow on scale at left-hand side no higher than pH 4 *(1)*

b

Substance	**pH**
Lemon juice	2 or 3
Water	7
Sodium hydroxide	12 or 13

(1) each

4 a Tube D (sodium chloride solution) *(1)*

b Tube A *(1)* Tube B *(1)*

c Gold rings do not rust *(1)*

Max 4 marks **Maximum 8 marks**

Pages 190–191

5 a One arrow pointing downwards labelled gravity and one pointing up labelled upthrust

(1) for each provided arrows are same size

b The forces acting on the boat are balanced *(1)*

Max 3 marks

6 a He should choose Bitch B and Dog C *(1)*

b Bitch B has the biggest litters so most puppies *(1)* but she is black and white, but as long as one parent is black, all the puppies will be black *(1)*, so Dog C

Max 3 marks **Maximum 6 marks**

Pages 192–193

7

To get sand from a mixture of sand and water	**Filtration**
To get water from black ink	**Distillation**
To get salt crystals from sea water	**Evaporation**
To find how many food dyes are in a blue Smartie	**Chromatography**

Max 4 marks *(1) each*

8 a i Sodium chloride *(1)*

ii (Common) salt *(1)*

b Sodium *(1)* and Chlorine *(1)*

c Because a completely new substance has been formed *(1)*

Max 5 marks

9 a

Source of information	**Evidence**
An experiment you carried out at school.	✓
What your Granny thinks.	
What your teacher thinks.	
The results of a survey published in a scientific journal.	✓
A TV interview with a famous scientist about an experiment she has been doing.	
Something written in your science textbook.	✓

(1) each

b i Independent variable – the amount of light given to a plant *(1)*

Dependent variable – a measurement of the height of the plant/thickness of stem/number of leaves *(1)*

ii Independent variable – the material the cups are made of *(1)*

Dependent variable – how long it takes for the liquid to reach room temperature/the temperature of the liquid at 1-minute intervals for 10 minutes *(1)*

iii Independent variable – volume of water *(1)*

Dependent variable – height of bean plant *(1)*

Max 9 marks **Maximum 18 marks**

Pages 194–195

10 a So it is possible to compare accurately the energy content of different foods without making allowance for different quantities *(2)*

b Food A *(1)*

c Weigh out the same mass of each food *(1)*

Burn the food under a test tube of water *(1)*

Measure how much the temperature of the water rises as each food is burned *(1)*

Max 6 marks

11 a Sulphur dioxide *(1)*

b The gas combines with the water vapour in the air *(1)* which then falls as rain that is a weak solution of sulphuric acid *(1)*

c The acid rain falling onto lakes and rivers can change the pH of the water from neutral to acid *(1)* The animals and plants that live in that habitat may not be able to survive in such changed conditions *(1)*

d Alkalis can be added to the water to restore the pH to neutral *(1)*

e Neutralisation *(1)*

Max 7 marks **Maximum 13 marks**

Pages 196–197

12 a Streamlined body position/Streamlined clothing *(1) each or for anything else sensible*

b Terminal velocity *(1)*

c Two arrows, one representing accelerating force in the direction the car is travelling and one representing the retarding forces of friction and air resistance *(1)* Forward force arrow bigger than retarding force arrow as car is accelerating *(1)*

d **i** 100 miles in 4 hours = 25 *(1)* miles per hour *(1)*

ii No *(1)*

iii The car will have gone faster at some times than at others *(1)* 25 mph is its average speed for the journey *(1)*

Max 10 marks **Maximum 10 marks**

Pages 198–199

13 a Volume of water/mass of jelly/size of jelly cube/amount of stirring *(1) each for 2 correct*

b **i** Graph axes correctly labelled and with suitable scales *(2)*

Points plotted correctly *(2)*

Smooth line of best fit ignoring anomalous result *(1)*

ii Circle around the point at 60 °C and 3.3 g *(1)*

Graph to show the time for jelly to dissolve in water at different temperatures

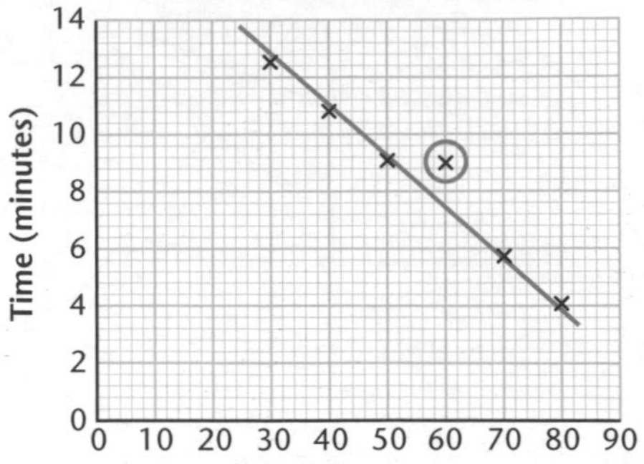

c **i** Because she did not refer to the evidence of her results *(1)*

ii The hotter the water the more quickly the jelly dissolved *or* The jelly dissolved more quickly if the temperature of the water was higher *(1)*

Max 10 marks **Maximum 10 marks**

Pages 200–201

14 a **i** The circulatory system *(1)*

ii Oxygen *(1)*

iii Oxygenated blood *(1)*

b No nucleus *(1)* Biconcave shape *(1)*

c **i** Respiration *(1)*

ii Glucose + oxygen → carbon dioxide + water + ENERGY is released

(1) for reactants (1) for products including energy

d The lungs *(1)*

Max 9 marks **Maximum 9 marks**

Pages 202–203

15 a **i** No *(1)*

ii They did not measure pulse rates before drinking the cola *(1)*

b **i** No *(1)*

ii Because although in this experiment the girls did have very slightly higher pulse rates, the sample was far too small to make such a general conclusion *(1)*

c Because there are so many variables that it is hard to control *(1)*

Max 5 marks **Maximum 5 marks**